MARVELS: The Life of Clarence B
*Botanist, Archaeologist, Artist*

SCIENTIST, ARTIST AND MAN OF LETTERS, Clarence Bicknell was a product of the late-Victorian enlightenment; he was motivated by the desire to understand our world and to express its enormous range through his own creativity. After thirteen years as a clergyman in England, he moved to Italy where he dedicated the rest of his life to botany, to archaeology in the high mountains, to Esperanto and to botanical art tinged with the whimsy of humour, story-telling, affection for his friends and arts-and-crafts originality. He remains a respected figure on the Riviera and in the Maritime Alps.

A treasure trove of research discoveries enlightens Valerie Lester's biography of this genial and unassuming scientist and artist. She has pored over hundreds of letters, diaries, botanical watercolours and designs in archives including the Natural History Museum in London, the Fitzwilliam Museum in Cambridge and Genoa University. Letters and diary entries reveal Clarence's voice; and drawings, watercolours and whimsical creations tell of his hand and his eye. There are remarkable insights into how and why this man strove for perfection in each subject he tackled. Here is a rich story that is brand new . . . a discovery for the reader.

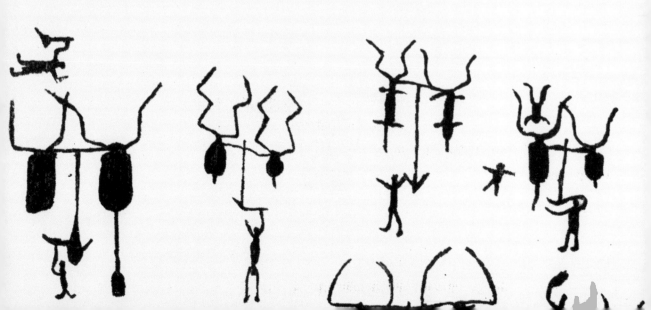

# MARVELS

## THE LIFE OF

*Clarence Bicknell*

# MARVELS

## THE LIFE OF CLARENCE BICKNELL

*Botanist, Archaeologist, Artist*

Valerie Lester

MATADOR

Published by Matador, an imprint of Troubador Publishing Ltd., 2018
9 Priory Business Park, Wistow Road, Kibworth Beauchamp,
Leicester LE8 0RX, United Kingdom. Tel: +44 116 279 2299
Web: www.troubador.co.uk/matador Twitter: @matadorbooks
Email: books@troubador.co.uk

in cooperation with the estate of Clarence Bicknell and the Clarence Bicknell Association
www.clarencebicknell.com  info@clarencebicknell.com

ISBN 978 1 7890 1494 5 hardback

British Library Cataloguing in Publication Data
A catalogue record for this book is available from the British Library

Design by Sally Salvesen
Maps by Martin Brown
Family tree by Gwyneth Hibbert
Photo research by Graham Avery, Marcus Bicknell, Helen Blanc-Francard and the author
Printed and bound by Gutenberg Press Ltd, Malta

FRONTISPIECE: Outside the Casa Fontanalba, left to right: Marco Novello, Clarence Bicknell,
Capitano Alberto Pelloux, Signora Bianca Pelloux, Luigi Pelloux. All four guests signed
the *Casa Fontanalba Visitors' Book* on 12 August 1913.

# CONTENTS

# PROLOGUE

WHEN CLARENCE BICKNELL WAS BORN in 1842, Queen Victoria was 23 years old, had been on the throne for five years, and already had two children. The Industrial Revolution was in full swing in Britain; the emergence of steam power, factory production, and a modern capitalist economy caused a decline in workers' living standards but fabulous wealth for others, among them Clarence's father Elhanan. The Mines Act of 1842 prohibited underground work for women and for boys under ten years old. Isambard Kingdom Brunel's tunnel under the Thames was completed; he had already run the Great Western Railway to Bristol; and was a few months from the launch of the world's biggest ship, the *SS Great Britain*. J. M. W. Turner had just exhib-

ited *Snow Storm – Steam-boat off a Harbour's Mouth* at the Royal Academy, and his new Swiss mountain scene *The Blue Rigi, Sunrise* had been snapped up by Elhanan.

J.M.W. Turner *The Blue Rigi, Sunrise*, 1842. Tate.

John Ruskin, art critic, artist and social thinker, was also 23 and living next door to Elhanan in Herne Hill. Clarence's uncle Phiz was 27 and had been illustrating Dickens's books for six years. Opera was all the rage; Verdi's *Nabucco*, Glinka's *Ruslan and Ludmilla*, and Donizetti's *Linda di Chamounix* all had premières in 1842.

In the natural sciences Charles Darwin had published his monograph on the *Beagle* in 1839, crystallising early stirrings of the idea of evolution by natural selection. These ideas were to have a profound effect on the teachings of the established church and posed intellectual challenges to men like Clarence Bicknell. It is no wonder that, after a formal education and 15 years in the Anglican church, he left Britain, and devoted the rest of his life to botany, archaeology, writing, painting and philanthropy on the Italian Riviera and in the nearby mountains.

Clarence Bicknell

**William Bicknell** = **Elizabeth Randell**
1749 – 1825     1756 – 1821

and 7 siblings

**Hannah Wootton Langton**
1788 – 1815
1st wife   1.

**Mary Jones**
1795 – 1827
2nd wife   2.

**Ethanan Bicknell**
1788 – 1861
Shipowner   3.

**Lucinda Sarah Browne**
1801 – 1850
3rd wife

**Ethanan Bicknell II**
1813 – 1860

and 2 siblings died young

**Mary Ann Bicknell**
1817 – 1858

**Henry Sanford Bicknell**
1818 – 1880

**Christine Roberts**
1821 – 1872

**Herman Bicknell**
1830 – 1875

**Ada Bicknell**
1831 – 1911

**Edward Berry**
1817 – 1875

**Algernon Sidney Bickne...**
1832 – 1911

**Margaret Serocold**
1867 – 1957

**Edward Ethanan Berry**
1861 – 1931

and 5 siblings

1 adopted child

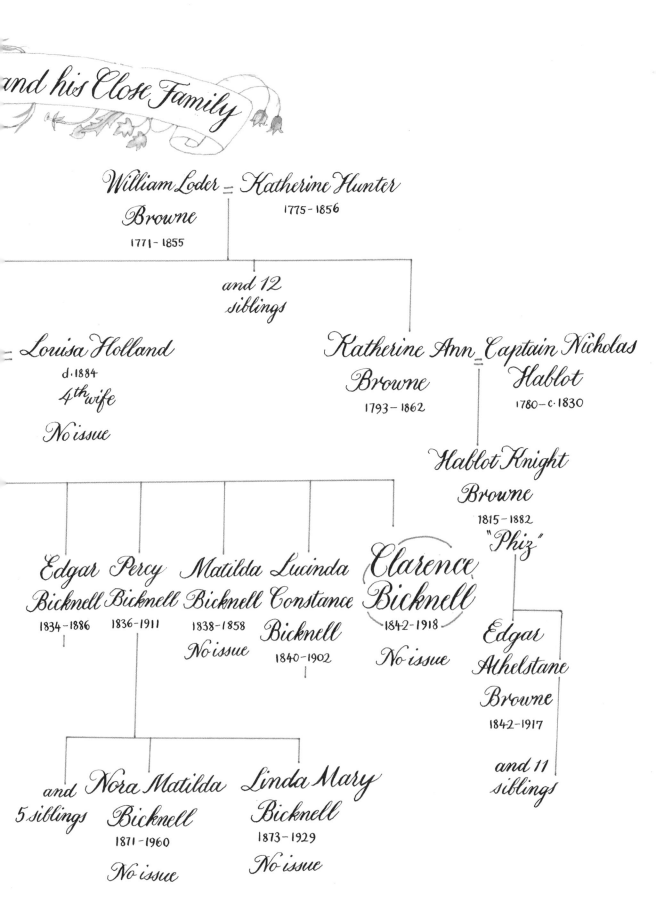

William Loder
Browne
1771 - 1855
=
Katherine Hunter
1775 - 1856

= Louisa Holland
d. 1884
4th wife
No issue

and 12
siblings

Katherine Ann
Browne
1793 - 1862
=
Captain Nicholas
Hablot
1780 - c. 1830

Hablot Knight
Browne
1815 - 1882
"Phiz"

Edgar
Bicknell
1834 - 1886

Percy
Bicknell
1836 - 1911

Matilda
Bicknell
1838 - 1858
No issue

Lucinda
Constance
Bicknell
1840 - 1902

Clarence
Bicknell
1842 - 1918
No issue

Edgar
Athelstane
Browne
1842 - 1917

and 11
siblings

and
5 siblings

Nora Matilda
Bicknell
1871 - 1960
No issue

Linda Mary
Bicknell
1873 - 1929
No issue

CHAPTER ONE

# HERNE HILL

CLARENCE BICKNELL WAS BORN on 27 October 1842 at Herne Hill, then a prosperous suburb a few miles south of London. He was the son of a wealthy merchant, Elhanan Bicknell, and his wife Lucinda Browne Bicknell, the sister of Hablot Knight Browne, 'Phiz',[1] the principal illustrator of the works of Charles Dickens. Elhanan, who made his fortune from sperm whale oil, which was used in those days for lighting and lubrication, already had five children by two previous wives before he and Lucinda so successfully produced eight more, of whom Clarence was the last. Elhanan spent little time with his children, but would occasionally entertain them by performing magic tricks, spinning coins, and telling stories at the dinner table. Lucinda was more interested in the children's physical education and insisted that they perform calisthenics, for which she purchased 'clubs, boards and poles, the latter often winging off and smashing windows.'[2]

In line with her desire for her children's physical fitness, and at a time when she was pregnant with Clarence, she and Elhanan took two of their sons, Herman and Sidney, hiking in Derbyshire. A year later, they took one-year-old Clarence, his nurse, Herman and Sidney to North Wales, where the older boys ascended Cader Idris and Snowdon, while Clarence was exposed for the first time to mountains.

Lucinda was a talented artist, pianist, harpist and singer, and she brought music teachers from London to instruct the children. Another of her passions was French, and a Monsieur Guillaume, who had 'an appalling accent', also showed up from London. To protect himself from marauding boys, he carried a bible in one pocket and a pistol in the other.

Lucinda's eight children – Herman, Ada, Sidney, Edgar, Percy, Matilda, little Lucinda and Clarence – were all born in the twelve years between 1830 and 1842. Sidney, whose diaries (East Sussex Record Office) are so informative, adored Herman, but had nothing pleasant to say about Ada, Clarence's favourite sibling. Sidney constantly carped about her, and his carping reveals the depths of his sibling jealousy: 'My parents were absurdly extravagant in providing teaching for my sister Ada . . . She was taught French, Italian, music, singing, elocution, dancing and other accomplishments by the best professors of London, though she never evinced the slightest aptitude for anything. My mother worshipped these masters, who flattered and fooled her about her daughter's genius.'

*Above:* Stephen Poyntz Denning, watercolour portrait depicting six of Clarence's siblings in 1841, left to right, Algernon Sidney, Percy, Herman, Ada, Matilda and Edgar. Victoria and Albert Museum, London.

*Left:* Thomas Philips R.A., *Elhanan Bicknell, Master of the Vintners,* 1853. Vintners.

*Facing page, top:* Photo by A.S. Bicknell, *The Residence of the late E. Bicknell Esq, Herne Hill, Dulwich, May 1859,* written on the back in Sidney Bicknell's hand.

*Facing page, bottom:* Photo by A.S. Bicknell, *The Garden at Herne Hill,* May 1859.

This jealously boiled up when, at the age of eight years and ten months, Sidney was packed off to Dr Laing's in Brighton, a school he loathed. He expresses surprise that his parents cared so little about their children's education, saying, 'I was sent about like a parcel, carriage paid, without more than the most superficial inquiry of acquaintance. Somebody had said Dr Laing's was a good school, and that was enough, it would do.' For Sidney, the only redeeming feature of Dr Laing's was that Herman also attended and suffered. They would be followed there by their younger brothers Edgar and Percy – but not by Clarence. By the time he was old enough to join them, Dr Laing had retired, and Clarence, fortunately, was parcelled out to a very different type of school.

He grew up surrounded by a beautiful garden, its long view reaching from the verandah to the distant Norwood hills. Even though London was only five miles away, no houses interrupted a vista that incorporated woods and meadows. Mature specimens of oak, ash, elm and a magnificent cedar of Lebanon cast their shade across closely clipped lawns. Young trees of exotic species and large shrubs were planted at intervals close to the sinuous paths that meandered around the large property and down the hill. As a budding botanist, Clarence could not have wished for a more entrancing environment. He was soon collecting wildflowers and making drawings of them, and he was devoted to drawing and painting from his earliest youth.[3]

The mansion in which he was born had the air of a prosperous Late Regency matron: imposing, bosomy, pale and stucco-fronted; but it lacked the elaborate trim so beloved of the Victorians. It made up for plainness with a columned portico, sash windows, octagonal gables, tall chimney stacks, many roof lines, a 120-foot long conservatory, and a labyrinth of rooms.

The original building was fairly modest, but as Elhanan's family and wealth increased and his pre-occupation with modern British painting grew, he extended the house and added two large wings, one at either end. The family lived upstairs and he turned the ground floor into an art gallery with reception rooms. He also created a library that contained not only books but musical instruments, telescopes and microscopes. He added a billiard room and a cellar, that absolute necessity for a Warden of the Worshipful Company of Vintners. Outdoors, he made sure his establishment was self-supporting by adding a dairy for his small herd of cows, a pig sty, a kitchen garden, greenhouses, stables, chicken coops and a carpenter's shop.[4]

Elhanan had a sharp eye for contemporary British artists but no time whatsoever for Old Masters. 'On returning from an extensive tour in Italy, undertaken for the purpose of seeing works of art, I remember hearing him say he had not seen a picture he would give a damn for', recounts Clarence's cousin and direct contemporary, Edgar Browne, Phiz's son. Elhanan made a point of getting to know both the person and the work of modern British painters such as Turner, Landseer, Stanfield, Etty, Collins, Denning and Callcott, and fashionable sculptors such as Baily. A special friend and contemporary was the artist David Roberts, a prominent orientalist, whose daughter Christine married Henry Sanford Bicknell, Elhanan's son by his second wife.

Elhanan avoided dealers like the plague, buying directly from the artists themselves, befriending them, commissioning them, and entertaining them at Herne Hill, some of them long before they became famous. He had a special eye for Turner, and at a time when that artist was not yet in fashion, before Ruskin singled him out for fame, Elhanan bought a number of his paintings that had been left unsold after being exhibited at the Royal Academy. His association with and admiration for Turner endured for many years.

J.M.W. Turner, *Giudecca*, which hung in the drawing room at Herne Hill.

The old drawing room in the centre of the house, whose walls were lined with mahogany to keep out damp and then covered with white and gold rococo panelling, was used to display watercolours. Instead of framing the paintings, he set them into panels in the walls and, according to Edgar Browne 'if I remember correctly' even went so far as to decorate the door panels with Turner's *Rivers of France*. In the new drawing room, he hung several of Turner's masterpieces including *Giudecca, La Donna della Salute and San Giorgio*.[5]

Clarence's mother Lucinda was born in 1801, although she always claimed a birthdate of 1804. She was thus 13 years younger than her husband.[6] Lucinda was the seventh of the 15 children of William Loder Browne and his wife Katherine Hunter. Talented and absolutely charming, she was according to Edgar Browne 'a notable woman, and managed her household affairs with a skill truly early Victorian.'[7]

The Brownes were descended from Michel Bruneau and his wife Hélène Descharmes, both of them Huguenots who came to London as refugees from religious persecution in France sometime in the early 1700s. Wanting to assimilate, they changed their names to Michael and Eleanor Brown, and then to Browne. They lived in Spitalfields where Michael was a maker of wires used in weaving velvet and tinkered with watchmaking. Many of their descendants, like Clarence himself, had a talent for working on a small scale, and many of them were remarkably good artists.

Samuel Drummond, *Mr William Bicknell Senior, Master of an Academy at Tooting, Surrey, late of Ponder's End*. 1813.

Elhanan Bicknell's parents were William Bicknell (1749–1825) and his wife Elizabeth Randall. William worked for many years in his family's 500-year-old, prosperous wool-combing and serge business in Taunton, but just before his 40th birthday, when Elhanan was a year old, he broke with family tradition and became a schoolmaster. He was greatly loved, a voracious reader, a charming and witty conversationalist, a dedicated and conscientious worker and a lover of

Samuel Drummond, *Elhanan Bicknell*, a youthful 42 years old in 1830.

William John Huggins (1781–1845), *The Whalers*, painted from a sketch by Thomas Beale, *A South Sea Whaling Voyage*, and the inspiration for J.M.W. Turner, *Whalers*, 1845. Courtesy of Mark Bicknell.

music – many of his happiest hours were spent at the spinet, the harpsichord, or the organ. He believed in a happy family life based on civilised appreciation of the liberal arts, a belief strengthened by his staunch Unitarianism.

Thus Elhanan grew up in a large and attractive property until he was 16, at which point his father moved the school to Surrey Hall, near Tooting Common in London's southern suburbs.

Elhanan (1788–1861) was William and Elizabeth's fifth child; he was given the name Elhanan – 'God is gracious' in Hebrew – in honour of the American preacher and Universalist, Elhanan Winchester, whom William had met and greatly admired during Winchester's six-year stay in England. Elhanan's life echoed his father's in his committed adherence to Unitarianism.

Having finished his education at his father's school, Elhanan worked there as an assistant teacher until he was 21, when he decided to become a gentleman-farmer. He studied at Cause, near Shrewsbury, but was not cut out to be a farmer and when, a few months later, at the end of 1809, he received an invitation from his uncle John Walter Langton, he leapt at the opportunity. Langton wanted to retire from his business as a ship owner, merchant and manufacturer of candles; he proposed that Elhanan join his son John Bicknell Langton as a partner in the enterprise. Elhanan accepted the offer and returned to London to join the firm at 3 High Street, Newington Butts, then a hamlet just north of Camberwell, but now part of Southwark. He soon cemented the partnership by marrying his cousin Hannah Wootton Langton, John Bicknell Langton's sister. Elhanan turned out to have powerful business and financial acumen, and under his guidance Langton & Bicknell became a prosperous concern, operating a fleet of more than thirty ships with a monopoly over the Pacific sperm whale fishery until free trade opened up the market to all comers.

Merchants were prepared to underwrite dangerous sperm whale expeditions because the reward was great. The sperm whale carried a pot of gold in its head: the prized spermaceti oil. It also provided regular oil rendered from its blubber, whalebone used in corsets, and ambergris, a fixative used in the manufacture of perfumes. When Elhanan started work with John Langton, whaling was at its height and the Pacific trade was opening up. Though the range of the sperm whale was world-wide, the hunting grounds off the east coast of Australia and around New Zealand were particularly abundant, and that is where Langton and Bicknell concentrated their efforts.

In 1819, a mere nine years after joining the firm, Elhanan was wealthy enough to move his family to the house he had built at the top of Herne Hill. By that time, he had three living children: a son, also named Elhanan, by Hannah – she died of consumption in 1815; then Henry Sanford and Mary Ann, by his second wife, Mary Jones – she died of heart failure at Herne Hill in 1827. He married his third wife, Lucinda Browne, Clarence's mother, two years later. As a music teacher, she may have been brought from London to instruct Elhanan's children by his two earlier marriages, thus offering him the golden opportunity to court this lovely young woman with beautiful hands and elegant neck and shoulders. They were married on 5 May 1829 at St Matthew's, Brixton, and Lucinda was the great love of Elhanan's life.

∼

One of Elhanan's first gestures of help to a promising artist occurred around 1830, shortly after his marriage to Lucinda. He perceived that his young brother-in-law Hablot Knight Browne was showing extraordinary artistic talent but he also recognised that the large and perennially penurious Browne family could become a drain on his financial resources. Rather than give Hablot money, he decided to invest in the boy. He removed him from boarding school in Norfolk and apprenticed him to Findens, the London engravers. Thus Elhanan launched the career of Phiz – Hablot's pen-name – whose illustrations for the novels of Charles Dickens would soon be recognised around the world.

Clarence's uncle, Hablot Knight Browne (1815–1882), 'Phiz'.

By 1838, with his fortune assured, Elhanan began seriously collecting modern British art. His taste was eclectic, running to, among others, Roberts's foreign landscapes, Etty's nudes, Turner and Stansfield's marine paintings. It also included several works by Gainsborough. 'There is nothing remarkable in a rich man making a collection of pictures', states Edgar Browne, 'but it was not so common in the early Victorian days, and this was done entirely at first hand, on his own judgment, and without the aid or intervention of dealers . . . he must have had a shrewd idea of their pecuniary value and prospects, as the collection sold for about three times its original cost.'[8] Yes, Elhanan had a sharp eye, keen instincts, and financial acuity when it came to buying paintings – and not just paintings. He sought out sculptures too, in particular the work of Edward Hodges Baily, sculptures that included *Eve listening to the Voice, Cupid, Psyche, Paris* and *Helen*. Baily had studied with the great English sculptor John Flaxman and he became well known for his monumental work. His fame skyrocketed when he carved the statue *Horatio* for the top of Nelson's Column in Trafalgar Square, where it still

Clarence with his donkey in 1850.

towers over Edwin Landseer's lions. In spite of his successes, Baily was chronically short of money and was grateful for Elhanan's loyal patronage.

Lucinda passed on to Clarence a passion for drawing wildflowers, playing the piano and singing. She may also have kindled in him an interest in foreign travel by reading aloud from the letters of her six brothers and one sister who variously travelled as far as the West Indies, Latvia, India, Australia, New Zealand and Mauritius. And no doubt she would have shared with him her pride in the artistic accomplishments of Phiz, who remained in England. By the time Clarence was eight, Phiz was famous, having already illustrated *The Pickwick Papers*, *Nicholas Nickleby*, *The Old Curiosity Shop*, *Barnaby Rudge*, *Martin Chuzzlewit*, *Dombey and Son* and *David Copperfield*. His carefully executed, detailed etchings of scenes from the novels would have made a strong impression on Clarence, whose own talent for illustrating on a small scale was rapidly developing.

As a Unitarian, Elhanan did not believe in sending his sons to public school because, as Sidney writes, 'My father ... from his being a nonconformist by birth as well as choice, viewed with entire disfavour the religious education, the religious tests in force, the system of fagging, and much besides, which his sons would have encountered at a public school or university ... it would indicate weakness of character if he allowed us to say we believed in the Trinity.' Instead, Elhanan had his children educated by tutors before sending Herman, Sidney, Percy and Edgar off, one by one, to Dr Laing's dreadful school in Brighton. Clarence remained at home with his sisters, Ada, who was 11 years older, and Matilda and Lucinda, respectively four and two years older. He also spent time with Edgar Browne, Phiz's son, born like him in 1842, who lived in nearby Thornton Heath. Each boy had a pet donkey, and Edgar and his siblings even had a goat that pulled the younger Brownes around in a cart.

Browne described his uncle Elhanan as a large, handsome, red-faced man, and his Bicknell cousins as all above average in personal appearance and intelligence. He adds an interesting note about the way they talked. '[Elhanan had] a rather thick utterance, which in his children became converted into an extreme difficulty with the letter 'r'. In order to improve their speech some of them, at all events, were taught elocution by a distinguished actor of the day, Alfred Wigan. Whether it was owing to his efforts, or some other reason, the difficulty disappeared as they attained adult age.'[9] Perhaps this was not so in the case of Clarence. G.B. Briano writes in *Vita esperantista di Genova e Liguria dal 1900 al 1975*, 'According to the testimony of a contemporary, Bicknell spoke Esperanto fluently, even though he suffered from a slight stutter which he had from birth.'[10]

The Bicknell home was often overrun with painters, sculptors and critics of the day. John Ruskin, a young neighbour from across the road, was a constant presence. Browne refers to him as 'a vehement young man who was greatly attached to my aunt. He would read to her long screeds of a work in manuscript. Sometimes he would set the whole household running about fetching colours, brushes, paper, that he might on the spur of the moment copy a flower from the conservatory.' Throughout Clarence's early years, the parties for artists and critics continued apace. Here is an invitation from Elhanan to William Etty, written on 20 June 1845:

My dear Sir

I have called to ask you to dine with me on Tuesday next to meet Turner & two or three other RA's [members of the Royal Academy of Art] if I am not disappointed owing to the shortness of the notice Turner having only just fixed the time. His head is full of fish just now & he wants to get away after others.

Dinner at ½ p. 5 – if walk in the garden before

Yrs very truly E Bicknell, Friday Noon.

He followed this up later the same day from his office:

Newington Butts, June 20th.

My dear Sir,

After I had written my note to you at your house I peeped into your Studio and saw a little picture of an Indian & a female figure. I wish you would let me have this nicely finished – My house much wants something of yours in it.

Yrs very truly
E Bicknell[11]

Could this be the very dinner party where Sidney witnessed the following well-known episode? He recounts how much Turner disliked having his portrait painted, and how two of the other guests, Count d'Orsay and Sir Edwin Landseer, decided to play a trick on him. 'Whilst Turner unsuspiciously chatted with a guest over a cup of tea in the drawing-room, d'Orsay placed himself as a screen beside him to hide, when necessary, Landseer sketching him at full length in pencil on the back of a letter.'[12] Sidney also mentions that Landseer included the Louis XIV panelling and the piano inlaid with Sèvres plaques in the background of the drawing.

D'Orsay redrew and enlarged the sketch and sold it to the print seller J. Hogarth, for twenty guineas. '[I]t was then lithographed and published by the latter, January 1st, 1851, with the title of Turner's mysterious poem, "The Fallacy of Hope," at the bottom.' There is no record of what Turner felt about this deception, but Sidney declares grandiosely: 'I knew Turner extremely well, and I have always considered [the sketch] to be a most admirable, truthful likeness; indeed, the only one exactly portraying his general appearance and expression in his latter years.'

In 1845, Turner exhibited two paintings, both called *Whalers*, at the Royal Academy, and in 1846 another two whaling paintings. It is thought that they were part of a series either commissioned

Count d'Orsay, *The Fallacy of Hope*: Joseph Mallord William Turner (1775–1851) in Mr. E. Bicknell's drawing room from a sketch by Sir Edwin Landseer.

by Elhanan Bicknell or painted expressly with him in mind as a possible buyer. Elhanan had put at Turner's disposal one of his four copies of Beale's book *Observations on the Natural History of the Sperm Whale* and one the firm's portraits of a whaler by the marine artist William Huggins – still in the Bicknell family. Early in 1845, Turner wrote to Elhanan, 'I have a whale or two on the canvas', and asked him to call in at his studio in Queen Anne Street at his earliest convenience to take a look. Elhanan did just that, and later, after the first two paintings in the series were exhibited at the Royal Academy, he took one home. Alas, according to John Ruskin senior, '[Bicknell] found Water Colour in Whalers & rubbed out some with his Handky. He went to Turner who looked Daggers & refused to do anything, but at last he has taken it back to alter . . . all say it is not finished. They account for his hurry & disregard for future fame by putting Water Colours by his stronger passion, love of money.'[13]

This was Elhanan's last dealing with Turner, and he did not buy that painting. *Whalers* (also called *The Whale Ship*) now hangs at the Metropolitan Museum of Art in New York where it emanates its own particular atmosphere of light and fury.

~

J.M.W. Turner, *Whalers*, 1845.
Metropolitan Museum.

Toward the end of February 1850, when she was 48 years old, Clarence's strong and vibrant mother became catastrophically ill. Clarence later wrote about her illness and dying on the front endpaper of the Bible she had given him when he was a little boy. On the right side, he has written his name in his childhood hand; inserted among the pages, are three religious cards of distinctly Roman Catholic sentiment. On the left side, Clarence has written in a mature hand:

> My mother died at 7.30 a.m., March 6th, 1850. When saying goodbye to my eldest brother Herman, she said, 'I know that at the present day there are many temptations to infidelity. Do not be led away by them, whatever may be the arguments of those who support them. I wish to be interred in Norwood Cemetery. I wish my funeral to be as plain as possible. I hope that you will think of me when I am gone, even as I have thought of you. I rely firmly on the wisdom & goodness of the Almighty, and look forward to a cheerful immortality. Without that hope these moments would indeed be dreary. God bless you.'
>
> She died after 10 days illness of peritonitis; she suffered great pain, & scarcely slept at all, morphine only making her delirious; but when not under the influence of medicine her mind remained perfectly clear. She took leave of her elder children separately, & said the Lord's Prayer out loud a few minutes before the end.  R.I.P.

There is something significant about the sentence: 'She took leave of her elder children separately.' It sounds as though Clarence and his two young sisters were not allowed to bid individual farewells to their mother, but said their goodbyes as a group or were entirely excluded.

Clarence's claim that Lucinda died of peritonitis is not at odds with Sidney's statement that she died of enteric fever, which is another name for typhoid. A serious complication of typhoid is intestinal perforation followed by septicaemia and peritonitis. Sidney scotched a rumour that his mother had died from swallowing a bone, saying there was no foundation for that absurd story. He recounts that his mother's death made the children feel as though they were orphans because their father was an unsympathetic parent, esteemed but not loved, who had never taken any interest in their education. Herman was desperately sad and he suggested the family wear black for the rest of their lives. Signor Magrini, the children's Italian tutor, was so distressed on learning the news that he wept, raved and tore his hair. Elhanan's grief can only be imagined.

Lucinda's body was first interred in the catacombs of West Norwood cemetery, and then moved to a large tomb next to Elhanan's after his death in 1861. The two tombs are to be found in the unconsecrated section of West Norwood cemetery – that is, the section in which non-conformists were buried. The tombs of Elhanan's three other wives are nowhere to be seen in West Norwood cemetery. The first two died before 1837 when the cemetery opened. By the time his fourth wife died, she had converted to Roman Catholicism and chose eternal residence elsewhere. Lucinda's inscription is simple, although even in death she appears three years younger than her actual age. Perhaps Elhanan was ignorant to the end about her little deception.

Lucinda Bicknell<br>
Born 30th May 1804<br>
Died 6th March 1850

Immediately after her death, Elhanan lost no time in making contact with his old friend Edward Baily, the sculptor, who hurried to Herne Hill to make a death mask. His subsequent marble bust of Lucinda is a lovely memorial to a lovely woman.[14]

A year later, Lucinda's personal effects were divided up among the children. The four eldest boys, Herman, Edgar, Percy, and Sidney chose books according to seniority. The girls inherited her jewellery. Sidney, who can never resist a jab at his bossy sister, points out that Ada received a valuable diamond ring and other rings, and the greater part of the rest of the jewellery, even as she grumbled about not receiving a share of the books. He adds that, according to his sister Lucinda, Ada ultimately obtained all the jewellery. Clarence is not mentioned in the division of spoils, being too young to enjoy the books and unable to sport the jewellery. His bequest must have been the Bible in which he reported his mother's death.

In the 1851 census, five people are listed as living at the Herne Hill mansion: Elhanan, ship-owner and merchant; Ada, who is given no role; and Matilda, little Lucinda and Clarence who are referred to as 'scholars at home.' It is surprising that no live-in servants are mentioned.

In the months following his wife's death, Elhanan may have distracted himself from grief by reading a new book, published in England in October of that year. It was *The Whale* by Herman Melville, published a month later in America under the title *Moby-Dick*. Melville based his novel in part on the famous ramming and sinking of the whaler *Essex* by a gigantic sperm whale in 1820, an incident with which Elhanan would have been well acquainted. It is highly likely that Elhanan and Melville met in London during Melville's visit to London in 1849. Both were admirers of Turner – Melville collected Turners, in the form of engravings of the paintings[15] – and both were fascinated by whales. Elhanan had given Turner *The Natural History of the Sperm Whale*, and Melville wrote on his own copy of the book, 'Turner's pictures of whalers were suggested by this book.'[16] In Chapter 100, Elhanan would have noted with pleasure that Melville included a meeting of the *Pequod* with a whaling ship from London called the *Samuel Enderby*. The *Samuel Enderby* was a real ship, in which Elhanan Bicknell was the major shareholder.[17]

Ada, who was twenty at the time of Lucinda's death, suddenly found herself occupied with comforting her siblings and her father and running the household. She was strong and competent, in spite of Sidney's snide remarks. Edgar Browne describes Ada as being a large, striking person with a splendid physique, fine colouring and regular features. It was Ada, of all his siblings, with whom Clarence formed the closest attachment, and she and her family would play a major role in his later life. Elhanan disliked being unmarried, even though his daughter proved to be an efficient manager of the household, and two years after Lucinda's death he wed his fourth wife, Louisa Holland Jones, the widow of the brother of his second wife. They were married at St George's church, Brighton, by Dr Laing. None of the children attended. Elhanan was 62, Louisa was 47, and Sidney claimed that on her part it was simply a marriage for position and money. She did not like the children and they disliked her. David Roberts referred to her as 'the old hen', and complained mightily about her constant 'simpering and giggling'.[18] He also complained about 'that lout' Sidney, who had 'a habit of snarling'; Roberts found that he could silence Sidney by snarling back.

'Ada, who had been dethroned from management when the fresh mistress arrived, carried on a perpetual internecine warfare with her stepmother', writes Sidney. 'Indeed my sister's temper

Bust of Lucinda, Clarence's mother, in front of Huggins's oil painting, *Whalers*. Courtesy of Mark Bicknell.

seemed to keep at boiling point, and she tried to dominate with most aggravating and dogmatic interference, not only all her brothers and sisters, but my father as well. If it had not been for my sister's treatment of my father, he would very likely never have married again, and certainly not so soon.'

The world that Clarence knew had split asunder, and shortly after the wedding Elhanan decided it was time for him to be parcelled off to boarding school. Still opposed to public schools, he wondered where to send the boy, now that Dr Laing had retired. In the end he chose Rev. J. Edwards's school in Dorney, Buckinghamshire, a strange decision because Edwards had the reputation for preparing young men for entrance to Cambridge, a university of which Elhanan did not approve because of its religious requirements

In the cases of Herman and Sidney, Elhanan had allowed them to attend University College London, a university favoured by dissenters, of which Arthur Hugh Clough was the Principal. 'My brother disliked [Clough] extremely', says Sidney, 'and one day invited our uncle Hablot K. Browne to dinner in order that he might caricature him exactly with a sketch, which however he very naturally refused to do.' Sidney also mentions that he experimented with being a vegetarian while at university, 'After eating no meat for six weeks I found I had become extremely weak and derived no good. It is a silly craze – living like a monkey.' Clarence would have vehemently disagreed with this statement if he and Sidney ever talked about it; at least in later life, if not well before, he was a committed vegetarian.

After three years of grieving the loss of Lucinda, a joyous event occurred in the Bicknell household in 1853. Sidney describes it:

Since my mother's death we had had no grand dances in our house. Consequently we were overjoyed when my father gave us one on July 12. We had 'Weippert's Palace band', with harp, cornet, violin, violin cello, etc. and a couple of professional singers, whom of course the dancers – there were no 'wallflowers' – never listened to. The first supper was at 12.30, and the second at 1.30; it came from Bridgman, of Wigmore St, a very celebrated confectioner and cost 10/6 a head. It ended at 4.30. A ball at our house was quite an event to excite the neighbourhood, for the four drawing rooms, library, hall, and dining room, filled with works of art, and brilliantly lighted, as well as the splendid conservatory, with its enormous mirror reflecting 60 of the 120 foot length, presented a scene no neighbouring house could match. I also recollect the first ball we ever attended at home, in my mother's time, and how in her anxiety to look young – which she always looked without artificial tricks – she sent for a crack French coiffeur from town, but the man did her hair in such a way that he put on ten years to her age at least. Herman and I had magnificent hand embroidered waistcoats, costing I do not know how much, for the occasion, and I have seen nothing like them at a party since. The famous John Parry sang as well as Miss Louisa Pyne of the Italian Opera, the two Miss Williams, and Clara Novello . . . Herr König too, the best cornet player in the world 'blew our heads off' with his, I think, disagreeable instrument, though the waltzers adored it, especially those who danced in time with difficulty.

Ada married Edward Berry at the Unitarian Chapel in Brixton on 20 August 1857, a wedding that Clarence would have attended because it was held during school holidays. Sidney, as usual, has nothing nice to say about anything concerning Ada:

If I had ever been in the least inclined to join my Father's faith, I am sure that gruesome spectacle would have deterred me. The bride and bridegroom stood on one side of a mahogany table beneath the reading desk and pulpit, and the minister in an ordinary dress was on the other. There was no music, not even a hymn; a Unitarian form of marriage service was read, and the happy pair walked away very shortly as man and wife. At the grand breakfast at home I proposed the Bridesmaids, and I remember saying that like Curtius arrayed in his chamber they were all ready, arrayed in white, to jump into the gulf – of matrimony; a sentiment which my brother in law Dr Edgar, a barrister, afterwards told me, was the best thing said, and in the only good speech there was.

When he was 16, Clarence received the news that his sister Matilda had died of scarlet fever on 22 January 1858. Sidney, for once, has something pleasant to say as he clearly much preferred Matilda to Ada; when he notes Matilda's death, he calls her 'a cheerful, bright, goodlooking girl', who would have been twenty on the first of April.

One by one, all Elhanan's children left Herne Hill. In 1860, Edgar decided to marry Elizabeth Hill, a union that Elhanan considered highly unsuitable. Sidney, ever censorious, has this to say:

What chance would any family ever have of keeping up a decent position, and of advancement, if children are to be allowed to marry any woman they fancy, quite regardless of the relationship she may have to others who are vile. In Edgar's quarrel with my father he was not only wrong throughout, but he went needlessly out of the way to hurt his feelings by violent language, and finally by insulting him by celebrating his marriage at the church on Herne Hill, close to my father's house, and thus prominently drawing the attention of the neighbourhood to it.

Sidney subsequently tried to smooth over the estrangement between father and son, but Elhanan made his feelings known in his will. As Sidney says: 'When my father died, on Nov. 27, 1861, it was found he had left Edgar only £5000 absolutely, instead of an equal share in trust to those brothers, who were not residuary legatees.'

The last of Elhanan's children to leave Herne Hill was little Lucinda. On 1 August 1861, she married the Chaplain of the Guards, the Rev. Henry Maxwell Egan, at St George's, Hanover Square,[19] thus firmly turning her back on her father's Unitarianism. She was certainly not the only child to do this. At the age of twenty, Sidney himself was baptised at St George's, Bloomsbury, on 2 October 1852, and he recounts what happened as he left the church: 'My grandmother had decked herself out very gaily for the occasion, and put on a white veil, so when I came down the great flight of steps with the ancient dame on my arm, to go to our carriage, the mob outside mistook it for a wedding, and called out "What an abominable shame" – "poor young man", and other very uncomplimentary exclamations.'

Elhanan began slowing down, even as the whale oil business dwindled because of a diminishing supply of whales and the use of kerosene and gas for lighting. He retired in 1859; he bought fewer paintings and he held fewer gatherings of artists and critics. His health began to fail but his staunch support of the Unitarian church never wavered. In early 1861, he pre-empted his own will by donating the then 'timely and munificent sum of £1,000' to the British and Foreign Unitarian Association.[20]

David Roberts visited his old friend regularly, enjoying dinners at Herne Hill with Elhanan, especially if 'that lout Sid' was absent. Roberts continued to visit up until the evening of 22 November 1861. Then he writes to his daughter: 'I passed The Evening with poor dear Mr Bicknell ... But I can see he is breaking fast. The swelling in his legs increasing. See him as often as you can.'[21]

Elhanan had been a healthy man until late in life, claiming never to have taken a dose of the simplest medicine in forty years. Sidney blames his death on a severe fever, caught on a trip to Bologna in 1857. It left him with a chronic chest disease, and forced him to consult Dr Williams, of the Brompton Consumption Hospital, once a week. Elhanan took to his bed on 24 November 1861 and died on the afternoon of the 27th. Sidney adds: 'Only about a couple of hours before, he had signed an important codicil to his will, and conversed in full possession of his faculties, till he expressed a desire to sleep a little, and never woke again. The funeral, by his express desire of the plainest kind, took place on [Tuesday] December 3, when he was buried in the unconsecrated division of Norwood Cemetery, near the chapel used by Nonconformists. A plain altar tomb marked the spot till 1875, and then the executors replaced it with a handsome monument designed after a sketch by David Roberts, R.A.'

Elhanan Bicknell's commitment to his religion and to his 'gallery' shines out in the obituaries written after his death. Here is one from *The Christian Reformer*: 'He was a man of genial temper, of high and noble principles, one that sought and loved the truth with his whole soul, and who thought no sacrifices too great in its behalf . . . His zeal never flagged and never degenerated into bigotry.'[22] And here is what *The Art-Journal* has to say: 'A visit to his elegant suburban villa was a treat of no ordinary kind to all who could appreciate those luxuries which elevate the mind, and that wealth which confers honour on the possessor.'[23] Elhanan's grandiose tomb bears a simple inscription:

In memory of
Elhanan Bicknell of Herne Hill
Born 21st December 1788. Died 27th November 1861

CHAPTER TWO

# THE CHURCH

ON 26 APRIL 1861, in an act of flagrant rebellion against his father's Unitarianism and as a first step in his ever-deepening attachment to high church Anglicanism, Clarence had himself baptised into the Church of England at the church of St James the Less in Dorney, Buckinghamshire. This move was probably encouraged by Mr Edwards, his schoolmaster in Dorney, as part of his preparation for university. Clarence was 'admitted pensioner' – that is, he received no financial support – to Trinity College, Cambridge, on 8 January 1861, and went up in the Michaelmas term of that year.[24] The very name of the college, Trinity, must have sent shudders up Elhanan's Unitarian spine. At the time, Trinity was the largest and most academically competent college in the university and rightfully proud of its reputation for good teaching and serious-minded tutors who fostered a love of learning in young men who were not particularly inclined to studious work.

Clarence received the news of his father's death six weeks after beginning his studies at Cambridge. Assuming he attended the funeral, returning so soon to Herne Hill would have been a challenging experience. On the one hand, he would have been happy to see his remaining brothers and sisters, although Ada could not attend as she had moved to Canada with Edward Berry. The much-travelled Herman showed up, on leave from the army, but 'seemed virtually untouched by his father's death . . . but then one could not exactly judge Herman by the rules of ordinary people.'[25] On the other hand, Clarence was already committed to his studies, and after his recent conversion to the Church of England it would have been disconcerting to be subjected to the full blast of his father's Unitarianism at the funeral.

Clarence was now truly an orphan, and there seemed to be no escape from death because two weeks later, on 14 December 1861, Prince Albert died. The husband of Queen Victoria and Chancellor of Cambridge University, he was a national, if not universally beloved, figure whose early demise at the age of 42 shocked the country. In concert with the funeral held at Windsor, the entire city of Cambridge came out to watch their own city's spectacle in honour of the Prince Consort. The churches muffled their bells and rang the dumb peal. The Rifle Corps, bearing flaming torches, marched through the town and assembled opposite the University Library, while the torchlit Band of the University Rifles played the Dead March on the steps of the Senate House. It was a season of lament.

Sale of Elhanan Bicknell's collection of drawings at Christie, Manson and Woods, from *The Illustrated Times*, 1863.

The prospectus for the Christie's sale of 25 April 1863.

Two years later, on 25, 29 and 30 April and 1 May 1863, the auction of Elhanan Bicknell's collection took place at Christie, Manson and Wood's.[26] It turned out to be the art sensation of the season. Potential bidders flocked to preview the works while they were still in the gallery Bicknell had constructed in his Herne Hill mansion.[27] Outside the house carriage after carriage lined up in the road, the occupants waiting their turn for a chance to take a look at one of the largest collections of modern British art ever accumulated.

Elhanan Bicknell would not have approved of this scene. His great hope had been that his art collection would go to the nation after his death, and some of his heirs agreed. However, the majority favoured selling the collection, along with his land holdings. As the editor of *The Art Journal* of London commented: 'It is certainly much to be regretted that a collection of pictures got together with so much judgment and at a large expenditure of money should be dispersed. What a noble addition would it have made . . . if bequested to the nation! This, however, could not be expected with justice to Mr. Bicknell's family.'[28]

Once the property auction had taken place, the art collection was crated up and transported to Christie's auction house in King Street. As soon as the objects were ready for display, Christie's opened their doors for three days of private viewing, days in which their rooms were thronged. The first day's sale of oil paintings and sculptures broke all records for British art by realizing the unheard-of sum of £58,600, or roughly £127,000,000 in 2017. Most of the buyers were dealers, principally Agnew's, but in the case of three paintings, including Turner's *Palestrina* (1828), the buyer was Elhanan's own son, Henry Sanford Bicknell.[29]

Another of Turner's oils, *Giudecca, La Donna della Salute and San Giorgio*, for which Bicknell had paid 250 guineas in 1841, realised 1,650 guineas. Elhanan would be pleased to know that his good eye for painting has not gone unnoticed in the present age. *Giudecca* was sold in 2006 at Christie's, New York, for the astonishing price of $35,856,000.

The sales of watercolours, drawings and some beautiful enamels by Henry Bone took place in the succeeding days, but did not realise such large sums as the oils. All the same, a Turner watercolour, *The Blue Rigi*, which Bicknell purchased from the artist in 1842 for £84 sold for £310.16s. This picture would set another Turner record; Christie's sold it in 2006 for a stunning £5,832,000.[30]

Commentators on the Bicknell sale were puzzled by the high prices achieved; some of the Landseers fetched bigger sums than the Turners. The editor of *The Fine Arts Quarterly Review* wrote: 'The run upon such comparatively poor painters as Callcott and Copley Fielding, exceeding the run even upon so great a man as Turner, did not speak highly for the degree of artistic culture which our art-patronizing classes have reached.'[31]

The grand total raised by the auction of Bicknell's art collection was £78,271, a value in 2017 of £170,000,000. No wonder that this sum, along with the amount raised at the property sale, ensured economic independence for Elhanan Bicknell's heirs. That very same year, 1863, at the age of 21, a newly wealthy and independent Clarence made his first trip to Italy and Switzerland.

Clarence attained his B.A. in Mathematics in 1865 – mathematics dominated all other subjects at the university in those years – and his M.A. in 1873. While he certainly studied mathematics, he spent a great deal more of his time pondering the divine, a very consuming activity of the period. 'It is arguable that during the nineteenth century, British people of property and influence were more obsessed with religion than at any time before or since', points out John Premble, who cites John Addington Symonds's description of his undergraduate days at Oxford in the 1860s: 'We talked theology at breakfast parties, and at wine parties, out riding and walking, in college gardens, on the river, wherever young men and their elders met together.'[32] It is all too tempting to imagine Clarence punting and pontificating with friends.

Great Court, Trinity College, Cambridge. Clarence's rooms were through the door on the left.

Rev. Joseph Barber Lightfoot (1828–1889), later Bishop of Durham. Detail of a window in Auckland Castle chapel.

He had fallen under the spell of his first tutor at Cambridge, the quaint, erudite, pious and fearless Rev. Joseph Barber Lightfoot. A short, bald, stocky man, well-travelled, cheerful and witty, Lightfoot was a distinguished New Testament scholar, a classicist, a mathematician, and an amateur geologist. After his death in 1889, *The Times* wrote in his obituary that 'his belief in Christian truth and his defence of it were supported by learning as solid and comprehensive as could be found anywhere in Europe, and by a temper not only of the utmost candour but of the highest scientific capacity'.[33] Lightfoot's capacity for biblical scholarship and analysis of the highest order made a forceful impression on Clarence, who subsequently demonstrated an equally strong commitment to scientific scholarship. Lightfoot also enjoyed gathering together a group of like-minded students and taking them on expeditions.[34] What could have appealed more to Clarence than accompanying his tutor on walks in the countryside, all the while discussing Nature and the nature of religion?

In 1862, the year after Clarence went up to Trinity, Lightfoot became the Hulsean Professor in the Faculty of Divinity; he had been chaplain to Prince Albert and honorary chaplain to Queen Victoria. He was replaced as Clarence's tutor by two men, James Lempriere Hammond, a lawyer, classicist, and adorned with a pair of remarkable sideburns, and Robert Burn, a classicist and archaeologist.

According to the college archives, Clarence's career in mathematics was not particularly distinguished. In his first year, he was placed in the third of nine classes in the College Examinations, in the seventh in his second, and in the sixth in his third. As the college archivist explains, 'These examinations did not contribute to Bicknell's degree, but were used to weed out the complete no-hopers and give some idea of each student's progress. The comparatively good first year, when Classics dominated the subjects examined, may suggest that Bicknell took some time coming to terms with Cambridge mathematics. Nonetheless in January 1865 he graduated 15th among the Senior Optimes – the second class amongst the Honours mathematicians – which suggests he may have been better at the subject than his College exams suggested.'[35]

A typical day at Trinity consisted of Chapel at seven; tuition during the morning and early afternoon; a two-hour break for rest and recreation; dinner at four followed by a 'lounging time' until Chapel at six; and finally an evening of study. Dinner at Trinity normally consisted of a meat course with pies or puddings and cheese. The joints of meat were placed on the table and the diners carved for themselves. About twice a term there was a dinner party, and special festivities were held during the twelve days of Christmas, when dinner was served later with an extra course, and on several evenings was followed by cards, a cold supper of turkey, boar's head, ham and game pie, with punch brewed by one of the fellows.[36]

Clarence found himself caught up in a whirlwind of scientific and religious debate. Charles Darwin's *On the Origin of Species* had been published on 24 November 1859; like Luther's Ninety-five Theses, it had turned religious thinking on its head and was still the subject of much vehement debate. The young man, in his need for stability, was not yet ready to be shaken up by the concept of evolution or anything that deviated from Biblical 'truth.' He was more attracted by the leaders of the Oxford Movement who came to speak at Cambridge, where they found the religious temperature distinctly tepid compared with that of Oxford. They were determined to stir things up. In their lectures, they argued that the future of the church lay in the revival of high church principles. Anglo-Catholic in its intent, the Oxford Movement's structure and formality greatly appealed to Clarence, even as it would have been anathema to his father. Lightfoot, however, trod his own particular spiritual path between the extremes of the Oxford Movement and the Evangelicals, believing that charity and inward moral purity were more important than the outward appearance of religion.[37]

The Movement was initiated in Oxford in 1833, inspired by the Reform Act of 1832 which included Catholic Emancipation, and had as its prime movers John Henry Newman, Edward Pusey and John Keble, all great writers of tracts. Believing that the Anglican church had become flaccid in recent years, they desired to return it to its energetic pre-Reformation roots. They wanted to re-instate the ancient traditions and rituals of the early church's liturgy, vestments, incense and devotion to the Eucharist. They even set about forming religious orders for men and women and regarded themselves as missionaries within their faith. The movement was divisive, with critics calling its members 'Dissenters' or 'Tractarians' and claiming that it reeked of Rome to such a degree that some bishops refused to appoint its priests. This censure meant that only the poorest and least desirable of parishes would welcome Anglo-Catholic priests and thus, paradoxically, the Anglican high church began to prosper at the lowest level of society.

The moment Clarence attained his degree, he turned away from the study of mathematics and entered holy orders. In 1866, he was ordained a deacon in the Church of England and two years later he was ordained priest by the Bishop of London. He could afford to do whatever he wanted; his inheritance allowed him to be extraordinarily generous when he entered the church, and later to travel widely and pursue his passions for botany, archaeology and philanthropy with a free mind and an open purse.

$\sim$

Clarence was a young man in robust physical, spiritual and financial health, primed to devote himself to a cause, in spite of the fact that he had no home, no parents and scant contact with his scattered siblings. As a newly ordained deacon in the Anglican church, he found employment as

a curate at St Paul's, Lorrimore Square, in Walworth, Surrey, about three miles south of the Thames and three miles north of his old home at Herne Hill. He was joined at St Paul's by two like-minded friends from Trinity, Herbert George Morse and Frederick William Puller. The three young men, whom the vicar John Going called his 'three gallants', toiled assiduously for the good of the parish earning 16 shillings a year[38] – all the while celebrating the Christian faith in the most flamboyant and ritualistic Anglo-Catholic manner possible.

The three curates, a governor and a servant lived at 9 and 10 Lorrimore Square, two houses within the

St Paul's, Lorrimore Square, Walworth, in 1864.

Rev. John Going (c.1825–1899), Pastor of St Paul's, Walworth.

terraces that bordered St Paul's on three sides. Lorrimore Square also contained the parish house and all these church buildings were set among gardens. Therefore, even in the midst of Walworth's ever-pressing urban sprawl, Clarence had the opportunity to indulge in some horticultural adventures.

St Paul's was built in 1853, in the neo-Gothic style, to serve the needs of Walworth's rapidly expanding population. Destroyed in World War II, St Paul's is now a modern building, but in Clarence's day it had three naves and a bell tower topped by a spire. At the time of his arrival, the incumbent vicar, the Rev. John Going, an Irishman in his thirties, was a zealous, warm-hearted man, who did not merely think and talk about returning the Church of England to its pre-Reformation roots, but put his words into action. He was also a proficient fundraiser and a highly organised man, who drew volunteers to the church like moths to a lamp.

His first bold step was to abolish the renting of pews, a move that did not go unnoticed in the press: 'St. Paul's, till lately a pew-rented is now a free church, and its truly exemplary Incumbent, the Rev. John Goring [sic], has been lately mentioned in The Times as having for a time resigned his income, in order to free his Church from a debt contracted we may add under the ruinous operation of the pew-rent system.'[39]

Going then turned his mind to embellishing the church. With funds donated by a layman, he installed a stained glass window created by Charles Eames Kempe, another young man influenced by the Anglo-Catholic revival, who was at the beginning of an illustrious career. Going charged him with decorating the church and designing the clergy's vestments and tiles for the floor of the choir. The final flourish of decoration was the addition of a pair of large silver candlesticks on the altar.

Going then hired an organist, Mr J.E. Vernham, and a choirmaster, the Rev. James Baden Powell, who had only just received his B.A. from Exeter College, Oxford. Going clearly believed in giving opportunities to rising stars, particularly if they adhered to Tractarian principles, and Baden Powell composed a setting of Salva Festa Dies that is still in hymn books. For important festival occasions, Going brought in an orchestra or the band of Her Majesty's Theatre.[40] During the many services he led, including the Eucharist, he and his curates dressed in gorgeous ceremonial garments; they swung incense; the choir sang; and the organ thundered. He invited some of the strongest preachers in London to give sermons. This was religion as theatre, and the people of Walworth thronged to a church that provided such glorious entertainment. Attendance at St Paul's soared.

But John Going did not merely indulge in panoply and theatricality; he was deeply concerned about the welfare of his parishioners. He and his curates travelled door to door in the poorest sections of Walworth, assisting families in their misery, and ministering to them during a terrible smallpox epidemic. It would not be the only time that Clarence would put his own safety at risk in the service of others. They encouraged parishioners to send their families to St Paul's day school, Sunday school and night school. The school buildings had been constructed for the most part using funds contributed by the clergy. One of the 'three gallants' – most likely Clarence – donated the then enormous sum of £1,000 to the cause.[41] And John Going himself was generous to a fault; his pockets were always empty after he went visiting. The success of the clergy of St Paul's can be measured in the parish register in terms of the number of baptisms, marriages and burials they performed in the space of a few years. Clarence's signature alone appears on more than 120 pages.[42]

Going also instigated spiritual retreats, festivals, missions and even a children's mission, run by Joseph Tindall, a layman, who created a children's chapel in a disused railway arch on the Walworth Road.[43] In 1863, Going celebrated the first Harvest Festival at St Paul's, nowadays a much-loved and well-established service but then regarded as ritualism. He invited speakers to the retreats, among them Richard Meux Benson, founder of Oxford's Society of St John the Evangelist, the first religious community to be established in the Anglican church since the English Reformation. Other preachers included Luke Rivington and the silky-tongued Rowland Corbet, who had been two years ahead of Clarence at Trinity, and was poised to play an important role in Clarence's religious life.

Going's success in gathering a congregation of approximately 14,000 souls[44] – Evensong was often attended by as many as 1,000 people – was soon noticed by the more conservative members of the established church, and his religious leanings, his popularity, his insistence on confession and his disregard for the established Church drew unwanted attention to St Paul's. Shouts of 'Popism' greeted parishioners and clergy as they left the building. Posters defamed Mr Going's practices, protests appeared in the press, and an editorial in *The Church Association Monthly Intelligencer* in 1868 read: 'did we not know to the contrary, we should conclude that we had mistaken a Roman Catholic Chapel for a place of worship belonging to the Church of England . . . a brazen-face pertinacity on the part of the Incumbent and his friends has at length put down all active opposition . . . An essentially Romish establishment takes the endowments of the Church, and leads the people astray.'[45]

Clarence found himself swirling in the midst of a heady, divisive religious stew. He had to contend with accusations of 'Popism' in his workplace, and he was wrestling with the memory of his father's Unitarianism and a slew of controversial, much read works about evolution. He also had to come to terms with the wide proliferation of marginal sects and even the ecstatic raving and shaking of Mary Ann Girling, a self-claimed woman saviour right on his doorstep.

Mary Ann Girling (1827–1886).

Not far from the railway arch where Joseph Tindall had set up the St Paul's children's mission, things were jumping. Three evenings a week, starting at 6.30, outside another railway arch, crowds gathered, waiting for a chance to attend one of the meetings held by the Walworth Jumpers, otherwise known as the Girlingites, the Bible Christians, the Children of God, the Convulsionists and, later, the New Forest Shakers. With his mind full of questions about faith, Clarence must have been at least once in that crowd, but he did not fall under Mrs Girling's spell. Instead, he joined a community of celibate, religious thinkers in the nether regions of the Shropshire countryside.

~

Rev. Rowland Corbet
(1839–1919) in 1862.

Clarence had fallen under the spell of the Rev. Rowland Corbet, a mere three years older than himself, who had preceded him at Trinity. After graduating from Cambridge with a degree in theology, Corbet became a fellow of St John's College, Oxford, where he was exposed to the leading lights of the Oxford Movement. A particular influence on him was the Rev. Richard Meux Benson, founder of the Society of Saint John the Evangelist.

Corbet's father, Richard Corbet, was lord of the manor in the parish of St Peter's, Stoke-upon-Tern in Shropshire, and in 1869 he nominated his son as rector of St Peter's. The move to Shropshire offered Rowland an opportunity to construct a church because the original medieval building had burned down. Using the family's considerable funds, he set about rebuilding the church, but first erected a school that could be used on Sundays as a chapel of ease (a church building used for services, primarily for the convenience of those who cannot reach their parish church without difficulty) until the church itself was ready for services.[46] At the same time, Corbet founded his own religious community, the Societas Sancti Spiritus or Brotherhood of the Holy Spirit, closely based on Benson's community. He drew to it like-minded priests desiring a return to the early Church within a close community of brothers, and sought and gained the benediction of Pope Pius IX for his new brotherhood, on condition that the brothers say the canonical hours together.[47] It is a great shame that the society's book of rules has been lost as it would have revealed the order for each day and what tasks the brothers fulfilled.

Meanwhile, back in Walworth, John Going was increasingly exhausted by the demands of his enormous urban parish and by opposition to his work; his curates were worn out too. When Clarence received the invitation to join Corbet's brotherhood at Stoke-upon-Tern, he leapt at the opportunity to lead a religious life in the countryside, along with a chance to indulge himself in another of his passions: botany. He signed the baptismal registry at St Paul's for the last time

Clarence Bicknell, *St Peter's Church, Stoke-upon-Tern, under construction*, 1873.

on 31 August 1873, and made his way to Stoke-upon-Tern, arriving there at a point when the rebuilding of St Peter's was nearing completion. He signed the parish's baptismal register there for the first time on 2 November 1873.

What a change of scene Clarence experienced! While St Paul's had operated in a noisy, over-populated parish, rattling with the sounds of carriages and trains, resonant with the cries of hawkers, prey to diseases like cholera and smallpox, and often smothered in London's smoke and fog, St Peter's, with its nine hundred parishioners, was set in the middle of nowhere, beside a stream, surrounded by green fields, sweet with the scent of flowers in the fresh air, chirping with birdsong, and now buzzing with the effort of building the church. The villagers pitched in, providing time and energy. The most useful of them all was Tom Dutton, the Shropshire Giant, whose extraordinary height, strength, and skill as a mason enabled him to place the heavy stones used in building the church tower.[48] Tom was seven foot three inches tall and weighed 23 stone. He spent some time as a soldier and he also worked in a travelling circus, playing the part of 'The British Soldier Giant.'

The Shropshire Giant, Thomas Dutton (1853–1926) and his wife Betsy.

As St Peter's gradually rose from the ashes of the previous church and revealed itself in its neo-Gothic glory, Clarence began to feel at home. The church, with its two naves, and a chapel next to the presbytery, was built in the same style as St Paul's. Charles Eames Kempe – the same artist who had made the windows at St Paul's, Walworth, and was much in demand by this time – created a stained-glass window for St Peter's. Corbet also installed a magnificent Grindley and Foster organ and a tall and ornate font. The main difference between the two churches was scale. St Peter's was smaller and featured a sturdy square tower instead of St Paul's tall and elegant spire. All the same, it was a large church in a small parish.

For the church's construction, the masons used local pink sandstone, quarried at Stoke Grange Woods. Inside, Corbet installed the monumental Elizabethan tomb of Sir Reginald and Lady Corbet, recovered from the remains of the medieval church. He placed it at the front of the south

St Peter's Church, Stoke-upon-Tern.

nave, not far from the altar, thus acknowledging the Corbets' status in the parish and proclaiming his own fine breeding. Four large steps led up to the altar, whose scale was somewhat at odds with the church's dimensions. He designated two pairs of wooden benches for the brotherhood, setting them in the choir facing the altar, and built a vestibule with a door through which the brothers could enter and leave. A bell, hung above the doorway, was rung to call the brothers from the parish house to the church for services and prayers.

During Clarence's time at Stoke-upon-Tern, the brotherhood consisted of twelve men, either priests or laymen preparing for the priesthood. They were referred to as missioner priests and they lived in an open community, as opposed to a closed monastery. The group of twelve was astonishingly well-educated: four, including Clarence and Rowland Corbet, were Cambridge graduates; five were Oxford graduates; and the others were products of Lichfield Theological College. They lived in a one-storey building with a cloister just east of the parish house. The parish house itself was spacious enough to host conferences and retreats attended by theologians, priests and interested participants who arrived from all over the country – and even from abroad. The stables and carriage houses were located on the south side of the parish house, with a forge close by, much used owing to the frequent missionary journeys the brothers undertook on horseback or in horse-drawn carriages. Clarence himself went on missions to Edinburgh in 1874 and 1875 to found a temperance society on the lines of Stoke-upon-Tern's.[49]

Even without the book of rules for the Societas Sancti Spiritus, it is possible to imagine how the brothers spent their time. The little bell over the presbytery door would call them to 'hours' several times a day. They performed baptisms, marriages and burials; they listened to confessions; they went on preaching missions to surrounding towns and villages; they grew vegetables and raised farm animals.

Henry Slocombe, *Thursday (Monks Fishing)*, etching after a painting by Walter Dendy Sadler (1854–1923).

In St Peter's church today hangs a marvellous old print of a band of brothers fishing, etched by Henry Slocombe from a painting by W. Denby Sadler. These are generic brothers, clearly not members of Corbet's brotherhood, but the fact that the image hangs in St Peter's is a clue to one way in which some of Corbet's men used their time: fishing, and thus providing food for the community. However, Clarence, who would later become an animal rights activist, might have preferred to head off into the fields and by-ways, botanising and sketching to his heart's content.

The spring of 1874 arrived and with it came St Peter's inauguration. Corbet, the brothers and the congregation celebrated jubilantly, even as the parishioners might have been stunned by the Anglo-Catholic display. A journal article written on 30 May 1874 made clear that St Peter's followed very much in the tradition of St Paul's, Lorrimore Square: 'on every side there was a profusion of exotic, scented flowers ... a richly decorated cloth on the altar ... decorative tapestries surrounding the altar ... brass standards in front of the altar ... a processional cross carried in front of the choir ... the missionary priests of the community.'[50]

Alcoholism in British cities in the middle of the nineteenth century was a terrible scourge. Once the church was fully up and running, Rowland Corbet, bowing to the wishes of his bishop, instigated the Stoke-upon-Tern branch of the Church of England Temperance Society. He named it 'The Guild of the Holy Redeemer.' and Clarence was a founding member and administrator. He may or may not have been a teetotaller at that point in his life – there's plenty of evidence that he was not a teetotaller in Italy during the second half of his life – but even without alcohol, he brightened the guild with his talents.

Clarence's copy of *The Handbook of British Ferns* by Thomas Moore is dedicated 'Clarence Bicknell, From the master of his class as a reward for industry and good conduct, June 1855'. The book plate of the Societas Sancti Spiritus in Stoke-upon-Tern would have been added in the 1870s. BibCiv.

Meetings were held on Tuesdays, alternating weekly between a service and address held at the church and a social event and business meeting held at the school. Refreshments and entertainment were provided at the social event and the line-up of performers was drawn from the brothers and members of the congregation.[51] Clarence was indispensable; at the very first meeting, he sang 'Nazareth'; Purcell's 'How Great is the Pleasure'; 'When the Swallows Homeward Flee'; and participated in the round 'Chairs to Mend', a song that would have strongly reminded him of the street hawkers in Walworth. But he did not just sing; he accompanied himself and others on the piano. His mother Lucinda's insistence on his learning to play the piano was paying off. Soon enough he became vice president of the guild, a role he fulfilled particularly efficiently when he had to stand in for the president, Rowland Corbet, who in 1874 took himself off on holiday – perhaps Corbet counted it as work – to the Italian Riviera and to Rome.

Songs, poems, readings, recitations and lectures were the staples of the entertainment. Clarence, showing the thoroughness with which he tackled any project, was soon a popular lecturer, although he sometimes went on at too great length, putting a strain on his rather thirsty audience. On 7 November 1876, he gave a lecture titled 'Mohammed', illustrated with a drawing of Mecca and a map of Arabia. The minutes state, 'After lecturing eloquently for 2 hours, he consented to finish his lecture at a future meeting.' This he did at the next meeting, in a lecture that explained the tenets of the Mohammedan faith and the teachings of the Koran. He probably gave these two lectures as a tribute to his brother Herman, who had died the year before. Herman, a surgeon, soldier, linguist, orientalist, botanist and explorer was the first Englishman to visit Mecca undisguised. Before going there, however, he took the precaution of thoroughly acquainting himself with the rituals and customs of the religion, going so far as to have himself circumcised, just to be on the safe side.

It is tempting to believe that it was Herman himself who sent the drawing of Mecca and the map of Arabia to Clarence, his youngest brother by 12 years. He may have communicated directly with Clarence about his exploits in Persia after his visit to Mecca, thus firing Clarence's interest in other religions and filling him with the desire to travel.

Herman spent many years in Persia, labouring on his masterwork, a translation of the poetry of Háfiz. In all he completed 189 odes, 69 tetrastics and 42 substantial fragments. Sadly, he died before he could bring them to publication; complications following a climbing accident on the Matterhorn contributed to his death. Sidney Bicknell took up the task of publishing the poems, writing a preface and the introduction, and choosing the decorations and illustrations, some of them prints from Herman's own sketches.[52] In his preface Sidney mourns the loss of his brother: 'In addition to being dear to me for his accomplishments and his single-minded amiableness and truth, my Brother had been my oldest companion through life . . . as Háfiz says, "Would that I could see but the shadow of my friend!"'

~

By the mid-1870s, Darwin's theory of evolution had taken a firm hold in Britain. Clarence, a serious reader, was extremely interested in scientific writing – at the end of his life, he still had *The Descent of Man* (1879) and the 1880 edition of *The Origin of Species* in his library. Even in rural Shropshire, he would have heard about the evolutionary theorist and anarchist Peter Kropotkin, who arrived in England in 1876 for a short stay after escaping from prison in Russia. Kropotkin was full of his own evolutionary philosophy, and he would later make an impact on Clarence, even landing him in a spot of hot water.

Rowland Corbet came back from his travels on the Italian Riviera during the winter of 1876 with wonderful tales to tell of Bordighera, a pretty little town, sun-drenched and filled with flowers, just over the border from France and within easy reach of the Maritime Alps. He had been invited there by Mrs Rosa Fanshawe, the self-appointed empress of the English community, a widow who spent the winter season with her daughter in Bordighera at the Villa Rosa. Clarence paid close attention to what Corbet had to say about the charm of Bordighera – and its flowers. During his walks in the Shropshire countryside, Clarence had the opportunity to notice the subtle, seductive workings of Nature and found himself, perhaps unconsciously at first, becoming an evolutionist too and drifting towards a life of observation, led outdoors, even as the ritual and rote of the Anglo-Catholic Church slowly began to lose their appeal. After five years of living in a little village in a close-knit brotherhood, with all the stresses and strains of a small religious community, lacking the leavening influence of female company and scant contact with the outside world, Clarence began to feel the need to broaden his experience. He gave his last lecture to the temperance guild on 4 December 1877. The topic was, presciently, 'Flowers.' The minutes state, 'The excellent manner in which he explained his splendid drawings made us more appreciative of the marvellous works of the Creator. A hearty vote of thanks was given to him, and wishes expressed that he would give us another one after Christmas.'

He did not. Instead, he left the country. Probably at the instigation of Rowland Corbet, Clarence had been invited to stay with Mrs Fanshawe in Bordighera where he would be considered for the post of chaplain in the Anglican church for a year. Mrs Fanshawe was 'an ebullient personality whose enthusiasms were contagious ... socially esteemed as the person to know ... quick to seize opportunities to help people but not without a view to her own advantage ... also something of a gossip.'[53] Most important among her connections in England was William Makepeace Thackeray, the author, whose nickname for her was 'Pincushion' because of her small, plump stature. Her invitation to leave Stoke-upon-Tern for the Italian Riviera was the turning point in Clarence's life.

As for Rowland Corbet, in the entry for 24 February 1879, the minutes of the temperance guild state: 'Ordinary meeting under the Presidency of the Rector. Only a few members were present. With the object of disbanding the Guild, the Rector announced his intention to retire from the post of President.' It seems that, without Clarence's energy, the life had gone out of the Guild. Corbet later disbanded the brotherhood itself, became a mystic and a popular speaker, and married in 1884. He and Clarence remained in touch with each other, but 'according to a member of the younger generation, Rowland Corbet would eventually become garrulous and self-satisfied ... and pampered by his adoring wife, herself considered unworthy of him by his even more devoted lady admirers.'[54]

~

Clarence continued to thirst for clarity of thought in his religion. Once he began to travel, he became more and more interested in the varieties of religious experience and less in the dogma of an individual faith. After his first winter in Bordighera, where his faith was sorely tested, he attended the Broadlands conference of August 1879. These conferences were religious retreats, organised annually between 1874 and 1888 by William and Georgina Cowper-Temple (later Lord and Lady Mount-Temple). They invited broad-minded European and American speakers, as well as English friends and friends of friends to participate.

William Cowper-Temple (left) and his second wife, Georgina. University of Southampton.

Broadlands is a sixty-room stately home with gardens designed by Capability Brown, set in five thousand acres of rolling Hampshire countryside through which the river Test meanders. It was the perfect environment for seekers of spiritual refreshment. If the weather were fair, attendees would gather under the great beech trees to offer up prayers, read from scripture, provide short addresses, and engage in discussion of personal experiences of grace. Here is a typical programme for the daily routine in 1876:

08.30 Prayer in the Beech Grove
09.30 Breakfast
11.00 Bible Study
14.00 Luncheon
15.30 Meeting in the Beech Grove
17.30 Tea
20.30 Dinner[55]

Apparently the meals were delicious. Emelia Russell Gurney, whom Clarence had already met in Bordighera, was a close friend of the Cowper-Temples. She leaves a charming description of the Broadlands conferences:

As we sat together morning after morning under those over-shadowing beech trees, the breeze now stirring and now dying into silence amongst the abundant leaves, and heard the wild doves' voices in the intervals of our own prayers and hymns, it did indeed seem as if one heart were shared by all. We seemed together to ascend higher and higher, and, in

*Broadlands in Hampshire, England* from
Morris's *Country Seats* (1880).

the rarefied atmosphere that we breathed in common, to gather
courage to make a fuller and more joyful consecration of body,
soul, and spirit to our Lord.[56]

Coincidentally, the Cowper-Temples were interested in the New
Forest Shakers, the sect formed by Mary Ann Girling, of whom
Clarence was aware in Walworth.

Although they did not apparently practice spiritualism at the
Broadlands conferences, the Cowper-Temples, and particularly
Georgina, were renowned for their use of it. Clarence may have
dabbled in it too. While recounting incidents about the success of
dowsing is not exactly spiritualism, he nonetheless wrote letters about it in 1879 to *The Spiritual
Magazine*;[57] and he is listed in 1887 in *Psychical Research* as an associate member of the Society
for Psychical Research.[58]

Rowland Corbet was a regular attendee and speaker at the conferences, and it is likely that
he proposed that Clarence attend in August 1879. Clarence was completely smitten by the
open-mindedness of the group. In the short period of the conference, he cemented several
long-lasting friendships with the Mount-Temples themselves, Emilia Russell Gurney, the writer
and mystic George MacDonald and his wife Louisa. Clarence's thank-you letter to Mrs Cowper-
Temple reveals how much he was basking in the spirit of ecumenism displayed at Broadlands.[59]
One sentence is particularly striking: 'It was very refreshing to me, after so many years of contro-
versy & discussion to find that so much might be said and done with so very very little of what
dear Mr. Macdonald called the "impertinence" of thrusting our own particular opinions in other
people's faces.'

Clarence also corresponded with the beautiful Emelia Gurney, a widow and nineteen years his
senior. He became deeply attached to her and they entered into a lengthy exchange. His letters
to her were steeped in religious turmoil. One in the Shropshire archives may be a mere draft, so
rambling its thoughts, so poor its handwriting. It sounds as though Clarence is reeling incoher-
ently in religious intensity. It bears a date of 17 August, and unfortunately includes no year but is
probably 1879. He writes:

> Dearest Friend,
>
> ... Is not the devil just the temptation to learn of the inward by the outward which we can-
> not – and to try and make the transitory order the witness to the eternal, which it is not
> and cannot be – Christ's temptation notably to wish to be sinless these conditions God
> manifested outwardly with glory, worship, power? In fact to deny that God, or Being is
> good, though at present it is manifested of faith – The horrors we see & the pains we feel
> do not shew forth – [or] – they are as the vestige of 'Clouds & thick darkness'.

And so on. Then the voice suddenly changes, and Clarence returns to the mundane:

> Goodbye. I like your letters – they always come as cups of cold water to a pilgrim in a
> thirsty land.

Time and again, Clarence tried to pin down the Ineffable and jousted with a very slippery Creator as he came to terms with the dreadful, disorganised mess called religion. What Clarence's tabulating mind needed most of all was order, truth and evidence.

Clarence's decision to move to Bordighera provided the answer to how he wanted to live his life, but perhaps not the one he expected.

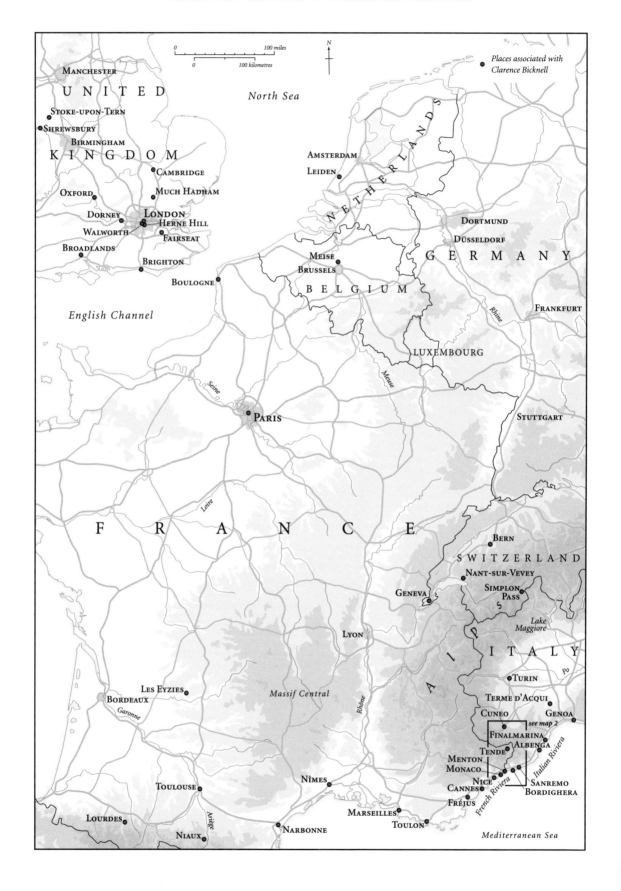

CHAPTER THREE

# ARRIVAL IN BORDIGHERA, 1878

IN EGYPT AT THE END of the fourth century A.D., there lived a man called Ampelio in a religious community at Acori near Thebes, near present-day Luxor. The community was self-supporting and each member had an assigned role. Ampelio was a metalworker who made and polished beautiful utensils and other items essential to the community. His work was of the highest order and he was also renowned for his moral perfection and religious virtue. One night when he was working late in his workshop, the hazy figure of a woman appeared before him, flattering him and trying to seduce him. Ampelio was horrified. He shouted at his temptress, telling her to go away. But it was no use; she persisted. Desperate to shake her off, he reached his bare hand into the fire and grabbed a red-hot iron and hurled it with all his strength at the woman. She fled, cursing furiously.

The fame of Ampelio's ability to handle red-hot metal with his bare hands soon spread and he was besieged with visitors wanting to witness his miraculous skill. One of those visitors, a man named Palladio, remembers meeting Ampelio, who welcomed him graciously and kindly. 'He communicated many other admirable things to me, and very satisfying were his sweet and edifying reasoning . . . Besides, he exhibited a miraculous gift . . . he managed the metal that he pulled red-hot out of the fire with his bare hands, without suffering the least wound.'[60]

Ampelio was a quiet man, who found celebrity a strain. He decided to leave Egypt to search for a place where he might live in solitude. Carrying with him date palm seeds from his native country, he travelled north to the shores of the Mediterranean and from there sailed west, making landfall in Italy at Cape Bordighera. He made a home in a grotto in the rocks, planted his seeds and enjoyed solitude for a while before his fame caught up with him. He was greatly revered in Bordighera and after his death a cult began to form even as his palm trees flourished. Bordighera still has the northernmost palm grove in Europe and provides palm fronds for the Vatican for Palm Sunday. The dates are of the species *Phoenix Dactylifera*.

St Ampelio became the patron saint of Bordighera, the patron saint of blacksmiths and a great hero of Clarence Bicknell.

'On a fine sunny afternoon of early April in the year 1840, an elegant travelling carriage was rattling, at the full speed of four post-horses, over the road, famous among tourists as the Cornice Road, and which runs along the Western Riviera of Genoa, from that city to Nice.' So

*Saint Ampelio Church on Cape Bordighera,* c. 1870, watercolour.

begins *Doctor Antonio,* Giovanni Ruffini's 1855 novel, a book that was the single most important factor in luring the British to Bordighera. Ruffini, a political exile from Italy living in Britain, wrote the novel in English with the help of two friends, Cornelia Turner and Henrietta Jenkins. Published by Chambers of Edinburgh, it soon became a sensation. Readers loved the story of the romance between Miss Lucy of the broken leg and the mysterious Doctor Antonio, but most of all they loved the descriptions of Bordighera and its surroundings. Already the English had been flocking to the South of France during the winter, seeking health and sunshine in Cannes, Nice and Menton in particular. But here was something new: a little paradise with palm trees just over the border into Italy where they could visit the sites mentioned by Ruffini and enjoy for themselves Bordighera's particular, quiet allure. They packed their suitcases and set off. It was not long before Bordighera's winter population doubled and then surpassed the local population of 2,000 people.

Clarence Bicknell left Stoke-upon-Tern by train for Paddington on 25 September 1878 in the company of Brother Frederick Parrett, to whom he refers as 'Br.' Clarence never liked to travel alone and Parrett was another member of the Societas Sancti Spiritus. After sightseeing in London with a 'countryman' they met on the train, they dined with Clarence's sister Ada in Bedford Square and played Verbarium – a word game in which the players are given a set of letters and must form as many words as possible – before they retired to a hotel for the night.[61]

They were up early the following morning to catch the 7.25 train to the coast for a calm but lopsided voyage to Boulogne: 'All the weight was on one side, for we were terribly down in the water, dangerously so, had it been rough . . . the Captain ordered the immediate removal of the barrels [of herring] across the boat – a heavy wearisome job – the fish smell was only a trifle better than the engine one – but . . . I managed to escape illness, & to a certain extent enjoy the deep blue sea.' After an easy landing and a hearty meal on the pier, Clarence and Parrett travelled to Paris, where they finally went through customs. 'The douanier spoke sharply & seemed to think suspiciously about my 2 boxes of "revalenta Arabica" – my explanation of their contents probably did not enlighten him much.' This is not entirely surprising as *revalenta Arabica* is the ground-up root of *Glossostemon bruguieri*, best known for its ability to stimulate lactation! But it was also known to ease gout, a condition from which Clarence suffered, at least in later life. Once through customs, the men were lucky enough to secure the last two – minuscule – rooms at the Chatham hotel on the rue Neuve-Saint-Augustin. Paris was crammed with visitors attending the *Exposition Universelle,* the great World's Fair of 1878.

'What a sight on entering the exhibition grounds!' Clarence exclaimed the following morning. He was right to be amazed. The fair covered sixty-six acres, received thirteen million visitors in the course of six months, and displayed art, architecture and inventions from all over the world. These wonders included Alexander Graham Bell's telephone, Augustin Mouchot's solar-powered engine that converted solar energy into mechanical steam power and the newly completed head of the Statue of Liberty. Clarence and Parrett were unflagging in their sightseeing, even though Clarence was suffering pain (this must have been the reason why he brought along the *revalenta Arabica*). They visited the various national pavilions and salons. Clarence particularly enjoyed their architecture and the flower beds surrounding them, and he was full of admiration for new American inventions such as envelope folders and needle threaders. He was pleased to see familiar artists represented in the English salons, but 'alas I saw no Turner, Stanfield, Roberts &c.', those painters he remembered so well from Herne Hill. He deemed the French salons the best, even though the paintings included 'an inordinate number of naked women in anything but graceful attitudes.'

On their third day in Paris, the two men went to High Mass at the Madeleine, where Clarence was critical of the sermon: 'Very dry & useless – the preacher lamented the ways of the "world," & exalted the holy Church of course – when will priests learn to be men, & find they must talk as men to mankind?' After church they visited the Louvre and then gawped at the descending *ballon captif,* Henri Giffard's huge tethered balloon in which passengers who paid 20 francs could ascend 500 metres into the air over Paris before being brought back to earth by a cable powered by a steam engine. They gawped, but apparently did not ascend, preferring instead to walk to the Bastille and then visit the Père Lachaise cemetery. 'What a striking burial ground it is, interesting in character . . . and glorious in situation.'

Henri Giffard's captive balloon at the Tuileries, Paris, 1878.

After losing their way back to the hotel, they bolted down a quick dinner before rushing to the station to catch the train south – by 1870, trains were running daily from Paris to Menton; the service from Ventimiglia to Genoa was inaugurated in 1872.

'The train seemed very full but . . . we passed the night fairly, getting out to have some coffee at Lyon about 4 a.m., buying fruit at Avignon, & more breakfast at Tarascon where we changed for Nimes.' They disembarked at Nimes, found a hotel where they had their third, but first *real*, breakfast before setting out to sightsee. They went as far as the Pont du Gard, 'a splendid work. We refreshed ourselves at the little rim, & then crossed the new bridge, & walked thro' the aqueduct, & scrambled about on either side & sketched a little & at 6pm. started home again.' The oncoming traffic made the journey back to Nimes perilous, but 'the fresh air, starlight, & strangeness of the scene however made [it] far less wearisome.'

Next day they travelled to Toulon with a stop for a stroll in Marseilles, 'greatly delighted with those splendid bustling streets, with the huge plane trees – the flower stalls, the fish stalls tastefully arranged with seaweed, cockles &c – the fruit shops – the magnolias in seed, palms &c &c.' The south had begun to work its magic on Clarence, although the Toulon hotel did not: 'A Frenchy hotel, men house maids, rough & ready waiters . . . I was terribly eaten, unawares by mosquitoes.' On the train to Nice during the following few days, the magic continued: 'It was all so beautiful . . . about Les Arcs & Fréjus the verdure began to become more sub-tropical, & . . . at Cannes the gardens of palaces & oranges & lemons, & the pomegranates, & cactus & aloes, & the mountains & valleys leading into them met our eyes.' At last they crossed the border into Italy and disembarked at Ventimiglia.

'Mrs. Fanshawe's man, Antonio Imperiale soon discovered us, & helped us to get our luggage examined & given us, when in one of the rattling rumbling shaky sort of open cabs, 2 horses took us quickly to Bordighera.' It was not long before they caught sight of Mrs Fanshawe and her daughter Rosa Fanshawe Walker waving at them from the balcony of the Villa Rosa. 'Soon we had turned up their grove of pepper, olive, eucalyptus & palm &c, & were at the pretty brown house, & church embosomed in the trees.' Clarence was particularly struck by the garden: 'All the trees, except olives, were grown from seed sown 6 years ago! wonderful – mesquite, strelitzia, palms, oranges, lemons, eucalyptus, peppers, acacia, mimosa &c . . . But there has been little rain lately . . . in fact the whole climate is changing.'

Mrs Fanshawe had become a semi-invalid, and spent most of her time in her apartment, so dinner for four was served at a table upstairs. Clarence presented her with gifts from England, and they all spent a merry evening. Finally, it was time for bed. Clarence and Br were accommodated in the artist's studio downstairs, where Clarence slept in a 'pretty little white bed with long hanging mosquito curtains', a real boon to someone as fair-skinned and tempting to mosquitoes as he was.

⁓

Clarence felt immediately at home in the Villa Rosa. It was a newish house, built ten years previously by the Fanshawes themselves. Mrs Fanshawe and her husband, the Rev. Charles Fanshawe, began going regularly to Bordighera for the winter season in the late 1860s.[62] Like migrating birds, they left their home in Southampton in hopes that Liguria's mild climate would alleviate Charles's chronic asthma, and they brought along their daughter Rosa Ellen. They loved Bordighera so much that they purchased a large piece of land on the flat part of town near the sea – that is, Borgo Marina as opposed to the old town, Bordighera Alta, far up on the hillside. They built the house just off the via Bischoffsheim, now the via Vittorio Veneto, naming it after Mrs Fanshawe herself.

Of solid three-storey construction, its top floor was dedicated to bed-rooms, while the other two floors contained reception rooms, an art-ist's studio and a music room. The outstanding exterior characteristics were the pitched roof, the wooden balconies with simple crisscrossed railings and a traditional front door, all bearing testimony to the desire for a simple, airy home that took advantage of its beautiful mediter-ranean surroundings.[63]

The Villa Rosa in Bordighera today.

The Fanshawes' daughter Rosa Ellen married Dr Sanderson Will-iam Matthew Faithful Walker at the British Consulate in Turin in 1870, and in 1871 she gave birth to a baby, but was inconsolable when it died; in its memory she donated land on which to build a chapel for the use of the Anglican community, which had outgrown its earlier meeting places, first at the Hôtel d'Angleterre and then at the Lozeron du Parc.[64] A plaque commemorates her dona-tion: 'In memory of her babe, born MDCCCLXXI, the site for this chapel was given by Rosa Ellen Walker, née Fanshawe.'

The Fanshawes' efforts to heal Charles with fresh air and mild winters were eventually unsuc-cessful; he died and was buried in Bordighera in 1873. Later that year, Mrs Fanshawe and Mrs Walker gave money in his memory for the erection of the Anglican chapel on the land already donated. They hired the famous English architect, George Edmund Street (1824–1881), best known for his work on the Royal Courts of Justice in London, to design what would become All Saints, Bordighera.[65] When Clarence arrived, he noted that 'Mrs F's chapel is being enlarged & is not yet completed.'

After her husband's death, Mrs Fanshawe continued to spend her winters in Bordighera, accompanied by Rosa Ellen, whose own husband died in 1876. All this explains why they were only too happy to welcome a potential chaplain and his friend to their spacious home. Quite apart from anything else, having two single men to stay, in a town where women greatly outnumbered men, was a delicious coup.

Early in the morning following their arrival, Clarence and Parrett walked as far as the chapel of St Ampelio with the idea of taking a dip. Clarence was determined to teach his companion to swim, but the water was rough and deep and he balked. They spent the after-noon sightseeing, first walking in the hills above the house and then exploring Bordighera Alta. Clarence admired the little town with its 'arched gateways, high narrow winding pebble-paved, slippery, dark

The Chapel of St Ampelio in about 1900.

C.B., *Rocks near St Ampelio's Church* where Bicknell and Parrett swam. Watercolour, 1900.

streets with just room for a mule to pass, people sitting working, eating, gossiping & doing nothing at their doors & on their steps.' He found the parish church 'bright rather tasty tho' with an over amount of gold & colour', and was amazed by the proliferation of palms everywhere, 'many tied up (& so uglified,) to bleach the young leaves for sale ... many very beautiful with their clusters of dates, rather green now, but the stems brilliant yellows & oranges.'

The bleaching of palm leaves was an ancient industry in Bordighera. Legend has it that in 1586 the architect/engineer Domenico Fontana was put in charge of re-erecting the great obelisk in St Peter's Square, Rome. He commissioned 900 men and 75 horses for the work, but the task was so difficult that Pope Sixtus V insisted the workers kept silent in case they lost their concentration. A sailor from Bordighera broke the prohibition. Seeing the ropes smoking and fraying from the friction, he screamed 'Water on the Ropes!' and saved the day. Naturally he found himself in front of the Pope for disobeying orders, but the Pope forgave him and asked what he wanted as a reward. The sailor requested that palms for Palm Sunday at the Vatican be provided from his family farm in Bordighera, a tradition that remains to this day.

On their way back down to Borgo Marina, the two men stopped at the English cemetery, where Clarence sketched while Parrett read to him '& little troublesome ragazzi [Italian for boys] behaving like monkeys around us, worried us terribly.' But even the attentions of the ragazzi could not entirely distract Clarence from the wildflowers which grew everywhere. 'On the rocks of the hills near the cemetery were abundance of flowers mostly new to me: the shrubs chiefly thorny or aromatic – but rosemary grew everywhere & a kind of juniper; myrtle is on the hills above our house, Villa Rosa, a pretty little chocolate & green striped arum under the olives – Eryngia [sea holly], a beautiful Statice [sea lavender], a kind of sea cabbage, spurge, & many other flowers by the sea, including also Glacium luteum, [yellow-horned poppy] & on the rocks & everywhere is a handsome composite flower.'

Already, on his first day in Bordighera, Clarence had begun listing the flowers he saw and the places in which he saw them. He also made a note of the rocks he came across. At the beach 'a large coarse yellow limestone or sandstone, with here & there little angular pieces of many kinds of rock cemented together – higher up above the town is a coarse conglomerate, with very big pebbles, looking like artificial concrete.'

The swimming lesson the next day was also a failure. 'We bathed on the shore close by – very deep & the Br. stood a naked Apollo, ankle deep in water', but on the third day, 'Found the right bathing place at last, just where the train emerges from the little tunnel under the capo – a famous dressing place. Hidden from the road by rocks – less deep water – here we had a grand swimming lesson.' By the fourth day, Clarence was able to note, 'A nice bathe – Br. improving.' On 7 October Clarence enjoyed his swim, 'but water slightly rough, so Br. cdnt swim – he says he never will because he is not like other people, being so heavy that the water doesn't bear him up – at the same time he is also so light that there is great danger of his being carried out to sea.'

Clarence Bicknell had arrived in his own particular kind of heaven, a heaven of rocks and flowers and good company. He and Parrett had immediately taken to Mrs Fanshawe: 'Our hostess delightful – we talk of many & deep things – & oh how we do laugh sometimes at the pickle of the world, & the ideas men have of God & the ways & beliefs of Christians.' From the start, Clarence and Mrs Fanshawe seem to have been completely in harmony about their religious inclinations, and Clarence immediately interested himself in the building of the chapel and its history: '[It] is the private property of Mrs Fanshawe, built originally by her husband, who intended to minister in it to any who liked to come. It is not the recognised English Church – there is not one – consequently there are English visitors every winter who growl & grumble – want a consecrated building, & a licensed priest &c, &c, the Bp. [bishop] of Gibraltar also seems to seek to exercise authority here – why or wherefore I know not!' He found that he did not need a licence to perform services, and 'if I recognise Bps it is the Bp. of Ventimiglia I must own.'

Even as he watched the enlarging of the chapel, he found himself wishing that 'a so-called English church may be built, & that Mrs F's house & chapel may some day become a useful institution for invalids or anything else.' Mrs Fanshawe wished the chapel to be truly open to all, a place 'where the R.C. priest if he will, or the English clergyman, or the Vaudois pastor, may minister to their respective flocks if they can agree to do so without fighting & tearing [one] another.'

Work proceeded on the building, with the object of being ready for services by All Saints day. The apse would be completed later, '& then must come some hangings on walls or painting on ceiling – At present there is a very well painted *eye* in a triangle of yellow light ... We want a Dove – & perhaps a figure of S. Ampeglio, the patron S. of Bordighera, who prayed once on a time & promised the people rain for their olives in a time of dearth & trouble, on one of the walls.' This particular desire of Clarence's was not fulfilled.

Padre Giacomo Viale (1830–1912), Bordighera's parish priest for 50 years.

Ezio Benigni. *The English Church in Bordighera* in about 1900. BibCiv.

While waiting for completion of the church, he regularly administered Holy Communion to Mrs Fanshawe in her room and attended Matins in the parish church of Santa Maria Maddalena. After his first visit there, Clarence wrote, 'The priest, the Franciscan curé, had a nice face & seemed very reverent indeed – & the people behaved fairly well, & did not spit or talk more than usual . . . After the gospel the vicario preached a long sermon on the Rosary – horrible to hear indeed – he told us how . . . if we only said the Rosary, we should avert pestilence in our country, sicknesses in our homes, devils in the house of death, destroy the enemies of the Cathk Church &c &c . . . this awful rubbish was ended by an impassioned prayer to the Queen of Heaven & Mother of Mercy, with eyes fixed & arms extended towards the glittering dolls.'

Even though Clarence despised these rituals, he soon came to appreciate the parish priest, Father Giacomo Viale. Fourteen years older than Clarence, he was a tiny man with a huge mission: to work tirelessly for the welfare of his parish. He had arrived in Bordighera in 1863 from Ventimiglia as a temporary priest, but remained there until his death 48 years later. His four predecessors as parish priest had all left because of illness, but Padre Giacomo thrived. At the time of his arrival, the town of 2,000 was still asleep – no tourists, no villas, no hotels; just olives, fish and poverty. The parish church did not even have a rectory and the church itself was falling to pieces.[66] Padre Giacomo set to work, but he did not believe in doing the work alone. He was a consummate salesman; he could persuade anyone, Catholic or Protestant or Jew to comply with his wishes, from the lowliest fisherman to the great architect Charles Garnier, the designer of the Paris opera, a winter resident in Bordighera. Soon enough Clarence, too, found himself working alongside Padre Giacomo and providing generous financial support for the priest's ambitious plans to ameliorate the lot of the town's aged, sick, poor and homeless people.

By 12 October, he was once again in the grip of what he called his 'rheumatic pains.' Throughout his life, Clarence was plagued by lumbago/sciatica, often severe enough to send him to bed for days or even weeks on end. On this occasion, help was at hand: 'I could only dress with difficulty – however I toddled off with Br. to the bathing place, & he took my boots & trousers off for me, & in the water I could swim about without a single ache. But after breakfast I became stiffer & more utterly helpless, so I resigned myself for the day to the tender nursing of the ladies, & Br. put on & changed my linseed poultices often – I did not go out but talked & read in the "Paradiso", i.e. Mrs F's delightful room upstairs, all the afternoon, with hot water bottles at my back, & Br. moved me whenever I needed it – he found me a fine heavy baby.'

His condition improved, and then followed enjoyable days of exploration in the countryside and trips to San Remo and Ventimiglia. By 17 October he was able to write: 'the reredos &c is up & the chapel looks most chapel-like – we hear that the top Bp. of Gibraltar has issued a pastoral, in wh. he says that he cannot allow anyone to preach more than once in a church in his so-called diocese, without his licence.' This meant Clarence would have to get a licence and face up to having a superior.

He moved away from church matters in his entry for 18 October: 'I finished a pair of woollen baby's boots & gave them to Imperiale – he is such a dear fellow.' Clarence took his knitting seriously. He then embarked on a kettle-holder for Imperiale with his monogram in the centre. It was not entirely successful: 'A "work of heart": that is all I can say about it, for the design is weak & the execution worse.' Parrett too was working away, making 'carpet fringe at a fine rate' and the Fanshawe ladies 'beat Kidderminster, Brussels &c &c hollow, by their pretty & comfortable mats & carpets.' A few weeks later, Clarence took crochet lessons from a Miss Stubberd.

On the 22nd Clarence and Mrs Walker succumbed to temptation; they ate the giant peach 'which had long been carefully preserved on the top of the clock, with the words painted on it "questa pesca sara la ricompensa di Fra Frederico, quando può nuotare" – it was getting over-ripe.' [This peach will be the reward for Br Frederick, when he can swim.]

Suddenly the Villa Rosa's population increased by three, 'a lady & her 2 daughters, named "Patrick", Scotch people, one of the girls, a novel writer in weak health – they are to live in the bottom flat.' With the addition of the household staff – Bianca (maid); Jannetta (cook); Mary (English girl); Giuseppe (lad); Giovanni (gardener and odd-job man); Antonio Imperiale (builder, coachman, factotum); Trot, the black and tan terrier; and Black Pussy, shortly to be followed by kittens – the Villa Rosa was humming with activity. The Patrick girls soon set up a business teaching English in the house.

The Villa Rosa was humming and a few metres away construction was continuing apace on what would become the first tennis club in Italy, and the second in Europe, after Wimbledon and

*Left:* Attributed to Albert Trachsel (1863–1929), *Tennis net under olive trees*, Bordighera, watercolour.

*Bottom left:* Sandro Migliarini, *The English Church and the Tennis Club in about 1905.*

*Below:* Photo by Ezio Benigni, *The SIRT tennis raquet makers at Bordighera.* c.1905. BibCiv.

before Paris. Players in the English community had until then strung nets between the olives trees. Charles Lowe, a wealthy philanthropist, who lived across the road from the Villa Rosa, provided funds for the courts – and later for the Victoria Hall and the public garden.

Tennis became all the rage, so much so that Christian Garnier – son of Charles – complained bitterly about the English addiction to it: 'I find it scandalous that, in a place like Bordighera, a perfect centre for outings, they pass all their time playing tennis instead of going for walks.'[67] The addiction became so great that in 1901 the SIRT tennis racquet factory was established just a few metres from the club.

'Lo! & behold! on entering our room, oh what a transformation had taken place!' So wrote Clarence about the scene at the breakfast table on Sunday 27 October, his 37th birthday.

There was a great high vase with a branch of yucca blossom, bunches of roses, & sprays of mimosa flower &c & great bouquets of roses, heliotrope, chrysanthemum, geranium &c &c, surrounded by Nespola [Japonica] leaves, all facing my seat, & each with the name of the donor written on it, & a bundle of some good wishes in an envelope besides – from Giovanni the gardener, Janetta the cook, Bianca the maid, Mary the English girl, Imperiale & Giuseppe . . .

But stop, grandest of all was my chair, with branches of pine covered with cones tied on the sides & a sort of canopy of a creeper wh grows luxuriantly here, across the top of all – Then suddenly everybody appeared & wished me a happy fête . . . Bianca, of course, threw her arms about, & told me with great glee, that that was all the breakfast today, flowers wd be sufficient . . . However, they gave us breakfast as well.'

Later in the day, delighted to find a few shops open on a Sunday, Clarence and Parrett laid in a supply of biscuits, cakes and macaroons, and in turn surprised the Villa Rosa staff with a little fête especially for them. 'We . . . lit about a dozen candles, piled up our cakes, & chocolate & chocolate creams, & invited [them all] to come in & have a little wine – This was *my* party, they jangled glasses & all seemed to enjoy it much – So ended this wonderful festa.'

Although the household staff spoke French, Clarence was finding it more and more necessary to speak Italian. At dinner one evening, he struggled to converse with Signor Tessitore, the organist from the parish church: 'We had to talk Italian all the time & it was fatiguing work – I looked up words in the dictionary, & in great straits appealed to Mrs W.' He soon remedied this problem; three weeks later, he and Mrs Walker started taking Italian lessons from a Professor Grusardi:

A pleasant man & seems prepared to let us have our own way which we much like . . . Our lessons with him are great fun – we write letters or sentences, which later we give one another, & he corrects them. Mine, at least are blunders from beginning to end. We puzzle him terribly poor man with our English though not so much as he does us with his, & when he begins to give us sentences to turn into Italian we generally go off into uncontrollable fits of laughter.

On Hallowe'en, walking at sunrise with Parrett, he had his first sight of Corsica on the horizon: 'I had no idea it would look so high – at first I cd hardly believe my eyes – the outline of it is very beautiful.' In fact, Clarence was finding almost everything he saw beautiful, but he was seeing the world through rose-tinted glasses. All was not perfect in paradise. Entries in the first weekly newspaper for Bordighera's expatriate community, the *Via Aurelia,* in its edition of 27 October 1878, complained about the appalling state of the roads and pavements; the necessity for improvement in the delivery of letters; the dangers to walkers because of the huge heaps of olive branches left in the groves after pruning; and bad drainage in the Via Vittorio Emanuele. The good news was that the Anglican church would be open for services the following week: 'We are requested to inform our English readers that the Chapel in the grounds of Villa Rosa will be opened for services in English on All Saints' Day, November 1st, when there will be Holy Communion at 8 a.m. and Prayers with sermon at 11 o'clock. On Sundays, until further notice, there will be Morning Prayer and sermon at

10.30 a.m. and Evening Prayer and sermon at 3 p.m. with Holy Communion on the first and third Sundays of the month at 11.30 and on others at 8 a.m. Until the building is completed there will be no service on week days.' Clarence was about to go to work.

Services did, indeed, begin on All Saints day.[68] Clarence wrote in the chaplain's book for that day: 'Private Chapel Bordighera Villa Rosa. Opened for the season 1878–79 by Holy Communion (according the rites of the Church of England) on Nov 1st 1878. C. Bicknell M.A.' In his diary he wrote: 'We had H.C. at 8 a.m. Mrs F was carried downstairs & sat in an American folding chair – 2 ladies were there – the altar was bright with 2 vases of flowers, & a floral † made by Bianca from a bright orange creeper in the garden & scented geranium leaves. At 11 we had matins, a congregation of 16 – Mrs W played the Harmonium excellently well, though she was very nervous & all went smoothly.' And then came the important news: 'I heard from the Fr. that he wd. like me to stay the whole winter, if I approved of it.' The Fr. to whom Clarence is referring is probably Rowland Corbet, his erstwhile superior at Stoke-upon-Tern.

As if he had not had enough religion for the day, Clarence went to Vespers at the parish church, a candlelight service, during which the priest gave a heated sermon on God's love as the Consuming Fire, 'of which I heard but little owing to the noisy boys, who were nearly lighting my trousers & coat tails just behind me.' Two days later, on the first Sunday of his tenure as chaplain, Clarence celebrated Matins at All Saints Church and gave a sermon on the parable of the Marriage Feast, to which 30 people came. At Evensong, 15 people showed up. It was all 'simple, hearty & pleasant'. Later, he attended Vespers in the parish church, 'The Church crammed & the singing delightful – a grand spectacle with more candles than on Friday.'

For a change of scene and atmosphere, Clarence and Parrett headed out to Monaco with Giuseppe, Mrs Fanshawe's lad, the next day, where they were impressed by all the decorations. 'The previous day had been a grant fête there, being the feast of S. Carlo Borromeo, their patron – the streets of the old town & roads leading up to it were lined with Venetian masts, painted like barber-poles, with flags flying, garlands across them, & banners with rough pictures of innumerable saints painted on them – also Chinese lanterns & much bunting of course.' They caught the end of a grand Mass, attended by the bishop, members of the court and municipality, and the prince himself, 'a coarse, ugly, brown man in gorgeous uniform.'

Clarence and Parrett then ventured to the casino, but Giuseppe was not admitted, being under 21. At the time, the Casino de Monte Carlo was undergoing expansion and refurbishment under the direction of Charles Garnier. Clarence was horrified by the gambling, but went to enormous lengths to describe it, even trying to work out mathematically how a gambler could possibly beat the odds. 'It was a sight to watch the people, all with their books, papers & pencils making calculations, noting what number had last occurred &c – & to see the piles of money, raked about . . . We watched this hell for ¾ hr . . . it is the devil in the garden of GOD . . . hundreds must get drawn in to play who entered the rooms without the least intention of so doing.'

Clarence continued to wander all over the countryside with Parrett, discovering more and more wildflowers, finding fossils and looking hard at everything. 'Oh how lovely this country is – at first I was disappointed, but it seems to grow in beauty & I think continually of the words "Blessed are the eyes that see the things which ye see."' Another beauty that delighted him was Italian shoes: 'Boots arrived, wonderful Italian boots – others sent to have "suole e tacchi" [soles and heels].' He settled into a routine of holding services in the church; hosting a weekly tea for parishioners; reading aloud in the evenings with the Fanshawe ladies – *The Hunting of the Snark*; *Romola*; *Helen's Babies*; singing duets with Mrs Walker, whose fine alto voice he admired; dining with other members of the expatriate community; tutoring a young Englishman in mathematics; visiting the sick; and all too often burying the dead. Admired from a distance, Bordighera was a place of sunshine, flowers and happy social get-togethers, but closer up it had a darker side. Many of the winter visitors arrived deathly ill, hoping for a reprieve in the warmer climate, some of them having spent the summer in sanatoria in Switzerland. Clarence eased the passage of the dying and comforted the bereaved.

Bordighera attracted wealthy people. Charles Henry Lowe, a philanthropist, lived in the very modest Casa Rossa, across the road from the Villa Rosa; the banker/philanthropist Raphaël Bischoffsheim lived in his elegant, Garnier-designed villa on the via Romana; and Charles Garnier himself, with his family, lived in the far-from-modest Villa Garnier, above the Arziglia beach.

Charles Garnier (1825–1898),

Louise Jopling, who stayed at the Villa Ruffini, was a painter, the first woman to be admitted to the Royal Society of British Artists, and a supporter of women's suffrage. She was interested in botany and walking in the countryside, so she and Clarence were naturally drawn to each other. She gave him news about the London art scene, and her friends included 'Jimmy' Whistler; Everett Millais; John Singer Sargent; George du Maurier; 'Kitty' Perugini, the artist daughter of Charles Dickens; and Marcus Stone and Luke Fildes, each of whom had illustrated just one of Dickens's novels – as compared with Clarence's uncle, 'Phiz', who illustrated ten of them. Mrs Jopling wrote about their friendship: 'One of the best friends I ever had, I met that winter – Clarence Bicknell. He had a beautiful little Villa, called the Villa Rosa.'[69] About her, Clarence said: 'She is a famous walker.' High praise indeed. Clarence was also impressed by her painting skill. In her studio at the Villa Ruffini, she was 'busy at work on 2 life size oil paintings of Indian Rajahs grandly dressed out with decorations & jewels . . . she is to receive 700 guineas for them, not a bad sum for a young woman to earn in one year.' Mrs Jopling was one of the foremost British woman painters of her generation.

Louise Jane Jopling (1843–1933), portrait by John Everett Millais, 1879. NPG

Clarence refers in less glowing terms to an unidentified woman he had known long ago in London 'when I was in the very deepest depths of the bondage of the Ritualistic creeds & methods.' This is strong language about his years in Walworth.

The weather turned cold, and by 10 November, it was so cold that the church attendees huddled and shivered. 'I saw people looking wretched, & . . . I heard complaints about it afterwards.' Clarence took matters in hand, and by the following Sunday, he was able to write: 'The Chapel was nice & warm today. Some sugar was burnt by Imperiale before service, as there was some smell of bricks & mortar – We had a fair congregation, but only 3 men – they are scarce here.'

Two weeks later, the mayor of Bordighera circulated a bill, urging citizens to go to the parish church the following day to celebrate King Umberto's surviving an assassination attempt. Clarence posted the bill on the door of All Saints and before beginning Matins the following day, 'I told the congregation I hoped they would go to the Parish Church if they liked, as there seemed to me no better way of worshipping God than in joining in the joy of our neighbours. We mentioned our thanks in our general thanksgiving.' He followed this up by writing to the mayor, 'telling how we English had rejoiced with them, & why should we not, seeing, notwithstanding our difference of tongue & manner, we were all one in the Unity of the Life of GOD.'

Clarence truly believed that All Saints could be a universal church, even as, later in his life, he would believe in a universal language. He later wrote in the diary that religion should be 'a common worship of all sects, & all men in a truly universal church – & I think it ought to be in the fields, tho' buildings might be useful for invalids &c.'

Giovanni Ruffini.

One day, as they wandered around the countryside near Taggia, Clarence and Parrett encountered an old woman, who told them that Giovanni Ruffini, the librettist of Donizetti's *Don Pasquale* and author of *Doctor Antonio,* the famous book that had drawn so many people to Bordighera, was still alive and living nearby. She explained the way to his house, and later in the day, they knocked on his door and sent in a card. 'After some arranging of his room and lamp lighting, we were ushered in, to a large square room on the 1st floor, where our host was sitting in smoking cap, dressing gown & slippers by the fire reading the paper – an old & grey benevolent & handsome man who received us cordially & told us he had heard of Mrs Fanshawe, whose kind regards we gave him, saying we have come expressly at her desire to see one who had done so much for the English & for the Italians. I told him of our universal church, & of our desire that it should be used by the R.C. clergy – He said it was long since he was in England & he had almost forgotten English, but really he spoke beautifully.'

Finally it was time for Parrett to return to England. On 18 December Clarence and Mrs Walker accompanied him to Ventimiglia, where 'we bid the dear Br. farewell – his luggage was not much examined & there was no crowd in the waiting room, so he wd. have a pleasant journey on this lovely day along the coast. Mrs. W. & I did not wait to see the train off – we walked to the mouth of the Roya, to get the fine view of Ventimiglia & the coast.' Mrs Walker instantly became Clarence's favourite new walking partner.

Clarence wrote in his diary that night, 'Now I begin a new life – May the Br. have a prosperous journey home – a happy Xtmas & a new year – & may God bring us together again before very long – he has been a most kind unselfish companion all these weeks & months past.' Br. Parrett never shows up again in any of the records.

~

Christmas was coming and with it much carol practice. All the while, poor Clarence had to deal with terrible tooth problems. Fortunately he found an American dentist, Dr Terry, in San Remo. On 23 December he took an early train there and was met by the dentist himself at 6.40 a.m. Dr Terry escorted him to his house, where 'we had breakfast & then about 8.30 or 9 he began operations on my teeth – he has various appliances I never saw before: most of his instruments . . . are fastened to a machine which by the use of a treadle, moved by the foot, makes them rotate with great velocity.' Dr Terry spent over three hours on Clarence's mouth, before he sent him away until New Year with 'a warning that I might have some little achings owing to all the shock of bone cutting & filling. A prediction to be alas, fully verified.'

After decorating the church for Christmas, Mrs Fanshawe's man, Imperiale, arrived with his 'instrument' and the carol singers gathered with lanterns and at 8 they set off singing around the town. Afterward, Clarence went with Mrs Walker to the Christmas Eve midnight service at the parish church, a service that, combined with his toothache, nearly drove Clarence mad. 'It was a Massa [sic] Cantata . . . awfully slow – music wretched – people laughing & talking . . . One said to oneself, is it so that Christians 2,000 years A.D. keep the Nativity by a service where no-one communicates but a few superstitious people think it an act of devotion to kiss a doll – horrible, horrible . . . Mrs W. & I felt more than I care to write down here & were heartily thankful when the mass was over, & we could worship Christ better under the midnight stars.'

Clarence earned his Christmas dinner by performing three services on Christmas day. Dinner was served in Mrs Fanshawe's apartment, which was decorated with holly, ivy, oak and two great palm branches that overshadowed her couch and made glorious shadows on the walls and ceiling. The Patrick family joined them for a meal of 'beef, roast beef & turkey & then a flaming plum pudding & mince pies!' Everything an Englishman needed was available in Bordighera. The evening was not an unqualified success; Clarence's toothache had flared up and Mrs Walker 'had neuralgia beginning.'

The two sufferers were worse the following day and, unknown to Clarence, Mrs Fanshawe sent for Dr Terry, who arrived at 8 the next morning. He painted Clarence's gums with iodine, advised ice if the pain returned, and gave him 'a pretty little bag of ginger & capsicums which he had made . . . the muslin & hot contents to be next the gum. The India rubber side next the cheek – I gave him some breakfast.'

Feeling better, Clarence celebrated New Year's Day by taking a dip in the Mediterranean, 'a pleasant bathe . . . water somewhat cold, but warm dressing, & I enjoyed it greatly . . . Returning home I had a pleasant walk with Mrs W. up the Borghetto valley, returning laden with stems of hellebore.' What a lovely way to start the year, but the following day Clarence was back in the dentist's chair, where he spent four hours and had four teeth filled. He had one subsequent session with Dr Terry, and never again complained about his teeth until much later in life.

~

On 5 February 'Mrs W. & I suddenly heard a strange rumbling sound – What is it? oh, a van coming down the drive – a heavy train going by . . . it was about 1.30 by our time. I went out on

the balcony – there I heard legs – coming back it seemed in the house, then in the chimney, & listening up the chimney there was a loud roaring – Can this be a fire? . . . no fire lighted in the drawing room, but noise greatly increased – the house seemed cracking & creaking.' Alfred Gurney, a winter visitor and brother of the psychic Edmund Gurney, suggested it was caused by 'spirits.' Clarence found a practical solution: 'I will exorcise them if they come again.' They did not. Gurney had come to Bordighera with his aunt, Emelia Russell Gurney, a friend of Rowland Corbet, who became another of Clarence's soul mates, particularly after their time together at Broadlands later in the year. About her he wrote in his diary, 'She has such a beautiful face, & is full of the things of good to overflowing.'

G. F. Watts, *Emelia Russell Gurney* (1823–1896). engraving, 1866.

After a grand tidying up of the rooms in his honour, none other than Rowland Corbet arrived at the Villa Rosa on 21 March. 'R.W.C. looking well', commented Clarence. He stayed for six weeks, during which he preached sermons at All Saints on several occasions, and he and Clarence enjoyed long walks and sightseeing as far afield as Cannes.

~

In May, Bordighera was in a frenzy of excitement over the celebration of St Ampelio's day. (Clarence's spelling of Ampelio/Ampeglio varies.) A week before the actual anniversary on the 14th, Clarence attended a service in the parish church where the parishioners 'were keeping a Novena for S. Ampeglio, his arm bone being on the altar in a [case], surrounded by candles . . . a litany sung & hymns & then the kneeling congregation . . . were blessed by the relic . . . I thought it all very horrible & was glad to be out again.' This revulsion did not dim Clarence's enthusiasm for the saint. On the Sunday before the anniversary, he gave notice of the feast of S. Ampelio to the congregation of All Saints, 'to the astonishment of Protestants & Anglicans who are so anti-Roman or so insular that they cannot understand how we can love to rejoice with them that do rejoice, & confess the unity of all without holding to strict doctrines of one kind or another.'

On 14 May itself, a crucial day in Clarence's religious journey, he wrote in his diary, 'S. Ampelio – Hermit of the Thebaid, blacksmith by trade, wafted in his westward wanderings to the Italian shore, to Bordighera where in a cave on the shore he is said to have lived & taught & died – We had our Chapel decorated & H.C. at 8. when I said a few words about the festival & why we sd. keep it right joyously, in order to rejoice with those who rejoiced.' The celebration of St Ampelio did not sit well with the conservative faction at All Saints. It smacked too much of Rome, but Clarence was eager to establish rapport with his fellow Christians in Bordighera, no matter what sect they belonged to. Peter Bicknell, who researched Clarence, and might have had diaries which are since lost, wrote in the 1970s; 'His religious doubts were growing. He found the church too ritualistic, too dogmatic and too chauvinistic . . . He gave up any active participation in church matters, asked not to he referred to as "The Rev." and ceased to wear a dog collar.'

To break away from the Anglican church completely was an impossible act since a person ordained as a priest continues to be in holy orders unless subject to expulsion by the Church, and Clarence was certainly not expelled. Nor did he send a letter of resignation to the Bishop of

Gibraltar; he did not need to since, like his predecessors, he was appointed for just one season. Nor did he give up his faith in the teachings of Jesus.

The heavens themselves protested the following weekend. Clarence was awakened in the early morning by 'peals & cracks right overhead, & the huge hail stones came down like bullets – in some places as large as walnuts . . . I jumped out of bed at last & putting on my Cassock ran upstairs to see the storm better – We had many inches of hail stones on the balcony, the garden & roads were perfectly white with them, & at Villa Pozzoforte a grand hail man was made wh. had not melted when I saw it late in the day.' And this was May.

Clarence continued to perform services at the church, including three on Ascension Day, but by 28 May he noted that attendance was becoming thin, and on Whit Sunday he performed only one service. The winter visitors were making their way back to Britain. Clarence, too, having been appointed for just a year, was getting ready to leave. 'Paid farewell calls the whole afternoon & hardly saw Mrs F. till the evening. She thought I had quite deserted her.' He gathered his last botanical specimens with Giuseppe, and made a final shopping trip with Mrs Walker to San Remo.

*Wednesday June 4th.* A last H.C. in Mrs. F's room. Giuseppe's father came with a bag full of magnificent lemons – At 12.30 I bid all goodbye & went off with Imperiale & Giuseppe to Ventimiglia, & with such a lot of luggage – a small black hand bag with provisions &c – a big one with pottery & lemons & mats – a bundle of umbrellas red, white & brown – my great coat – the palms in ties in my pockets – & a big portmanteau. I had no trouble at the douane – gave my good friends a farewell hug, Italian fashion, & about 1.15 was off.'

*Saturday June 7th [1879].* I reached Stoke Rectory where I had started more than 8 months before, little thinking I sd. be away so long, or find all so changed on my return. I must end, just expressing here, my deep gratitude to my kind friends in Italy, whose friendship in every way has been so thorough & so true, & to God the Author & Giver of all good things.'

A rare photo by Degioanini Giovanni of Clarence Bicknell in his 30s, shortly after settling in Italy. Bicknell Collection.

CHAPTER FOUR

# LIFE IN BORDIGHERA

DREAMING OF BUYING THE VILLA ROSA from the Fanshawes, Clarence returned to the Italian Riviera sometime in the autumn of 1879, after many months of spiritual reflection during which he dropped out of sight. It is tempting to believe that he might have travelled to New Zealand during that time, but a New Zealand trip is hearsay and impossible to nail down (See Chapter 16), and there are simply not enough uninterrupted months to allow for such a long trip in 1879. Nor do we have any sketchbooks or diaries to use as conclusive evidence for such a trip at any point.

Following his return to Liguria and after lodging first in San Remo, Clarence was indeed able to purchase the Villa Rosa from the Fanshawes. Rosa Ellen acquired another, smaller, house nearby that she named Casa Fanshawe,[70] and Mrs Fanshawe died there in 1885. Rosa Ellen stayed on.

As his right-hand man, Clarence hired Giacomo Pollini, a married man with several children, who originated from Stresa, on the shore of Lake Maggiore. Giacomo was the owner of Villa Elena,[71] a house he frequently let to English visitors during the winter season. Clarence described him as an outstanding cook, a keen fisherman with such sharp eyes that he could spot a mushroom on the opposite side of a valley.[72] Giacomo's then five-year-old son, Luigi, would prove to be Clarence's invaluable colleague in later years. In acknowledgement of their admiration for their employer, Giacomo and his wife Marianna named one of their daughters Clarenza. Clarence was a thoughtful and generous employer who inspired loyalty in two generations of the same family. He treated the Pollinis as though they *were* his family, paying no attention to social barriers, and far preferring their company to the gossipy world of the English colony.

Clarence set off in March 1880 on a six-week botanical jaunt to Corsica, taking Giacomo with him as a companion and assistant. They took a ferry from Marseilles to Ajaccio, the capital of Corsica. They tramped from village to village, climbing up into the mountains and descending to the shore time and again, botanising all the way, and finding lodgings – or sleeping rough – wherever they could. They did, however, take a break from botanising one day to go trout fishing.[73]

A poorly drawn but rather dashing sketch of mountains and a village appears in the middle of the sketchbook, and is signed with the initials G.P., indicating that Clarence had turned his album over to Giacomo so that he, too, could try his hand at immortalising the view.

Still restless in June, Clarence took trips to Bastia, Albenga and Iselle, near Simplon. He then crossed the Simplon Pass – the tunnel had not yet been opened – on his way back to England for the summer.

According to the dates and placenames on Clarence's watercolours in the University of Genoa,[74] Clarence reappeared at Stoke-upon-Tern in June 1880, and then spent nearly two months in Cambridge. By the end of his visit, Clarence was primed to return to Bordighera with its cloudless skies, the sound of the lapping Mediterranean and the soft citrus-scented air. The rocky shoreline with its rustling palms, lush, semi-tropical trees and indigenous vegetation again enchanted him. There he would devote himself for the rest of his life to the enjoyment and classification of Nature.

However, his arrival coincided with the start of a technological and cultural revolution of invention and exploitation. He watched as glittering new promenades, planted with trees and flowering shrubs, swiftly spread along the sea front, accompanied by their attendant restaurants, galleries and cafés. He witnessed shops, carrying every delicacy an English family could desire, wedging themselves among those carrying local merchandise. And behind the seafront, he saw new villas, magnificent white-fronted mansions and splendid and luxurious hotels, topped with cupolas and ornate carvings and adorned with balconies and intricate ironwork, rising along what would later develop into long shady streets and avenues.

With construction came wealthy new visitors: royalty, statesmen, businessmen and newly rich industrialists. Visitors from the British Isles and Northern and Eastern Europe arrived by boat and train as soon as the winter season began, often with large retinues accompanying them. Families came with their children, nannies and governesses to set up residence. All were impressed by the showy new buildings, many built in the neo-classical style. They were excited at the prospect of reuniting with friends from the previous winter and attending concerts, dances and social events.

Bordighera was bristling with energy; the locals were scurrying around, priming themselves for the deluge of winter residents that would arrive in October. The whole town resembled a building site. Clarence made himself scarce, botanising on longer and longer walks in the countryside. His nephew Edward Berry recounts 'Though slow in pace, Clarence's powers as a walker were extraordinary and he once walked from Bordighera to the top of Monte Ceppo beyond Baiardo about 5000 ft. in altitude – and back to Bordighera which took him 20 hours'.[75] Each evening when he arrived home, he listed the flowers and made a note of the place in which each was found; then he drew and pressed them. How satisfying it was to be able to pin things down so systematically.

At the beginning of 1881, the artist Louise Jopling reappeared in Bordighera with her desperately ill son, Percy. Clarence took them in and listened to Louise's outpouring. Percy had just returned from Australia, where he had been sent in an effort to cure his consumption, but his condition deteriorated and Louise arranged for him to come to Italy where she would meet him. She was in perilous financial straits, but had remunerative work awaiting her in London; however, she was unwilling to drag Percy back to an English winter. Clarence stepped in. As Louise recounts, 'Percy was installed in the most delightful bedroom, and sitting room adjoining. The nurse had carte blanche to order anything she wanted for the patient's comfort, and I felt freed from care . . . While I was there, the beautiful Mrs. Morris, the wife of the poet, came to lunch. She was a strikingly handsome woman, the original of the Rossetti type of beauty.'[76] This was Jane Morris, the artists' model, Rossetti's muse, whose husband William later became a leader of the Arts and Crafts movement. It may have been she who sparked his interest in the movement.

Louise fell ill in Paris on the way to England. She eventually made it safely home, but it was not long before Clarence had to write to her that Percy was becoming daily weaker and 'it would be wiser to let him start for home at once.' Percy survived the journey, but died three days after reaching home. Louise wrote,

> He was so happy at being home again . . . Percy had an extraordinary sense of humour, and Dickens was his favourite author. All the last night of his dear life I read *The Pickwick Papers* to him. What a persistent effort it was to give the right tone of amusement to my voice! . . . Kind Mrs George Macdonald came to see me and begged me to let her clever son, Dr Greville Macdonald, come and see if he could do anything for my dear son, but, alas, no human help could save him.

Clarence was in Bordighera to witness an extraordinary natural phenomenon on 27 January 1882. Frederick Fitzroy Hamilton describes it: 'Towards one o'clock in the afternoon, a fog . . . spread itself over the sky and soon a wide and luminous circle was formed some distance around the sun; a few moments later two mock suns (*parhelia*), coloured like the rainbow, appeared on the outer side of the circle, on a line with the sun and to the east and west of it. This striking phenomenon lasted for more than an hour. At one time it was possible to see an arc of the counter circle above, which is a detail of great rarity in parhelia, even in those regions where they frequently occur.'[77]

Rather surprisingly, in light of Margaret Berry's statement that Clarence had bought the Villa Rosa in 1880, Clarence based himself for part of the winter of 1883 in Finalmarina,[78] a coastal town about 90 kilometres northeast of Bordighera. Later, in a letter to Arturo Issel Clarence wrote about an incident in Finalmarina, which may refer to the mysterious Alice Campbell. 'Something strange happened to me yesterday. I invited a lady to lunch, a friend of many years who with her mother, now dead, and other friends spent the winter of 1883 with me at Finalmarina. . . At one point she said to me: "Do you remember that long walk we took in the countryside near Finalmarina, when we found cliffs covered with mysterious carved figures?" I was struck dumb, remembering nothing, and said "no". Then she said. "In the middle of a rugged desert, some polished rocks – and you said to me, how interesting they are; they must be 'prehistoric' symbols."

> And by the way, this lady demonstrated an extraordinary memory, therefore I said, that regarding these rocks she was right. But how could I remember nothing? Did she dream it? Or did she read my thoughts by telepathy or "clairvoyance" etc.? I don't understand, and I'm trying to find a solution. For me the only explanation would be that we saw modern incisions, and I, as a joke, did not speak seriously. But is there anything like this known near Finale?[79]

Apparently, he received no definitive response from Issel, but in 1898, Clarence went back to Finalmarina, to visit the carvings near Orco Feglino, first obtaining directions from Father

C.B., *Cliffs at Finalmarina*,
watercolour, 1890.

Ammirani at the Collegio Ehulene. He wrote again to Issel, telling him that the path he then followed was exactly the same one he had taken in 1883 'with the Scottish lady of whom I spoke in my letter.'[80] He recommended that Issel go there because he would be far better able to judge the engravings than he was.

In 1884, Claude Monet roamed the same hills above Bordighera as Clarence did. He told Alice Hoschedé, later his wife, in a letter from Bordighera on 24 January 1884: 'I never stop walking; I walk here, there, and everywhere . . . I go on explorations down every path I find, always on the look-out for something new; so by dusk I've had it.'[81] This could be Clarence talking; indeed, the two walkers, artist and botanical artist, must have come across each other. They were operating in a small compass out in the wild and within the society of Bordighera.

Monet and Renoir had visited Bordighera briefly in December 1883, when the two artists were travelling together from Marseilles to Genoa, and Monet vowed to return. He had been overwhelmed by the light and the vegetation of Bordighera. In a letter to Paul Durand-Ruel, announcing his intention to spend time there, he refers to it as 'one of the most beautiful places we saw on our trip', adding, 'From there I have hopes of bringing you a whole new series of things.'[82] And return to Bordighera he did, on about 20 January 1884, with the intention of spending three weeks.

At first, Monet was discouraged. The town was busier than he recollected, and he found himself booked into a hotel where, when coming down for his first dinner, he was completely surrounded by Germans. This did not sit well with him; he moved out immediately and eventually found accommodation in a hotel that catered almost exclusively to English people, whom he apparently tolerated more easily.[83]

After the muted tones of northern France, working with so much bright light and colour proved challenging and required a palette Monet had never used before. On 26 January, he wrote to Alice: '[I]t's hard-going: those palm trees make me curse and swear; and the motifs are terribly hard to get hold of and put down on canvas; everywhere is so luxuriant; it's gorgeous to behold ... As for the blue of the sea and the sky, it's beyond me.' Three days later, he wrote: '[I]'m appalled at the colours I'm having to use ... the light is simply terrifying.' But by February he was able to write: 'Now I really feel the landscape, I can be bold and include every tone of pink and blue: it's enchanting, it's delicious.'[84] Like Clarence, Monet was taken by the wildflowers and the way they seemed to be charmed out of the ground, even anemones, roses and carnations: 'They are everywhere to be found, growing wild.'

Having finally found his motifs, Monet became extraordinarily productive. He extended his stay in Bordighera through February, March and into April, painting furiously, liberated by the light and colour. The weather was beautiful and he painted all day, experiencing the same kind of freedom and creativity that Clarence felt when he arrived in Bordighera. Monet reinvented his colour palette and dared to splash pinks and oranges and blues all over his canvases, telling Alice 'A most extraordinary pink tone predominates here.'

*Villas at Bordighera.* 'I'm appalled at the colours I'm having to use ... the light is simply terrifying', Claude Monet (1840–1926).

He returned to Giverny with approximately 45 glorious canvases, an extraordinary total, averaging one painting every two days. Despite his anxiety about their reception in Paris, they sold extremely well, helping to make 1884 one of his most successful years ever.

Monet was by no means the only artist to be captivated by Bordighera; the town became a magnet for European artists, many of whom arrived, looked and fell in love. They included Lovis Corinth (1858–1925) from Germany; Hermann Nestel (1858–1905) from Germany; Pompeo Mariani (1857–1927) from Italy; Alexej von Jawlensky (1864–1941) from Russia; Giuseppe Piana (1864–1956) from Italy; Baron Friedrich von Kleudgen (1856–1924) from Germany; and the architect/artist, Charles Garnier (1825–1898). Clarence struck up particularly warm friendships with von Kleudgen and Hermann Nestel, who presented him with a large and lovely painting of the Sasso Valley, which can still be viewed in the Istituto Internazionale di Studi Liguri in Bordighera. Edward Lear (1812–1888) also drew and painted in Bordighera, but made his home in nearby San Remo.

Clarence certainly had the opportunity to befriend, and be befriended by, a thriving, international artistic community, far more appealing to him than the tea-party types that congregated in private homes and later in the Bordighera tea rooms adjacent to the tennis courts. Also in 1884, he would have encountered literary figures when visiting George MacDonald, writers such as Mrs Oliphant and Emily Lawless.[85] Clarence made a particularly strong connection with the

Hermann Nestel (1858–1905) who settled in Bordighera in 1887, *The Sasso Valley*. IISL.

writer George MacDonald at Broadlands. Like Clarence, MacDonald had retreated from the church over doctrinal issues, preferring his own brand of mystical spirituality. By 1879 he was already famous for his fantasy literature, realistic fiction, non-fiction and poetry, and he would eventually exert an influence on the works of Lewis Carroll, G. K. Chesterton, C. S. Lewis, J. R. R. Tolkien and J. K. Rowling.

George MacDonald and his wife Louisa had a large family; they felt the need of southern warmth during the winter and were drawn to the idea of Bordighera. At the end of 1879, by which time Clarence had returned to the Italian Riviera and was staying at the Villa Diana in San

Remo, he wrote two letters to Louisa MacDonald, referring to his time at Broadlands and offering his help in the matter of acquiring housing in Bordighera. Then he came to the heart of the matter, telling Louisa how kind and friendly she and George had been at Broadlands, and how much George's books had helped him spiritually. 'I may add that having got somewhat stranded myself in many ways, and in a great puzzle as to what I ought to be trying to do *particularly*, or clerically, I feel drawn to attach myself to any who at all hold out sympathetic hands and heart.'

William Jeffrey (1826–1877), *George MacDonald* (1824–1905), albumen print in the 1860s.

Louisa Powell MacDonald (1822–1902).

Now comes the moment in the letter when he first expressed his desire to buy the Villa Rosa. 'I wanted to ask Mr Macdonald if *he* saw any *light* about my idea of taking Mrs. Fanshawe's house & private chapel – opening the former to receive poor sick people (or possibly a family) while offering the latter for the use of the English as a regular English church, reserving it to myself to teach in or invite conferences & meetings of other than so-called religious kinds, viz plays, concerts, lectures, etc.' But Clarence expressed doubts about his ability to effect this, feeling that such action would drive certain members of the congregation to raise money and build a proper church for themselves, 'consecrated, Gothic, etc. etc.' He also felt that he would no longer be acceptable as their regular chaplain after the events of the previous season. 'They said, some of them, I taught heresies, etc. that I taught and said many wrong, or at least very partially true & very many foolish things I have no doubt, but to myself my gospel seemed truer and better than what I had originally learnt of men.'

Clarence was, indeed, replaced as chaplain to the Anglican community the following season by P. C. Wodehouse, who had also preceded him, and the year after that by Charles Egerton Fiennes Stafford. Stafford had been at St Paul's Walworth with Clarence and a member of the Brotherhood of the Holy Spirit at Stoke-upon-Tern.

Although his idea to buy the chapel fizzled, his dream of a community centre never left Clarence's mind. In the event, the congregation did as he had prophesied. They banded together, raised money, and in 1883 enlarged the Anglican chapel, making it into exactly the sort of Gothic church that Clarence had imagined they would. His dream of a community centre would have to wait.

As he approached the end of his letter to Louisa, Clarence expressed anxiety about the damage a place like Bordighera with its tight English enclave might wreak on his philosophy:

There is especial danger of being considered (or becoming) very schismatical in spirit. I do myself, rightly or wrongly, long that Mrs. F's chapel should be a place as it has hitherto been, where a larger gospel might be taught, where any man lay or clerical might be invited to speak out what God had taught him – and where the 'Church' might be declared to be more Catholick than Italians or English seem to realise, and Xt more the all and the in all.

I fancy if one offered the chapel for regular English services & reserved to oneself the above-mentioned rights, one would do all that seems true and good. My only difficulty is the answering the question:

'Ought a youngish man of 37, strong and well off, to take what seems an easy post abroad in a pleasant climate & where the difficulties and opposition seem likely to be greater than the encouragements (and this I thought your husband might see some light about)' and 2, which I only can answer, and of course hardly with a yes:

'Are you, C.B. fit for this'?

but one's answer to all questions is 'God'.

On Christmas Eve, Clarence sent a poem to the MacDonalds especially written for them. It acknowledged the losses the MacDonalds had endured, and offered a message of hope for the New Year. Then he wrote again to Louisa, on 30 December, with news of a villa in Bordighera that they could rent with an option to buy, and accompanied the letter with a drawing of the building and a list of its rooms. Clarence's help in finding lodging for the MacDonalds resulted in their arrival in Bordighera in the winter of 1880.

In the two years prior to their arrival, George and Louisa MacDonald had already felt the lure of the south and headed to the health-giving warmth and sunshine of Liguria. In 1878, they found an enormous villa to rent, perched on the hillside above Nervi. It needed to be enormous; they had eleven children, one of whom, Mary, was severely ill with tuberculosis, which MacDonald called 'the family attendant.'[86] George himself was unwell, but he soon began to thrive with the change of climate; poor Mary succumbed to her disease. During the winter of 1879, the family again sought the sun, this time renting a large villa in Portofino. Again George thrived while another child, Maurice, succumbed.

In 1880, they followed Clarence's recommendation and came to Bordighera, where they had taken up the option to buy the Villa Patrick. Unfortunately, the villa was no longer for sale when they arrived, but they were able to rent it for the season. Then the Fanshawes offered the MacDonalds a plot of land on which to build a house in the heart of the English colony, just a few metres from the Villa Rosa and the Anglican chapel. The MacDonalds took up her offer and, excited by the prospect of building and owning their own home, George immediately started drawing preliminary plans to enlighten his Italian architect about what he desired in a house that would accommodate a large family.[87] In addition to family quarters, the MacDonalds needed a house large enough to welcome visitors and those in need, a house that included a living room that could double as a performance space for their theatrical presentations, concerts and religious meetings. The architect and the builder/ contractor, Antonio Imperiale, the builder of the Anglican church and Mrs Fanshawe's right-hand man, were sympathetic to their needs, and they ended up with a four-storey, oblong house, built of light grey stone, which had 13-foot ceilings, and whose drawing room measured 52 by 26 feet.[88] Friends and admirers, including Lewis Carroll, provided

Casa Coraggio in Bordighera; part of the MacDonalds' enormous living room where plays and lectures took place – 'a temple, a theatre, a museum, a club, an academy, an inn', according to Edmondo De Amicis.

funds to help with the construction. The MacDonalds named the house Casa Coraggio, which was linked to the family motto 'Corage! God Mend All'. The spelling of courage without a 'u' is intentional as the motto is an anagram of George MacDonald.[89]

George MacDonald was a handsome man with an arresting gaze. One of his sons, Ronald, describes him: 'In my earliest memory he was a man of forty; tall, with the build of an athlete, narrow-flanked and broad-shouldered; the hands and feet long and very finely formed; a head with brows and nose of great power; the hair and full beard as black as I have seen where there was no sheen of blue in it; and the eyes rather deep set, of a blue liquid as southern sea-water at rest, keen as a northern sky in cloudless frost at mid-day – the only eyes I have known with always a spark and sometimes a flash in them.'[90] By the time Clarence met MacDonald, that raven-black hair had turned a snowy white, but the keen blue eyes had lost nothing of their spark and flash.

Louisa Powell MacDonald, two years older than her husband, was a tiny, determined woman, and a support to George during the many vicissitudes of their long life together. She was gifted theatrically and extremely musical – she played the piano and the organ and had a beautiful singing voice – and she was the driving force behind the family's many theatrical productions. Louisa and George were regular worshippers at All Saints, where George often read the lesson[91] and Louisa became the valued church organist and choir director. George took to supplementing his religious observance at All Saints by conducting religious services in his own home on Sunday afternoons.

～

By 1880, Bordighera was a veritable building lot, a fact brought close to home for Clarence when construction started next door on the Casa Coraggio. As soon as the house was completed, George and Louisa and their remaining nine children moved in. In addition to their own family, the MacDonalds had taken in Madame Desaint, a consumptive widow with two little girls who lived with the family for seven years until her death.

Clarence must have been greatly impressed by the MacDonalds' inventiveness and industry. Because their shipment from England had been delayed by bad weather at sea, their house was unfurnished. Undaunted, they set to work making furniture themselves as an interim measure. The boys built chairs and ottomans that their sisters upholstered. The whole family worked at staining the woodwork and painting the walls, and one of the daughters, Grace, decorated the walls of her mother's room with artistically designed eucalyptus leaves. This decorating of walls was an attractive idea that Clarence would later pursue himself.

Even though they had barely settled in, by Christmas the MacDonalds decided to present a series of religious *tableaux vivants* to the community, inviting English residents to attend one day and the Italian community the next. When over 100 Italians showed up, the MacDonalds were particularly pleased because, like Clarence, they were eager to make friends in the Italian community. Greville, the Macdonalds' eldest son, describes the extraordinary beauty of these representations and the gorgeous effects they attained considering how small the cost and how simple the lighting. 'It was my mother's genius that managed all these things, showing yet again how much the true artist can do with the poorest material.'[92]

The MacDonalds also began to hold *conversazioni* and readings in their large living room on Wednesday afternoons and services there on Sunday evenings. The setting was high Victorian. 'The window-curtains, of dark-blue velvet, form a curious contrast to the olive-green walls; the floor is carpeted chiefly by rugs of various sizes and shapes . . . a yellow shawl [hangs] over the back of a chair', writes an anonymous visitor.[93] Every colour seemed to be carefully thought out, including red and blue vases, crimson and violet anemones, even scattered oranges. MacDonald's special chair was dark green 'lightened by a judicious touch of brighter drapery carelessly hanging on the arm.' MacDonald himself added to the palette with a bright crimson necktie adorning his black velvet coat. Musical instruments, books and portfolios were strewn over every possible surface.

On Wednesdays he read from Shakespeare, Dante, or his favourite poets, Wordsworth being high on the list, and offered interpretations of the more obscure lines. On Sundays he would pick a passage from the Bible and lecture on it; Louisa and the children lightened the atmosphere during breaks with their piano playing and singing.[94] The writer and translator Linda Villari describes her visit to one of the Sunday evening services: 'Logs flame cheerily in a huge, tiled hearth; and there by the fireside, facing the reverent throng, sits a gentle, white-haired man, Bible in hand, expounding the law of Christ in eloquent northern speech.'[95] She points out that MacDonald's sermon was no formal harangue, but more like a chat about holy things, and she quickly recognised what solace the gatherings brought to those driven abroad by illness and suffering from homesickness, and how comfortingly George MacDonald's words, spoken in his Scottish accent, fell on their ears. When he concluded the service, MacDonald would kneel down and pray, and then deliver a blessing, after which Louisa softly played Handel's *Largo*. 'Still and quiet even now, the guests would at last rise and go down the wide stone stair and out beneath the flashing stars of the huge Italian sky.'[96]

It is unlikely that Clarence showed up on Wednesday afternoons – too busy botanising – but he might well have been drawn to the Sunday evening sessions. Having known MacDonald at Broadlands, he was particularly interested in George's approach to theology which mirrored his

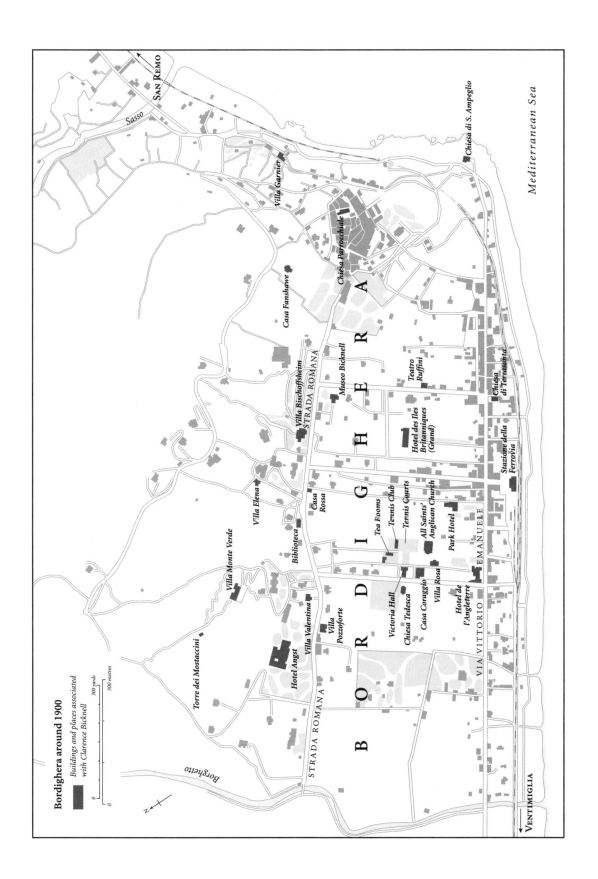

**Bordighera around 1900**

Buildings and places associated
with Clarence Bicknell

0     300 yards
0     300 metres

N

*Mediterranean Sea*

SAN REMO

*Sasso*

Villa Garnier

Chiesa Parrocchiale

Chiesa di S. Ampeglio

Casa Fanshawe

Villa Bischoffsheim

STRADA ROMANA

Museo Bicknell

Teatro
Ruffini

Hotel des Iles
Britanniques
(Grand)

Chiesa
di Terrasanta

Villa Elena

Casa
Rossa

Tea Rooms

Tennis Club

Tennis Courts

All Saints'
Anglican Church

Park Hotel

Stazione della
Ferrovia

Bibliotica

Villa Monte Verde

Victoria Hall

Chiesa Tedesca

Casa Coraggio

Villa Rosa

Hotel de
l'Angleterre

VIA  VITTORIO  EMANUELE

Torre dei Mostaccini

Villa Valentina

Villa
Pozzoforte

Hotel Angst

*Borghetto*

STRADA ROMANA

B   O   R   D   I   G   H   E   R   A

VENTIMIGLIA

61

own. MacDonald was also 'zealous for the truth alone and unwilling to proclaim that his thinking offered the last word on Christian doctrine.'[97] Religious systemization was anathema to both men; on his arrival in Bordighera MacDonald had decided that he would not offer to preach in any of the churches because an unwelcome sect might form around him. It was natural for the two men to participate in each others' lives.

Clarence even participated in the MacDonalds' dramatic presentations. The whole MacDonald family had become a well-oiled acting machine long before their time in Bordighera. In England, during the 1870s, Louisa had found that putting on plays provided the family with much-needed income. The children made their own costumes and painted scenery, and they performed children's plays in places as various as Hastings, Bournemouth and the Working Women's College in London. Eventually *The Pilgrim's Progress* became the family's most often produced play. When they decided to put on *Twelfth Night* in the living room at Casa Coraggio, the cast was too large for them to rely solely on family members, so they invited Clarence to play Orsino, opposite their lovely, dramatically-talented daughter Lilia as Viola. Such was the success of *Twelfth Night* that the audience declared the play must go on tour. Emboldened, Louisa arranged for a performance in San Remo and hired the Theatre of Cannes for a performance there on 11 January 1882. Lilia later remarked that Clarence was 'a regular whopper of a stage duke in blue satin garnished with yellow' and that his was the only costume the girls felt unable to make themselves.[98]

It certainly cannot have been peaceful living next to the MacDonalds, what with the children's singing and Louisa's playing the piano or the organ, and various orphan children running in and out. And then there were the dances: 'Our boys, and in fact the whole of young Bordighera, have gone mad on the subject of dancing, and have been giving dances all over the place', Lilia MacDonald told her friend Jane Unwin.[99] The atmosphere at Casa Coraggio with the clamour of noisy children was far different from that of the Villa Rosa with its thousands of mute drawings and dried flower specimens.

Increasingly, as time went by, both Clarence and George became exasperated with the narrow English colony. Greville MacDonald speaks of his father's feelings of oppression 'in Bordighera's stifling, chattering little community, with its constantly flitting additions from pleasure-seeking, wealthy trippers.'[100] And Clarence, in a letter to Baroness Helene von Taube, would later state: 'I am so sick of all the ordinary tea party, church-going people who are so conventional and such gossips and have so little of an international spirit.'[101]

CHAPTER FIVE

# BOTANISING IN THE HILLS

The happiest man is he who learns from Nature the lessons of worship.
Ralph Waldo Emerson

CLARENCE WAS NOT ALONE in his passion for wildflowers.[102] All Europe, but especially Britain, had become obsessed with botany. Amateur and professional botanists sprouted everywhere, with the professionals looking down on the amateurs, while the latter quite frequently had something to tell – and show – the former. Thanks to the Swedish botanist Carl Linnaeus and his system of classification according to binomial nomenclature, it had become much easier for the average person to identify plants accurately. An example of binomial nomenclature close to Clarence's heart would be *Pimpinella bicknellii,* a plant that he was to discover and which would be named after him some years later.

Botany was embraced by the middle classes and even by the poor. It enabled people to spend time out of doors, and it required very little equipment: a vasculum – a cylindrical metal box containing a base of wet moss, carried horizontally, in which specimens were transported – a hand lens for scrutinising them, absorbent paper for drying, some watercolours and paper. All over the countryside, people scoured the landscape for new flowers, mosses and ferns, and tried valiantly to identify and preserve them. Botanising was considered a suitable hobby for women, being the outdoor cousin of flower arranging and painting. It was a genteel pastime for women and children because flowers did not kill and copulate to the extent that animals often so embarrassingly did.

A healthy pursuit, it offered refreshing exercise and mental stimulation. As Susan Orlean comments in *The Orchid Thief,* 'By the nineteenth century curiosity had changed. It might have been the moment when cynicism was born. The Industrial Revolution was proving that not all man-made advances were perfect and many could be awful . . . Nature by contrast seemed pure and bewitching.'[103] Botany also offered the opportunity for women to meet interesting, albeit

A painted tin vasculum for collecting plants, of the sort used by Clarence.

sometimes eccentric, men who shared their interest in and curiosity about the subject. Botany was considered to be pious, because the study of nature – God's handiwork – confirmed His creative powers. Scientists such as Gregor Mendel and Charles Darwin soon blew apart this conventional thinking.

Clarence never claimed to be a professional botanist. He wrote about botany, he collected and preserved flowers, he drew and painted them, but his contribution to the field was enormous – precisely because he was an immensely capable cataloguer in an era when men and women were determined classifiers, list-makers and name-givers. By bearing down passionately and precisely on one topic, Clarence could shape his world into a manageable size and not worry about its uncontrollable hugeness. The thrill of discovering a new wildflower, believing in the perfection of its creation, and giving it a name and a place in the world's great catalogue gave Clarence the deepest satisfaction – and thrill.

Unable to find a handbook to the flowers of the area, he consulted John Traherne Moggridge's magisterial *Contributions to the flora of Mentone, and to a winter flora of the Riviera, including the coast from Marseilles to Genoa,* published in 1871.[104] He soon realised that Moggridge's book was incomplete, and indeed Moggridge himself, in his preface, exhorted others to keep adding to his inventory, an invitation Clarence took to heart. Moggridge states: 'The want of an illustrated Continental Flora has long been felt by tourists, invalids and others, who fail, either from want of power or inclination, to determine their plants by the present available means. Though unable at present to commence such an undertaking, I hope that the present work may afford some facilities which may induce not a few invalids and others to turn their attention to the study of the wildflowers of the district, and thus find a pleasant subject for recreation.' When he wrote this, Moggridge was dying of consumption. He then makes a heartfelt complaint, an issue about which Clarence also felt strongly: 'When considering the thousands of idle hands which every winter pull myriads of flowers to pieces south of the Alps . . . it becomes quite a marvel that these hundred-handed colonies of English should so rarely be set to work at drawing for publication some few of the wonderful objects of Natural History by which they are everywhere surrounded.'

Although Moggridge was unable to go on the kind of botanical expeditions that Clarence did, he had a loving father, Matthew Moggridge, who provided him with specimens to draw. He pays tribute to him, saying: 'My father was indefatigable in procuring subjects for my pencil, his knowledge of plants and great powers of endurance making him as able a collector as ever searched jungle or climbed Alp.'

John Traherne Moggridge (1842–1874) (left) with his younger brother Matthew and their cockatoo.

Clarence returned to Liguria during the autumn of 1879, after many months of spiritual reflection during which he dropped out of sight. No matter how or where he spent the missing months, he was back in Italy in time for the Christmas season. The temptation to return to a better climate, to the olive groves and citrus trees, to the Mediterranean, and most of all to his beloved wildflowers was clearly irresistible. He immediately resumed roaming over hills and valleys, seeking ever more exotic wildflowers, and noticing everything else: light and shadow, cloud effects, birds, butterflies, insects and stones.

Clarence took to heart John Traherne Moggridge's request that others add to his inventory of wildflowers. By 1884 he had completed over a thousand watercolour drawings of wildflowers, from which he redrew 82 onto lithographic plates to use as coloured illustrations in his own work, *Flowering Plants and Ferns of the Riviera and Neighbouring Mountains*. This luxurious volume, with notes on 280 species, colour plates with tissue paper interleaves and gilded sheet edges, was published by Trübner in London in 1885. It was reviewed in various British botanical journals. The reviewer in the *Journal of Botany (British and Foreign)* concluded that it was a handsome, expensive book, ahead of most of its class, and he enjoyed Clarence's modest tone and the care taken with drawing and description. He did, however, note that it was not on the same scientific level as Moggridge's book, and felt that the colour printing could have been better.[105]

The reviewer in *The Gardeners' Chronicle* was much more critical, commenting that the drawings were accurate as far as they went, but were more like rough memoranda than detailed drawings. He continued: 'The botanical details are not drawn to scale . . . in most cases only detached sprays, and what the old herbalists used to call "summitates" are shown . . . the illustrations seem to have been taken from specimens collected for a nosegay . . . The consequence is unfortunate for the illustrations have a stiff "weedy" look.'[106] And then, damning with faint praise, the reviewer admitted that Clarence had provided generally faithful drawings, whatever their technical defects, which would be of great service, and he would welcome a second series. In his preface to *Flowering Plants and Ferns of the Riviera and Neighbouring Mountains*, Clarence had mentioned that he was hoping to prepare such a second series, should there be a need for one.

Like Moggridge, Clarence complained bitterly in his preface that many of the coastal plants and those of the adjacent mountains 'are now to be found no more, and many others are becoming extremely scarce, owing to the ravages committed by horticulturalists' agents and winter visitors . . . Every autumn, too . . . a new road or villa or vineyard has caused the disappearance of some favourite old friends, while others had become extremely rare.'[107] Of course, Clarence

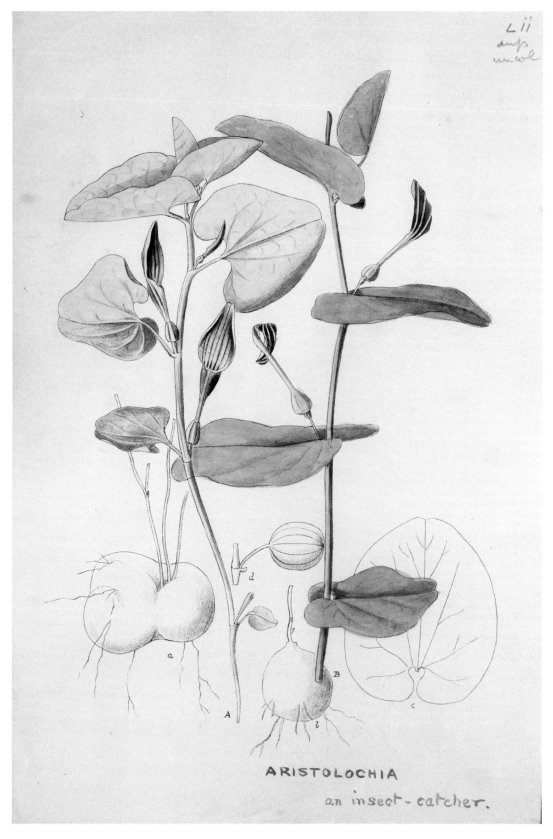

ARISTOLOCHIA

an insect-catcher.

himself was not entirely blameless. Although he seems to have left *in situ* most of the flowers and plants he painted, when it came to collecting for his herbarium, uprooting was a necessity to provide complete information.

Some residents of Bordighera, in despair, tried to stop the ceaseless collecting. Linda Villari in *Soggiorno a Bordighera* writes: 'The tourist greed for flowers that has already stripped the hills of their rarer plants, has evidently stirred residents to self-defence, for at many gates notice boards inscribed "Private" and "Do not take the flowers" in big capitals, warn off our countrymen's predatory fingers.'[108]

Clarence had published *Flowering Plants and Ferns of the Riviera and Neighbouring Mountains* in 1885, but this did not signal a halt to his botanical work. He continued to tramp up and down the hills and along the shore, listing all the wildflowers he saw. It was not long before he started climbing higher into the Maritime Alps in search of ever more exotic plants, carrying along with him Honoré Arduino's book *Flore Analytique du Département des Alpes-Maritimes.*[109] By May 1883 he had already made a trip up the Roya valley into the Maritime Alps as high as Tende and La Brigue, and on 6 June he made his first ascent to the Val Casterino (1,560 metres or 5,118 feet), a walk of three hours from Tende.[110]

Casterino! This is a name that would loom large in Clarence's future.

Fear that he might have left out a particularly interesting plant, being always obsessive about finding more, made Clarence reluctant to hand the manuscript of *Flora of Bordighera and San Remo* over to his publisher, Pietro Gibelli of Bordighera. The printer never had enough English type – the characters j, w and y do not exist in Italian; this slowed down the typesetting and caused Clarence to complain to the Swiss botanist Émile Burnat that the printer used an extraordinary mixture of type.[111] Not until 1896 was the handbook finally published. It contained a lengthy list of wildflowers, drawn up on the basis of Clarence's excursions, but not illustrated. His enjoyment of botanising is evident in the preface: 'There is no part of this district which may not be visited by a good walker, with the assistance of a carriage, within a day's excursion, and by an early start one may be among the larches, the gentians and the Edelweiss on a summer morning, and in the evening gather Oleander and Pancratium near the sea. It would be difficult to find another region of equal size with a richer or more varied flora, and after some ten years of botanical expeditions I have collected over 1700 species of vascular plants.' He then added wistfully, 'I think it well, with increasing years and decreasing walking powers, no longer to delay the publication of a catalogue of our plants.'

Clarence and Émile Burnat (1828–1920) learned of each other's existence sometime before 1885.[112] They entered into a correspondence that lasted for the next 31 years; Clarence wrote in French, the language of Burnat, and early in the correspondence apologised: 'Je regrette que j'écris si mal le français: je ne me puis (sic) bien m'expliquer.' [I'm sorry that I write so badly in French . . . I can't express myself well.][113] However, Clarence's lack of confidence about his French did not in any way impede the quantity of letters and postcards that flowed from his pen to Burnat; around 690 of them can be consulted at the Conservatory and Botanical Garden of

C.B., *Aristolochia, an insect-catcher*, hand-coloured proof for his book
*Flowering Plants and Ferns of the Riviera and Neighbouring Mountains*, 1885.

Émile Burnat (1828–1920).

the City of Geneva. Unfortunately, none of Burnat's responses has survived.

It comes as no surprise that Bicknell and Burnat should become such good friends. They were both passionate botanists and had many characteristics in common. In person, Burnat was tall, well-built, strong, a fine horseman and mule rider, and, like Clarence, an indefatigable walker until the end of his life. His sparkling eyes and great smile were said to have been unforgettable.[114] One way in which he did differ from Clarence was in facial hair design; while Clarence sported a full beard and moustache, Burnat was clean-shaven, except for his impressive long and bushy sideburns.

In his first letter to Burnat in 1885, Clarence invited him to stay at the Villa Rosa, and Burnat accepted.[115] The growing warmth of their friendship is demonstrated by the concluding phrases of Clarence's letters, which develop from the formal 'Agréez, Monsieur, mes salutations très cordiales. Votre dévoué, C. Bicknell' in the early letters to 'Je vous serre la main et me professe votre bien affectueux Clarence Bicknell' in 1887 and then to 'Mille choses affectueuses, votre très dévoué Clarence Bicknell' in 1897. However, Clarence never used Burnat's first name, addressing him always as 'Cher Monsieur'. Not only did they write to each other; they visited each other on many occasions.[116]

Their shared interest in the flora of the Maritime Alps meant that the two men had much to communicate botanically, but beyond the botany and the letters, they developed a warm relationship based on mutual respect and trust. They were generous to each other. They shared their finds. But unlike Clarence, who usually did his botanising alone or with Giacomo Pollini, using a minimum of equipment, Burnat travelled with a well-organised suite of assistants, a cook, botanical equipment, tents and mules.

Burnat and Bicknell's willingness to share knowledge and specimens is refreshing because botanists sometimes hoard their discoveries. This sharing was mutually beneficial, and they acknowledged their debt to each other in the prefaces of their published works. In his *Flora of Bordighera and San Remo* Clarence thanks 'chiefly Monsieur Emile Burnat, whose exhaustive work on the flora of the Maritime Alps is now in course of publication.' In turn, in Volume 1 of his *Flore des Alpes Maritimes,* Burnat thanks 'my friend Mr. Cl. Bicknell . . . who for six years has sent me numerous plants from different parts of the Maritime Alps for my *Flore*, of which several were new to me.' Clarence's friendship with Burnat led Bicknell to contribute hundreds of dried plants to Burnat's herbarium (now in Geneva). He also provided many descriptions of species to Burnat's monumental *Flore des Alpes Maritimes,* eventually published in seven volumes from 1892 to 1931.

Clarence paid the respect due to an eminent botanist 14 years his senior, and appreciated Burnat's botanical encouragement and advice on managing dried plants. In 1886 he wrote to Burnat 'This year I have begun seriously to make a herbarium and I will follow as much as I can your good advice.'[117] Clarence must already have recognised the value of his flower collection

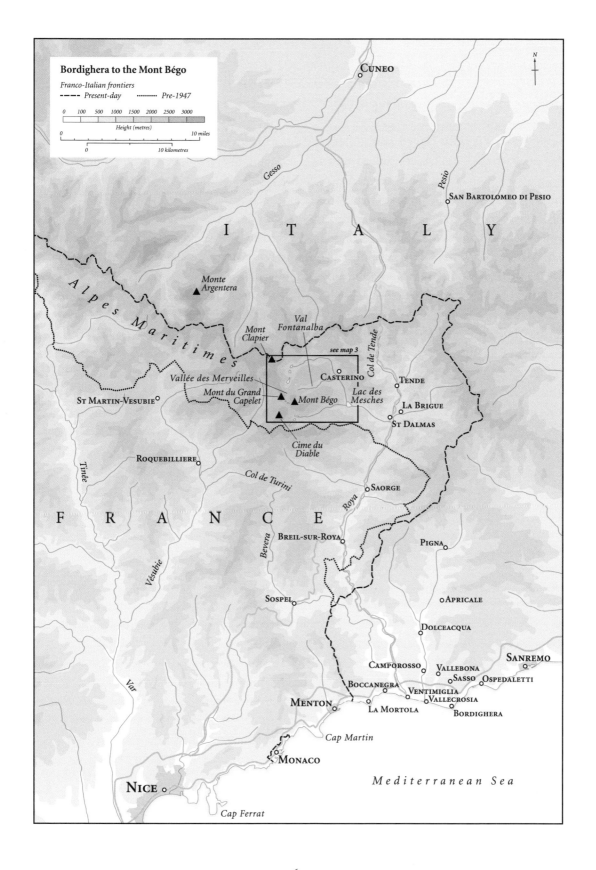

**Bordighera to the Mont Bégo**

*Franco-Italian frontiers*
- - - *Present-day*      ........ *Pre-1947*

0    100   500  1000  1500  2000  2500  3000
*Height (metres)*

0                                    10 miles
0                              10 kilometres

N

CUNEO

ITALY

*Gesso*

*Pesio*

SAN BARTOLOMEO DI PESIO

*Monte Argentera*

*Mont Clapier*

*Val Fontanalba*

*see map 3*

*Alpes Maritimes*

*Col de Tende*

CASTERINO

TENDE

*Vallée des Merveilles*

*Mont du Grand Capelet*

*Mont Bégo*

*Lac des Mesches*

LA BRIGUE

ST MARTIN-VESUBIE

ST DALMAS

*Cime du Diable*

*Tinée*

ROQUEBILLIERE

*Col de Turini*

*Roya*

SAORGE

FRANCE

*Vesubie*

*Bevera*

BREIL-SUR-ROYA

PIGNA

SOSPEL

APRICALE

DOLCEACQUA

SANREMO

CAMPOROSSO

VALLEBONA

SASSO

OSPEDALETTI

BOCCANEGRA

VENTIMIGLIA

VALLECROSIA

*Var*

MENTON

LA MORTOLA

BORDIGHERA

*Cap Martin*

MONACO

*Mediterranean Sea*

NICE

*Cap Ferrat*

because creating a herbarium requires the utmost care and persistence – and plenty of time. The process of drying plants is 'laborious, boring, and cannot be rushed. A diligent botanist tries to ensure that all the distinguishing characteristics of the plant are easily visible on the dried specimen. You need to dry a pressed plant quickly to avoid it getting mouldy, and to preserve as much of the colour as possible. Changing the drying paper every day helps the process. When the plant is neither dry nor fresh, it is floppy, and you have to lay the plant on fresh paper to avoid folding the leaves, petals etc. Changing the paper also gives an opportunity to rearrange the plant, which may not lie on the paper in the way that you wish: to see both surfaces of a leaf in the final specimen, for example, you need to arrange this when the plant is floppy.'[118]

In December 1886, Clarence wrote to Burnat that he was still struggling to dry the plants he had collected in the summer, and was discouraged by having to wait endlessly for the right equipment to arrive. Frustrated in his work and overwhelmed by the demands of Bordighera's social whirl of 'balls, meetings, committees, ecc. ecc.',[119] he made a quick dash to catch his breath in Berceto, a village in the Apennines. He spent ten days there during the Christmas festivities with the family of Dr Agnetti, his doctor friend, before gearing himself up for the advent of a nephew, a sister-in-law and many friends. This nephew was probably Edward Berry, son of Clarence's sister Ada, on an early visit to Bordighera that would have much bearing on the rest of his life.

With the publication of *Flora of Bordighera and San Remo* (1896) behind him and having edited 'an excellent map' of the Bordighera and San Remo district during his presidency of the *Società pel Bene Pubblico*,[120] Clarence felt restless enough to make a long-anticipated trip to Majorca. He took with him Luigi Pollini, Giacomo's son, who had taken over as Clarence's right-hand man when heavy labour at the Villa Rosa became too much for his father. However, Clarence kept Giacomo on as custodian of the Museo Bicknell until he died in 1913. To prepare Clarence for the adventure, the thoughtful Émile Burnat, who had already travelled there, sent him the guide to the flora of the Balearic Islands he had published in 1882.

At the time of the Majorca trip, Luigi was 23 years old, strong, willing, keen-eyed and absolutely devoted to Clarence. He turned out to be the perfect partner in all Clarence's endeavours, no matter how challenging and Clarence always treated him as an equal.

After an uncomfortable stop at Narbonne – no map, no directions and torrential rain – the two men continued their train journey as far as Barcelona where Clarence took the opportunity of purchasing the special cycling outfits and socks that Luigi wanted. Clarence explained to Burnat this was because 'He has been very courageous and useful, and is a good and intelligent assistant.' They had the intention of catching the first possible boat to Palma, but thwarted by the weather, Clarence made the unusual choice of sailing first class: 'We are still here because Tuesday's boat only had space in third class, and with this terrible wind, I dared not journey to Palma in third class, being always ill at sea . . . But I took advantage of the time to take a trip to Montserrat which is really charming.' Montserrat is a 1,236-metre mountain located about 48

C.B. *Pimpinella bicknellii* (Briquet). Clarence noted on the back 'Brought from Ariant near Pollensa, Majorca – blossomed in the garden at Bordighera May 8 1915'. The spelling of the species 'Bickneliana', in a hand other than Bicknell's, is incorrect. UniGen.

*Pimpinella Bickneliana* Briq.

kilometres from Barcelona; near its summit is perched the Benedictine abbey of Santa Maria de Montserrat, which contains a venerated and much-visited statue of a black Madonna, the Virgin of Montserrat.

In Palma they were 'well lodged but very badly fed', and the accommodation was quiet and so sunny that Clarence was able to dry his pressing paper in his room. He was enchanted by the island, its mountains and its clean and tidy villages. On their excursions, he and Luigi tried to trace the routes taken by Burnat, riding towards Lluch on mule-back through terraced foothills before ascending to Ariant. Clarence's mule was 'horribly stubborn on the rocks and scree' and the journey to the summit was difficult and painful. The mules lost their way in the fog, something which could have been disastrous, even fatal, but instead led to Clarence's miraculous discovery of a new plant 'sheltered among huge masses of rock fallen from stupendous precipices above, at a spot where another 1,000 feet of cliff shelves down to the sea below.'[121]

The plant, an umbellifer, had never before been identified, and was subsequently named *Pimpinella bicknellii* in Clarence's honour by John Briquet, the director of the Botanical Garden of Geneva.[122] A specimen collected in the same place two years later by Clarence and Luigi is now in the Oxford Herbaria. It bears a label in Latin stating that it was at a height of 4,500 metres on rocky slopes on the northern side of the hills between the two farms of Ariant (near Pollensa) and the sea.[123] In a letter to Burnat in January 1899, Clarence declared himself pleased with Briquet's write-up of *Pimpinella bicknellii*, which included a well-rendered plate of the plant. In the same letter, he said he was feeling remarkably healthy and free of colds. He put this down to the departure from the Villa Rosa of his nephew Edward, who always felt chilly. Now he could enjoy the weather – it is January – without having to heat the rooms.

# CHAPTER SIX

# THE MUSEO BICKNELL

CLARENCE FOUND THAT HIS HERBARIUM and paintings were taking up so much room in his home that he needed more space to accommodate them. At the same time, he realised there was a need for a building that could both house his collection and provide a community centre where people could enjoy concerts, talks, dances, lectures and fund-raising events. He had already thrown himself into activities which benefitted all levels of Bordighera society, and now he began to dream of a multi-purpose building, a museum that was also a hall with a stage and plenty of room for an audience. He wanted light and warmth in a place of refuge and culture, a place that celebrated the natural history of Western Liguria. He started doodling, putting ideas down on paper, and then in 1886 he took the first step.[124] He commissioned the British architect Clarence Tait, who elaborated on Clarence's ideas, applied his knowledge to them, and drew up the design for the building.

The work proceeded under the direction of an Italian architect, Giovenale Gastaldi of San Remo. Gastaldi was the same architect who built a villa for Edward Lear, and then an identical villa higher on the hill when the view of the Mediterranean from Lear's first villa was obscured by an enormous hotel. The general contractor for Clarence's museum was Francesco Giovanelli.

Clarence specified local sandstone from the Arziglia quarry for the window sills, the fireplaces and interior decorations, but he chose sturdier limestone from La Turbie for the exterior walls, the columns and capitals of the portico, the terrace and the remaining architectural decorations. The interior was plastered except for some brick stripes near the top and a floral band framing the apse and running along the entire perimeter of the hall. Outside, bands of sandstone were interspersed with bands of brick in pleasing stripes. Below the windows, Clarence and the painter/decorator Domenico Calori painted and inscribed Clarence's designs of fruit and flowers, fish and shells, birds, deer, hares and the heavenly spheres.[125]

Clarence sited the museum in a little park off the Via Romana, a park that he enlarged in 1890 when he bought some adjacent land. He hired a gardener, Ampeglio Bianchieri, and together they planted mostly indigenous flora but, following the example of his friend Sir Thomas Hanbury

Sir Thomas Hanbury (1832–1907) built the Giardini Botanici Hanbury at La Mortola.

Clarence in secular attire, Bordighera, early 1880s. Bicknell Collection.

in his gardens at La Mortola, near Ventimiglia, he imported a few exotic plants, such as *Bursera graveolens*[126] from South America, where it is known as *palo santo* or holy wood. A relative of frankincense and myrrh, it is used as incense, and its oil can be applied to aching joints to ease the pain of rheumatism.

Clarence also planted two Moreton Bay figs (*Ficus macrophylla*), descended from the first specimen brought to Italy from Australia by Lord Howe.[127] This was a great mistake. One of them has grown to such huge proportions – over 18 metres tall with vast, spreading buttresses[128] – that, today, it has all but gobbled up the museum's gate, designed by Clarence, crushed the garden's retaining wall, and played havoc with the path leading to the museum. It shows no signs of slowing down.

The giant *Ficus macrophylla* at the entrance to the Museo Bicknell in Bordighera. Photo courtesy of René Stannarius.

Photo by Ezio Benigni, *The wisteria on the face of the Museo Bicknell*, c.1900. BibCiv.

He also planted a wisteria (*Wisteria sinensis*) which has thrived to such an extent – 25 metres in length – that it reaches across the front façade of the museum and hangs down so low that you have to stoop to enter the building. Open to the sun when Clarence first established it, the garden soon became a riot of colour, a vision far different from the green shade with which one is greeted today, where the majority of plants under the giant ficus trees are shade-loving acanthus.

The New Museum, as it was at first called, would be the first museum in western Liguria, and although it was built with Clarence's own funds, he made sure that it was open to all. The architecture managed to blend the style of a Protestant church with a very mediterranean portico and decorations. The large hall was set up with an apse – that is, a semicircular recess at one end, covered by a half-dome – and this recess contained a stage.

One of two fireplaces in the Museo Bicknell has the initials of those that worked on the museum – CB, CT, GG and FG.

The hall was lit by a large, central skylight and by windows high up in the side walls. During the winter, it was heated by two impressive fireplaces, one on either side of the hall. Clarence decorated the fireplaces himself, one with leaves and flowers and the initials CB, CT, GG and FG, thereby immortalising the names of those who had worked on the museum. He decorated the other with leaves, berries and birds, and inscribed among them the words 'Non fa scienza senza lo ritenere avere inteso' from Dante's *Paradiso*. [Hearing without retaining does not make for knowledge.]

Work on the museum proceeded slowly at first because the winter of 1886 was one of the coldest on record. 'That year, the wind from the north and the snow, after having swept across the continent, came to caress the edge of the Mediterranean', writes Pierre Damon in his biography of Louis Pasteur.[129] Pasteur, his wife, daughter, son-in-law and two grandchildren were winter visitors to Bordighera in 1887, staying in the Villa Bischoffsheim, just across the via Romana from where the museum was rising. Pasteur, another visitor for whom the vaunted mild winter weather of the Riviera had proved treacherous, wrote to friends that for only the second time in the past nine years Bordighera had been subject to snow. He later complained: 'Yesterday, continual rain and snow on the mountains behind Menton. Damp and cold.' But he recognised that the storms – 'ces continuelles deviations atmosphériques' – did not endure, the sun would break out, and he and his family could soon wander among the palm trees, citrus trees and roses that abounded in Raphaël Bischoffsheim's garden. Once the weather had settled down, his main complaint was the tardiness of the Italian mail bringing him news from colleagues in Paris.[130]

As soon the museum was ready, Clarence moved his thousands of watercolours of wildflowers and his collection of specimens from the Villa Rosa into it. To these he added, in showcases on the floor, an assortment of items, testifying to the diverse history and natural history of the region. These were items he had indefatigably collected, annotated, conserved and systematically classified:[131] minerals, stuffed birds, Roman finds from the excavations at Albintimilium, prehistoric objects from the caves at Finale,[132] and even a fragment of a fresco from Pompeii. On one of his trips to England, he bought a large collection of exotic butterflies from the London naturalists, Watkins & Doncaster, which was held in two beautiful made-to-order cabinets.

Photo by Ezio Benigni, *Bordighera under snow*. BibCiv.

The museum also became the home of the English Lending Library, whose name was then changed to the Biblioteca Internazionale or the International Free Library. Until the library was moved to the museum, its books had been housed in the home of the Anglican chaplain, and it was referred to as All Saints' Library. When, by 1910, the space in the museum became too cramped for the rapidly growing collection of books, Clarence put up £1,000 – about £300,000 in today's money – towards the building of a new library specifically designed for the purpose. To this day, the International Civic Library is an exemplary building that contains over 60,000 books and more than 950 digitised photographs of Bordighera in the Victorian era.

The collection of butterflies in the Museo Bicknell.

Once the museum was completed and Clarence had moved his collections and arranged them to his satisfaction, he opened the doors to the public. It soon became the lively heart of the community, where people could attend meetings; conferences; dramatic presentations; gymnastic displays; exhibits of drawings, watercolours, photographs, embroidery; concerts that usually benefitted some good cause or other in Bordighera. Clarence's willingness to share his hall with all comers is apparent from the nationalities of the performers in a concert to raise funds for the *Asilo Evangelico* (the Evangelical Kindergarten).[133] Sponsored by the German church in Bordighera, the performers came from Bordighera, Germany and England. Few days passed without some form of entertainment or education being presented. Lantern slide shows were extremely popular as were travellers' accounts of their adventures in far-flung countries such as India, Tibet, Java, New Zealand, Fiji and Siberia. Especially appreciated was the talk by a certain Captain Empson who had travelled from Alaska to Australia.[134]

The English colony in Bordighera was well known for its good deeds, and was part of a larger tradition of British expatriates helping local populations. This generosity could sometimes be seen as patronising and yet another dependency-forming wedge that widened the chasm between rich and poor, but for the most part it was greatly appreciated.

People in need who appealed to Clarence for help were never turned away but he did not suffer fools gladly. His generosity was discreet and he managed that neat trick of providing compassion and monetary assistance without ever being patronizing. For instance, he would give funds to sick labourers, whose neediness had been brought to his attention, and he was always interested in anyone trying to get ahead academically. He

Ezio Benigni (attributed), *The interior of the Museo Bicknell in 1902.*
IISL.

provided money to a scholar to publish a work containing costly, elaborate charts, thus further-ing the young man's career.[135] Another act of generosity is particularly charming. Arturo Issel relates how Clarence encountered a foreigner, a botanist, in one of the Alpine huts he frequented. When the stranger asked him to recommend a place to stay in Bordighera, Clarence directed him to the Villa Rosa. The botanist took his advice, and stayed there for a few days, amazed by the attention he was given by the staff on orders of the patron. When it came time to settle his bill, he was stunned when his offer to pay was refused. It was only in departing that he realised the hospitality came from someone whose name he scarcely knew.

One day in 1888, as he strolled through Bordighera, Clarence heard a perfectly gorgeous voice, coming from someone singing to himself as he laid bricks. Clarence stopped and intro-

duced himself to the young mason, Pietro Zeni (1870–1932), then 18 years old. Knowing instinctively that Zeni's voice could release him from the bondage of brick-laying, Clarence arranged for him to go to Milan, and paid for Zeni to have private training and attend classes at the Conservatory. Zeni received top grades. When he arrived home from Milan at Christmas in 1894. Clarence told Burnat, 'his voice is much sweeter, and he will sing this evening at the museum.' What a delight for Clarence to hear his protégé singing in the museum, and how pleased the Bordigotti must have been to hear one of their own, now famous, in full, sweet voice, singing for them in their own town.

Pietro Zeni (1870–1932), the Bordighera bricklayer who became a respected opera singer.

In March 1895 Clarence wrote excitedly to Burnat that he was awaiting a tel-egram from Bergamo giving him the date of Pietro's debut, at which point he would set off immediately to attend the performance. Later that year, he wrote again saying he was going to see 'my Pietro' sing in Florence, taking Pietro's mother with him. He wrote yet again ten days later to say that Pietro had made enormous progress and had been very well received. 'I heard him twice in *Faust*, and he sang marvellously well, but above all I was happy about his conduct, his modesty, his thriftiness and his diligence in studying, always studying. The other tenor is unwell, and so Pietro must also sing in Verdi's *Aida*, which will be presented next Thursday for the first time, and I have great hopes that he will do very well in this opera, the music being less delicate than the French music.'

Zeni went on to sing in all the major opera houses in Europe, and his great voice even took him as far as America.

Clarence later provided considerable funds for major building projects such as the International Civic Library and a home for the aged poor. He was also known for his kindness to animals and was a staunch supporter of Bordighera's Society for the Protection of Animals. This organization was formed by the English colony to improve the lot of local animals, who appeared ill-used and often abused. The society's major contributions were lectures in the schools to teach children about treating animals with respect; the apprehending and punishment of those who performed acts of cruelty on animals; and the building of three low fountains in various parts of the town from which dogs and other animals could drink.[136] Each fountain bore the inscription: 'Siate buoni cogli animali' [be kind to animals].

# CHAPTER SEVEN

# TERREMOTO

A CATASTROPHE OCCURRED ON 23 FEBRUARY 1887, a catastrophe that called a halt to the building of Clarence's museum for several months. The previous evening, horses, mules, donkeys, cattle, dogs, chickens and even caged birds were distressed and agitated. From Nice to Genoa, animals sensed that something terrible was about to happen, and in Ventimiglia, a captive thrush honked like a goose.[137]

The following morning Liguria and the French Riviera were shaken to their foundations, though Bordighera got off relatively lightly. Many people were still in bed, but early risers were at church receiving blessings and the mark of ashes on their foreheads while the priest prophetically intoned 'Memento homo quia pulvis es et in pulverem reverteris'. [Remember you are dust, and to dust you will return.] It was Ash Wednesday.

All seemed well in the Ligurian Garden of Eden, but at 6.22a.m. the populace heard a deep rumbling and felt the earth lifting beneath their feet, immediately followed by a terrible swaying which swelled like a wave. This lasted for 12 seconds. Then came a tremendous tremor followed by a whirlwind. According to a contemporary account by Domenico Capponi, the noise resembled that of a heavy train barrelling its way through a tunnel at high speed, the noise growing louder and louder all the time.

Capponi swells to his theme: 'What a moment! In the houses, furniture was hurled about, doors and shutters slammed, bells rang, beams and roofs creaked, walls were torn apart, palaces collapsed, as did the tops of temples and workmen's houses. Twenty seconds were enough to change Liguria's Eden into a heap of ruins! Where just 20 seconds before Nature smiled, now there was nothing but immense desolation. The astounded people fled from the churches and houses; they spread out, they thronged, running for their lives towards the squares . . . Alas! How many more could not flee! Thousands upon thousands of people were buried beneath the ruins of churches and houses; hundreds upon hundreds died; numberless were the wounded. Alas, catastrophe, catastrophe, catastrophe! Liguria's garden of Eden is no more; the hand of God has struck and destroyed it!'[138]

The 1887 earthquake shook the whole Riviera and was reported in the *Illustrated London News*.

The earthquake originated off the coast at the depth of about 15 kilometres. The first shock was followed by two serious aftershocks, at 6.29 and 8.51 a.m., and these were followed by many more in the days that followed. An article published in 2012 relates some hard facts: 'The main shock of the Ligurian earthquake of 23 February 1887 was felt across a vast area that covered Switzerland and Austria to the north, and that reached as far as the eastern Pyrenees to the west and northern Sardinia to the south ... Almost 300 villages were affected by damage, 200 of which suffered great destruction.' According to the article, about 600 people died, and most of the deaths were caused by collapsing buildings. This figure differs from the estimates of 1,500, 2,000 and 3,000 that were bruited about shortly after the event. Unlike Diano Marina on the coast, which suffered catastrophic damage, and the inland villages of Baiardo and Bussana, which were completely razed and suffered much loss of life, Bordighera escaped without severe damage and experienced no loss of life.

After the first enormous tremor, everyone rushed outside in panic, and remained out of doors for most of the next two weeks – with the notable exception of George MacDonald, who stayed in his study, writing amidst a chaos of books flung from their shelves. Strangely, his little statue of Jesus remained perfectly in place on top of the bookcase.

The English houses suffered less damage than those of the Italians, being generally more strongly built, but MacDonald's daughter Lilia wrote witheringly about the English colony's reaction: 'The English about us have suffered not at all, and in some cases have behaved disgracefully,'[139] in marked contrast to her own family, which provided comfort to the homeless and gathered up friends to sew garments for those who had lost everything. At the moment when a massive aftershock occurred the following day, Louisa MacDonald was sitting at the church organ, taking a breather from the chaos at Casa Coraggio. Even though the church swayed so hard that it seemed about to collapse, she pulled out all the stops and launched into a thunderous version of the Hallelujah Chorus.

Louis Pasteur was so shaken that he bundled up his family and fled from Bordighera back to France.

Clarence's correspondent Arturo Issel, an archaeology professor at the University of Genoa and also a palaeontologist, geologist, malacologist, wrote extensively about the earthquake in his book *Il Terremoto del 1887 in Liguria*. In his introduction, he acknowledges Clarence's help and, in his exhaustive description of the damage wreaked upon Liguria, includes two interesting nuggets of information that relate to Clarence. The first is that on one his forays out of town to help others, keen-eyed Clarence noticed that the level of the spring of sulphurous water at Giancarello, just outside Bordighera, had risen by about a third, even though there had been no change in its temperature.[140] The second is that near Ventimiglia in the gardens of the Villa Hanbury, the home of Clarence's friend Sir Thomas Hanbury, the marble balustrades of an arcade completely changed their orientation from south to north, while the villa itself was undamaged.

Two weeks after the earthquake, Clarence wrote to Burnat about the damage to his home even as he kept hoping that Burnat's proposed visit might occur: 'If my house can receive you, I shall be very happy to see you here, but we have not yet begun work on the repairs. There is not a single room without more or less damage . . . huge pieces of fallen plaster – the ceilings, the walls are all cracked. We patiently await the end of the little tremors that plague us almost every night.'[141]

Clarence then reported to Burnat how he had assisted the Earthquake Help Committee in bringing relief to the terribly ruined little mountain villages, finding out what the villagers needed and returning with a mule cart laden with provisions and blankets. As for his own household members, they had taken up lodging in the garden, covering the bower with all the carpets of the house, making it into a kind of 'royal tent'. Four people slept in it, while the cook slept in Clarence's alpine tent. 'It's not as though we were timid, or were scared of new shocks, it was because one could not sleep tranquilly when the least shaking made the brick walls vibrate . . . the solid walls are not really damaged, but I could easily knock down the dividing walls with one hand.' He finished his letter with just one complaint: the earthquake meant that he was still behind in organising his specimens, 'still a quantity not attached to paper – still a hundred not identified.'

A few days later, on 4 March, in full, forthright, fund-raising mode, Clarence wrote to the editor of the London newspaper, *The Morning Post*, under the heading 'The Late Earthquakes in Italy.' The letter reveals the havoc wreaked in a village near Bordighera – and Clarence's scorn for the apathy of the municipality:

> Sir, If this should meet the eye of any of our numerous winter visitors, who either left us before the late terrible earthquake or who were driven away in consequence of it, perhaps they will feel disposed to help the little international committee which we have formed here for the immediate succour of the sufferers in our own commune and in the neighbouring villages. Hitherto the municipality of Bordighera has done absolutely nothing, except affix to the walls, and that only yesterday, a few undated telegrams from the Turin and other observatories, which might have been useful in calming the panic-stricken people a week ago, but are now as useless as they are ridiculous. Our committee, however, has been for some days actively at work personally visiting the villages round about us, and taking them food and coverings. We have in a few days collected over 3,000 francs, but this sum will soon be exhausted. We waste no money in printing or in paying secretaries, &c., but defray the few necessary expenses out of our own pockets. Today I have myself taken meat and blankets to the wretched population of Castel Vittorio, a town of which the newspapers have at present said nothing, situated in the mountains 17 miles distant. The 1,700 inhabitants are nearly all camped out under the olives and chestnuts, while the hills above them are still covered with snow. Four-fifths of the houses are beyond hope of repair, split from top to bottom; food, furniture, utensils, and clothing being in many cases buried beneath the rubbish of the fallen roofs and floors . . .

And so on.

By June Clarence was able to take a trip to England, where he stayed first in London and then with one of his brothers in Beckenham. He wrote to Burnat about how delightful he found the green of the English countryside, the flowers in his brother's garden, and the huge number of birds. He had no doubt been reminded of how voraciously his Italian friends consumed their songbirds and how bereft he was of birdsong in Bordighera.

When he arrived back in Bordighera, his house was still uninhabitable, so he spent the next two weeks taking care of 'une amie malade', at her house. Eventually, she recovered enough for him to leave the terrible heat of Bordighera which, he told Burnat, 'during the day made me suffer terribly and gave me a powerful skin irritation, and during the night I was unable to sleep because of the mosquitoes.' Taking Giacomo with him, he found pleasant lodgings in Ormea, a village in the mountains above Bordighera, where he revelled in the fresh air, the trees, the cold-water baths, the mushrooms, the flowers, the butterflies, and the excellent botanical excursions.

Unfortunately, he had to cut this visit short because his ill friend suddenly found herself alone, without help. He felt it was just as well that he returned because another English lady died two days later, and 'It was left to me to arrange the burial and to perform the service at the tomb . . . I hope that I was able to encourage and console her a little during the last two days of her life.' When needed, Clarence could still fulfil the role of a pastoral minister of the church.

Once the Villa Rosa was habitable, he and Giacomo set to work putting everything to rights. He told Burnat that as soon as he had liberated some tables, he would set to work on his herbarium and would soon send him some specimens. And the mosquitoes were still tormenting him.

By October, the bedrooms were all in order but the chairs and sofas in the salon were still encumbered with plants. Nonetheless, Clarence was looking forward to a visit from Burnat, and was actively house-hunting for him in an effort to bring the Burnat family to Bordighera during the winter.

In January of 1888, Clarence apologised to Burnat for the long interval between letters because of a terrible attack of sciatica during which he lay in bed for two weeks, reading 'the biography of Charles Darwin, published last autumn.'[142] In all likelihood, this book is *The life and letters of Charles Darwin, including an autobiographical chapter* (London: John Murray, 1887).

In April, Clarence expressed his sorrow over the death of Burnat's mother in a particularly interesting letter because he approaches the subject of God: 'I hope that He who understands everything, and loves more than we do, has done all for the best – but I doubt this sometimes. It seems to me impossible to console friends when they are suffering, but at least one can say to oneself "be more of a friend, stronger, more good, and ease to the extent that one can the sorrows of this life with sympathy and love," and that is how I am thinking right now.' Clarence then uttered a little *cri de cœur*: 'You were blessed to have your mother for such a long time . . . I lost mine, an irreparable loss for a child, when I was seven years old.'[143]

Burnat's wife died a mere month after the death of his mother.

By June, Clarence was still suffering from sciatica, perhaps as a result of hauling his various collections from the Villa Rosa over to the New Museum, as the Museo Bicknell was then called. Hoping to improve matters, he took himself off to Terme d'Acqui where he wallowed in the mud baths and complained to Burnat that he was suffering a great deal of pain, pain that was exacerbated, rather than assuaged, by the treatment. However, a few days later he wrote that he felt much better and had just arrived in San Bartolomeo di Pesio.

Carlotta – probably his friend Carlotta Gibelli, who ran the *Magazzino per Tutti* in Bordighera – and his right-hand man Giacomo Pollini were already there and everything was fresh and green. He spent the rest of the summer there botanising, and even enjoyed a visit from Burnat himself. On a subsequent visit to San Bartolomeo di Pesio, he received a joking challenge from Burnat: 'hunt for *Ranunculus lacerus*', a plant not seen since 1790. Such was Clarence's ability to find and identify plants that he was duly able to find a specimen and send it to Burnat.[144]

In October 1888, five months after the death of Burnat's wife, Clarence made his first visit to Burnat's home in Switzerland. Burnat had inherited property from his grandfather, located in Nant, a small village in the foothills of the Alps, above Vevey. It must have been a substantial establishment to house Burnat's vast collection of books and wildflower specimens. By the time of Clarence's visit, he was well on the way to a total of specimens that would reach approximately 210,000 by the time of his death in 1920. He was definitely a man after Clarence's own heart; they were bonded in personality, interests and collections.

In his letter of thanks for the visit, Clarence had a sad tale to tell. He had been the victim of a robbery on the train journey from Vevey to Turin. In a mere instant of inattention, a small case containing money, his barometer and Burnat's present to him of a fine bottle of kirsch had simply vanished. 'One must never for a moment leave alone little cases containing

C.B., *San Bartolomeo di Pesio, July 21st 1888*. View of the village in Clarence's pocket sketchbook.

items of value. Being honest myself, I expect honesty in my fellow man . . . but these unfortunate ones, are they really being very evil when they steal?' With this remark, Clarence seems almost too good to be true.

He writes to Burnat in the same vein when his son Jean is preparing to take his first communion: 'Tell him that I will think of him on Easter day and I hope he will learn from his first communion, and always more and more, all the beautiful truths that we practice with such great difficulty, the duties toward our neighbours, the support of the human race, the love for everyone, and in a word what St Paul has said so well "members of one body," "members of one another".'[145]

The following summer, he again escaped the heat and dust of Bordighera by visiting his sister Ada, then living in Much Hadham in England, going on to Gurteen in Shinone, Ireland, to stay with his brother Percy. Clarence was fond of Percy, much fonder of him than of Sidney, but often had to bail him out of financial difficulties. To Burnat, he described the lovely little flowers that

The faces in this photo show warmth and friendship: Carlotta Gibelli, wife of the printer and manager of the Magazzino per Tutti in Bordighera, sits next to Clarence, then the ever-present dog and Margaret Berry. The girls are Carlotta's daughters Emma and Ida.

grew in the quiet countryside and extolled the virtues of peat, but he had no time for Percy's neighbours, landowners who were 'neither Catholic nor Home-Rulers; on the contrary, all of them, except my brother, are very intolerant Protestants, and are convinced that all the nationalist chiefs are assassins and thieves. Next door to us lives a very grand proprietor who never wants to give work to a Catholic.'

Then Clarence suddenly mentioned his sister Lucinda, whom he had scarcely seen since her marriage to the Rev. Henry Maxwell Egan, the Chaplain of the Guards. In Clarence's opinion, Egan was despicable. 'My sister is probably going to spend the winter in Geneva. I would be happy to present her to you – because she has a charming daughter, quite disabled, very deaf and can't speak well – and two other little ones – but unfortunately her husband is so malicious, so everything that is horrible, that our sister has been completely separated from us, and I almost never see her, and I can never ask my friends to meet her.' Indeed, it is so surprising to hear him speak ill of anyone that it makes him seem more human and less saintly. The estrangement from his sister was particularly sad because Lucinda was closest to him in age of all his siblings – just two years separated them – and thus his earliest playmate.

When Clarence finally returned to Bordighera after his stay in Ireland, he described to Burnat the situation he found: 'The garden was more burned up and sad than in any previous year, but the rats had not eaten my poetry books (as they did once), nor had insects eaten my plants, about which I was happy, and in a few days, after I have sorted out my books and tidied drawers that I had left in great disorder, I hope to pay attention to plants and to send to you as soon as possible all those you desire.'

*Notes of a Tour in Italy. Egypt &c 1889 – 1890.*

Our party is composed of A, B, C & D.

A is an artist and able-bodied seawoman, prepared to nurse the other 3 landlubbers if necessary, on the water. B. is her sister provided with all the requisites for nursing A. C & D on land. C & D are proprietors in Italy, travelling for the benefit of their health under the care of the aforementioned A & B. lastly C is myself, who wrote this diary —

On Wed.ᵈ Dec. 4ᵗʰ 1889 they all started from Bordighera at midday, an international crowd having gathered on the station platform to see them off. How they travelled to Genoa in the sunshine, & thence to Bologna by night in the snow, & thence to Ancona in the early morning & in the rain need not be related in detail. They went 2ⁿᵈ class, had the carriages nearly always to themselves & reached Ancona at 8 am on Dec. 5ᵗʰ. Ancona is a picturesque town partly built on steep hills close to the sea & partly at their base: with a fine harbour, & a great many colliers discharging coal, and little fishing boats landing soles, mackerel, shrimps, & cuttlefish; a kind of white lobster and many small crabs and curious sea creatures. There are some broad new

The first page of Clarence's soft-bound Egypt diary.

86

CHAPTER EIGHT

# THE EGYPT DIARY

EGYPT WAS A FAVOURITE DESTINATION of travellers in the Victorian era. Clarence's trip is recorded in an illustrated diary. The juxtaposition of watercolour images with the text is one of the charms of this volume. Clarence may have preferred his botanical art, but he was also a competent landscape and seascape artist. Like so many of his Victorian contemporaries on their travels, he recorded his trips with sketches and watercolours. The diary opens with a description of his party, to whom he refers as A, B, C and D, rather than using their actual names. They were, as we find out much later, Giacomo Pollini, and Lucy and Fanny Leach, daughters of the late Robert Valentine Leach of Devizes and the Villa Valentina, Bordighera. 'A is an artist and able-bodied sea-woman, prepared to nurse the other 3 landlubbers if necessary, on the water. B is her sister provided with all the requisites for nursing A C and D on land. C & D are proprietors in Italy, travelling for the benefit of their health under the care of the aforementioned A & B. Lastly C is myself who wrote this diary.'[146]

An 'international crowd' gathered at Bordighera's train station on 4 December 1889 to wave farewell to the group. The train puffed its way through snow overnight to Bologna and then through rain to Ancona. There the travellers stopped to visit the Basilica de la Santa Casa at Loreto, a church built around what was said to be the Virgin Mary's house. In spite of being sceptical, Clarence played the role of pilgrim.

Of course I knelt down in that house – of course I kissed the shining blackened walls. Was it super-stition? Is that part of the old house of Nazareth, brought from there by monks and relic-hunters or borne through the air by angels . . .? Or is it some-thing else set up by deceivers to promote 'the devo-tion of the faithful'? . . . 'That is the window where the angel saluted the Madonna' said our guide! The Santa Casa I greatly liked – the 'business' about it, the 'roaring trade' not at all.

Ezio Benigni, *Train arriving at Bordighera*. BibCiv.

C.B., *On board P&O's Hydaspes, Brindisi to Alexandria,*
*8–13 December 1889.* Diary sketch.

Here, as so often during the second part of his life, Clarence acknowledges the mystery at the heart of religion while eschewing the trappings of superstition and the commercialisation of belief.

The travellers continued their journey the following morning, taking the slow train to Brindisi, where they boarded the *Hydaspes* and found their accommodation: 'A and B had *excellent* cabins. C in the 2nd class was well off. D the worst on the main deck near the sheep and far away from the saloon . . . We have about 100 1st class passengers, about 20 2nd. The Tsar's 3rd son with a large suite are on board, charming looking people . . . I am in a cabin with a Mr. Stead going to Australia and am very comfortable. A top berth *seems to me very attractive.*' Grand Duke George was the 3rd son of the Tsar. He and his elder brother Nicholas, the future Tsar, were on a grand tour that included Egypt, India, Singapore, and Bangkok. Although Clarence does not mention Nicholas, it seems likely that he was on the boat also, possibly travelling incognito.

The passage from Brindisi to Alexandria was pleasant and calm, even calm enough for sporting events on the deck: 'Cricket matches going on furiously, but every few minutes the string balls, made by the sailors, go into the sea and someone or other is fined 6d.'

The *Hydaspes* arrived at Alexandria at dawn and Clarence was on deck to watch the arrival: 'Soon the land became visible, and presently we were near the *outlying* flour mills and other buildings and the palaces and minarets of the East became visible. By about 7 we had entered the grand harbour full of ships and were soon alongside the quay and rejoiced in the first sight of the groups of men in lovely colours of skin and clothing.'

Clarence had booked a Cook's tour for their voyage up the Nile. Cook, the great travel impresario and founder of the Thomas Cook & Son travel agency, had been organising trips up the Nile since 1869, and Clarence was impressed by Cook's representative whisking them through Customs without their luggage being examined, 'by bribery, I suppose', in a place where the confusion was indescribable. Safely transferred to the train station, the four ensconced themselves in their second-class carriage for the journey from Alexandria to Cairo. Clarence, who insisted on travelling second class, pronounced himself delighted: 'We were the only 2nd class passengers: we were very glad of this

as lots of the natives came in from one station to another and we saw and learnt much. The 2nd carriages were like Swiss ones . . . The journey was one continuous wonder and surprise . . . The scene like a kaleidoscope, an ever changing picture of form and colour. The mud villages of Fellaheen . . . great groves of palm trees, very tall and looking quite different to our Bordighera ones, i.e. looking *at home* and much more beautiful and healthy. The multitude of people . . . and everywhere in the flat country, buffaloes, cows, sheep, donkeys and *piggeries*, while the air is full of wild birds, rooks and hawks and quantities of little ones, and some of them so beautiful . . . The camels are delightful.'

Once established in the Hotel Royale in Cairo the four set out on foot to explore the city, albeit unsteadily: 'We all 4 feel the effects of the sea so much. The earth seems to be *rolling* as in an earthquake.' Even so, entranced by everything they saw, they persisted and 'We walked till we could walk no more.'

The following morning, they took their first sightseeing excursion on donkey-back, guided by a dragoman, that is, an interpreter/guide, 'a splendid fellow, very pleasant and has the reputation at the hotel for honesty and experience, and he remembers well my brother [Herman] who made the pilgrimage to Mecca about 20 years ago . . . such strong good little donkeys! But mine set off galloping, I couldn't stop him, my stirrup broke and I thought every moment I would be pitched over

David Roberts R.A., *Mosque of Sultan Hassan, Cairo*, 1838. Clarence's half-brother Henry married Roberts's daughter, Christine.

his head or tumble off, but I clung on like grim death and survived!' But the end of the day, Clarence was able to write, 'It is immense fun donkey riding in Cairo: the beasts are so well-behaved and obedient . . . they are beautifully kept and have lovely embroidered and most comfortable saddles.'

That evening Clarence wrote to Émile Burnat: 'Oh! How beautiful this country is, the mosques, the streets, the palm trees and most of all these magnificent Egyptians. It is ravishing; all the books, paintings, photographs have never given me any idea of the movement, the colours, the

variety in this town. What has astonished me most is the countryside of the Delta . . . What a desert Italy and England are after that . . . I am completely enchanted with everything . . . I see beautiful *Cyperus* in the canals, some *Polygonum* and *Amaranthus,* several grasses.'

Day after day, from 13 to 26 December, the four went sightseeing in and around Cairo, never seeming to tire. They attended a performance by the 'howling dervishes'; they visited Rhoda, an island in the centre of Cairo, to see the Nilometer, a

C.B., *A mosque outside Cairo, 16 December 1889*, watercolour.

submerged column with marked levels for gauging the height of the river, housed within a grand building; 'We passed enormous rubbish heaps mountain high everywhere and then returned into the most wonderful streets of old houses and mosques without end.'

At night, they strolled in the streets 'where the lamps were being lighted in front of the

crowded shops and we *peered* into the barbers and arab *caffèes* and all sorts of strange places.' They visited the remains of Heliopolis, where they admired the Re-Atum obelisk. Clarence remarks 'We did not care to go and see the *Virgins* here', referring not to a brothel but rather to an account he must have read in Sozomen's *Ecclesiastical History* of the barbaric acts perpetrated against the holy virgins. Instead, they visited an ostrich farm. 'The first thing my donkey did was to tumble down so of course I was pitched over his head – so I said *bad donkey* to the boy and jumped up on another . . . There were 500 birds . . . In some of the pairs the male birds were sitting on the eggs in the sand.'

On their visit to the pyramids, the four felt impelled to climb the great pyramid. 'Of course it would be easy enough to go up quietly, and I cannot conceive anyone being giddy on such broad steps, but the arabs seize both one's hands and a third pretends to push behind, and so they drag one up and hardly allow one time to rest. We however insisted on stopping several times. The climb did not seem to me very long and soon we were on the flat platform . . . We stayed there a long time, but we were greatly worried by the men wanting us to buy things, talking incessantly about their "backshish" &c.', a constant annoyance throughout the trip.

Page 13 is typical of Clarence's diary. He writes his text round the sketches or watercolours afterwards.

Having descended from the top of the pyramid by jumping down from one large slab to the next, Clarence and the braver of the two Miss Leaches decided to see the interior of the pyr-

C.B., *The Great Sphinx of Giza*, watercolour, 23 December 1889.

amid, and 'with 2 men each holding candles went on alone . . . In the Kings' Chamber with its solitary red granite sarcophagus we lighted magnesium wire and remained a little while and then returned easily but very hot and dusty. They knew how to build in those days.' In the late nineteenth century, burning magnesium wire was a popular method of producing an extremely bright, white light.

Clarence was at first disappointed by the Sphinx, 'but gradually one recognised its colossal size and its strange beauty, which by degrees fascinates one – and there it has been, this great stone creature half beast half human looking out at the sunrise for who shall say how many thousand years.'

He was open to everything he saw, but he was disturbed by the almost invisible women who stayed inside their homes, cooking and cleaning and caring for the children. 'Selim [the dragoman] brought his pretty little girl of 7 to see us today, gorgeously arranged in crimson with a long net veil, artificial flowers in the hair and many bead necklaces. He has had 19 children by 2 wives and lost 17.

The women do not go to the

*Climbing a Pyramid*, c. 1885.

mosques, or pray like the men. Selim calls everything and everybody "he" – speaking of his wife he says "he always stop at home: he would be ashamed to be seen in the street".'

Clarence was impressed by how clean – although dusty – Cairo was.

Cairo is beautifully clean and sweet compared to most of the cities of Southern Europe. There are no heaps of rotting vegetables, egg shells and no filthy corners. The people don't spit. Their behaviour is very respectable. Beggars too are exceedingly scarce. People do not stare and are not half as troublesome as when one is sketching as in Italy. They seem very agreeable but at the same time one cannot help feeling that these Muslims hate the Christians.

Clarence had a wonderful Christmas Day. First, he went to Mass at the Italian church and to a fraction of a service in the Coptic church. 'Hardly anyone there, & the place very dirty, & the officials looking so also. The Coptic & Greek Xmas is much later than ours.' He and Giacomo spent the rest of the morning exploring and sketching before returning to the hotel. 'After a grand Xmas luncheon beginning with mince pies, we all took donkeys & went out to our favourite tombs of the Khalifs &

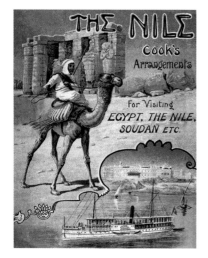

across the desert to the Red mountains, which we ascended for the magnificent view; the day was simply perfect, with the clouds casting deep purple shadows over the sand, the city bathed in light. A long Xmas dinner finished up the day, and nearly finished us up also.'

On Boxing Day, the second half of the trip began. 'Goodbye to Cairo at last!' exulted Clarence, glad by then to leave the teeming city. The four joined twenty others boarding the paddle steamer that would carry them up the Nile.

'There are some Italians, French, Swiss, Americans, Germans, many English & 3 brothers whose nationality I don't at present know. The boat is small but very comfortable with upper decks fore & aft provided with awnings . . . [it] goes very slowly – slow & sure – and on we go; the river is crowded with the beautiful feluccas.' The journey proceeded

with stops every so often when the passengers would disembark and hire donkeys for their sightseeing excursions. Time and again Clarence was struck by the beauty of the light: 'The light on the Nile is indeed wonderful . . . something we have not seen in Italy, a clearness, a transparency, a fullness of radiance . . . I had read & heard of the light & the colouring in Egypt, but it all far surpassed my most sanguine expectations & the quiet & peace of it all is pleasant after the streets of Cairo.'

Day by day they sailed up the Nile, admiring the scenery as they glided by, stopping every so often to visit a particularly interesting site but sometimes staying on board to sketch or to study their guidebooks.

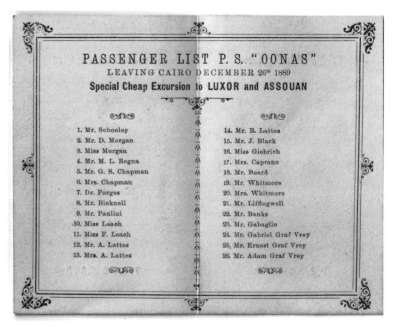

The 26 passengers on the excursion up the Nile are listed as if on a dance card. Giacomo Pollini's name has been spelled Paulini.

Clarence painted dozens of these Nile cargo boats, feluccas, in his diary, often several in a pose. Diary sketch.

After a night visit to Beni Hassan, Clarence wrote:

We start again for the tombs we had seen from the boat about 2–3 miles off, the boat captain cantering about on a fine Arab horse, the 3 soldiers on donkeys with their sticks, about 17 of us on donkeys with all their attendants, the sheik of the village and others carrying a sort of hatchet on the end of long sticks. We were advised to keep all together being assured that if we separated we might at any moment be mown down and robbed . . . The walls [were] covered with coloured hieroglyphics, beautifully executed but disappearing, and sadly spoilt by the hideous charcoal scrawls of visitors. I need not describe the pictures as the guide books do so thoroughly . . . It was a strange night, the moonlight without, & all the savage looking people & the men with guns at the entrance to the tombs, and the yawning pits inside into which someone's friend might easily push one.

An opening of the Diary showing the relationship between the sketches and the text.

Thomas Cook operated a fleet of a dozen ships on the Nile. Clarence was on the *Oonas*.

Time and again problems arose with the boat's engine, 'It was evident something was wrong as we stopped twice, and just after the end of dinner, past 10 o'clock, came a sudden stop, the anchor was let down . . . and we heard a screw of the cylinder had broken & we must stop till it could be repaired. Such a row & a talking, with all the sailors, captain, engineer &c gathered down below.'

All was well the following morning:

The engine was repaired during the night, & about 5 a.m. we started again, but going slowly, hoping to repair more thoroughly at Siout. The river was covered with the beautiful boats . . . they look like birds with their 2 great outstretched wings, dark against the southern sky . . . The hills with serial tombs, and more often quarries in the steep cliffs, always near the river, with stretches of undulating sand & then a narrow line of brilliant green by the shore, & lots of grasses & other plants, which I long to see near at hand; all very beautiful and enjoyable.'

Clarence was clearly thwarted in his efforts to botanise; there was never enough time, but on 30 December he and Giacomo arose early, and by 6.30 were 'out among the fields & palms looking for plants, of which we find a good many evidently wild, & others doubtful. Coriander seems much cultivated & 2 kinds of clover.'

Being away from home on the eve of a new year made Clarence reflective about the nature of the past in Egypt and the mystery of the future.

It is the last day of the year. May the cold winds go with it, & the new year bring us pleasanter weather. Yes, and to others as well as ourselves . . . The last day of the year brings many thoughts with it, and more than ever here one keeps wondering over the story of the byegone years & centuries & ages, & thinking of the lives of the early Egyptian architects & sculptors & painters, suddenly coming out of the unknown, with all their developed powers & then of the Israelites in Egypt, and many another race who sailed the Nile & lived on its banks. And then the suppression by force of the religion of the country by Xtian emperors, and the desert peoples with the monks & ascetics, soon to be swept away by Islam. What changes have taken place here in those 6000 years & now one rushes quickly by in a 2 1/2d steamer & passes ruined cities and empty caves, and abandoned churches & decaying mosques & wonders what will come next? A better religion? Who can say?

A better religion? It seems that Clarence never gave up on religion entirely, but continued to reflect on the variety of religious experience. But by the end of New Year's Eve, he was less reflective: 'The gentlemen are getting up a New Year's Eve entertainment . . . Before 9 we go down to play games, which with singing, much drinking of health in toddy, punch & champagne lasts till past midnight, but the boat goes quietly on till past 3 a.m., & starts again at 5.'

On New Year's Day, the boat reached the departure point for the temple of Dendera. The visitors disembarked and in about half an hour arrived to find the temple 'half concealed among enormous rubbish heaps & buried black brick walls . . . It is impossible to make out the story told on the walls, every inch of which in every chamber is covered with sculpture. As one penetrates further & further into the recesses towards the most holy place of all, which hardly any daylight reaches, it becomes more & more solemn &

C.B., *Hills behind Denderah, New Year's Day 1890,* diary sketch.

impressive, but the most interesting parts are narrow underground passages, the places for concealing the chief treasures of the temple . . . We resist all the attempts of the dragoman to make us come on, and with candles & guide books in hand go religiously through all the chambers, making out which were sacred to Osiris, which to some other divinity.'

Clarence was struck by the swarms of wasps everywhere, 'filling up the interstices of the sculpture with their mud homes', and noted that 'vandals had cut, painted and scrawled their names over everything, and torches have burnt & blackened the sculptured & painted ceilings. The colour has in great measure disappeared.'

Were he alive today, Clarence would be overjoyed to know that the careful cleaning away of soot on the ceiling of the Hathor Temple has revealed the original bright paint. In fact, he would be hard pressed to recognise the beautifully preserved site that today's tourists enjoy.

That night the boat made fast at Luxor. In the brilliant moonlight, Clarence could make out the majestic columns of the temple. 'Immediately some of us step off the boat, and are soon wandering about in the marvellous pile of ruins that lie close to the river side; then to bed.'

Thursday 2nd Jan. What a day of wonders! All the party off at 8, some of us having revisited the temple before breakfast. We cross the river in 2 boats, are carried ashore through the water & get onto donkeys, while a great camel is laden with the provisions of some 30 people.

The great ugly beautiful beast, looking so quiet & so restless so good tempered & so cross, so graceful & so ungainly, so stupid & so superior to everything & everybody, with the great proud nostrils, his strange furry feet, his strap for a tail, & his coat of old bits of worn out sheepskin of different ages & colours. Of course the first thing my donkey does is to tumble down & pitch me onto the hard sun-baked ground.

Clarence writes a lot about his donkeys, but this is the only watercolour of one in the diary. 'Keneh' 10 January 1890. Diary sketch.

Unharmed, Clarence proceeded along with the party 'up & down sand & mud dykes, & through flat green cornfields' until they reached the Valley of the Kings:

> a tortuous ravine of sand & stones, all white, red & yellow, without a sign of vegetation or life, becoming every minute more confined and at length where the limestone & mudstone cliffs are more perpendicular, we stop & with an excellent dragoman see 4 of these marvellous sepulchers, most interesting & most beautiful for all the brilliant colouring on the walls & roofs [it is interesting to note that it would be another 33 years before Howard Carter was to discover the tomb of Tutankhamen in the Valley of the Kings] . . . but it is misery to see temples & tombs with so many people, half of whom only look on the ground vainly hoping to pick up treasures . . . May I never travel again with a party.

Another irritant was the constant pressure from antiquity sellers: 'One carries a skull, another a mummy foot; one has pieces of painted wood, another scarabs, bottles, everything you can imagine.'

He toured with a vengeance the following day. 'Sketching in the Luxor temple in the morning before breakfast, afterwards with Dr Porges, an Austrian, & the American doctor, and our own dragoman and a porter carrying a huge basket of lunch, we started for Karnac along an excellent road, and on truly noble donkeys. I felt as safe on mine as on a granite sphinx; he never stumbled, walked at a marvellous pace, was No. 11 and called George Washington.' At the great temple of Karnak with its hall of 134 columns, 'of which one has heard & read & thought all one's life', Clarence admitted to being a little disappointed at first: 'It seemed so much less grand & so much less tall, less coloured & less perfect, but by degrees it began to grow upon one, and before long one appreciated the immense circumference & height of this glorious erection.'

The group continued 'into the great court, through the Gate of the large Pylon, & climbed to the top of it. Then back again to the hall of columns & the obelisks & so on & on from temple to temple longing to understand something, and see it all thoroughly & quietly.' On and on they went through the maze of ruins and among the palms and tamarisks, finally returning to the boat at sunset, in time for Clarence to draw in the Luxor temple. Then off he went to have dinner with friends at the Luxor hotel, returning in time to ride back to Karnak by moonlight

David Roberts R.A., *Column Hall of the Temple at Karnak/ Egypt in 1838.*

with Dr Porges. 'We were back about 10.30 after a most delightful excursion, but we hardly knew how to take leave of the great Hall of Columns, and the obelisks & the massive pylons, and it

was so weird trotting on in the brilliant moonlight & now in the deep shadow, accompanied by one of the temple guardians with his long stick, and of course several of his satellites, to whom the inevitable baksheesh had to be given before leaving; but one cannot grudge these trifling presents of a piaster or two to these poor & pleasant people.'

As the journey continued, the four would disembark to see special sights: 'Sometimes one sees men saying their prayers on the river bank, they never turn round

*Edfou. 8/1/90*

or look at the passing steamboat, but remain facing Mecca. Nor does one see women carrying anything on their heads but the water-pots, large or small . . . Some few have nose rings, all of them necklaces of beads or berries sometimes of cowries, bracelets & many cheap brilliant rings, also large earrings . . . Many of the men & boys work naked; indeed today most of the men were naked, though the wind was cool & the sun none too hot. How can they stand this, & what can they do in summer, if they can't remove their skins?'

C.B., *Pylon of the Temple of Horus at Edfou.* Diary sketch.

On Sunday 5 January, once again displaying his energy and curiosity, Clarence wrote: 'I got up at 3, and half-dressing went ashore in hopes of seeing the constellation of the Southern Cross, but I either did not see it because of some houses & trees hiding the horizon, or it was not visible . . . anyhow I enjoyed the strange quiet of the night's stroll, not even disturbed by the bark of one of the jackal-like dogs.' Later that day, the group went on donkey-back to see the temples at Edfou and Esneh, but

Clarence's day was not entirely devoted to temple viewing: 'Today I have added 2 more plants to my small collection . . . It is difficult to get anything when on donkey backs, as if I get off a crowd instantly assembles out of space, and every piece of the thing I am after is pulled off by the head, in the hope of attaining baksheesh.'

At Assouan (Aswan), 'charmingly situated among the palm trees, with the river full of great rounded granite rocks, and the long island of Elephantina a few hundred yards away', the group

visited the bazaar 'where the people were more interesting than their wares for there were many regular looking savages with plaited hair, & women with nose rings & nose ornaments, and all black as black as coal with immense white turbans . . . The scenery is strangely different here with all the islands dividing the Nile into narrow streams.' That night, Clarence went to bed early, 'glad to be away from the row of the natives ashore, & the vulgar American & his chief allies on board, who play cards & talk slang & behave badly.'

The following morning, 'We had 2 ½ hours to roam about and explore the ruins and gather the few wild plants that grew there. Very beautiful is this quiet spot, with its unsymmetrical temples . . . I found several new plants, and some bivalve shells in the river.' In the afternoon, 'we bade adieu to Assouan & at a great pace went down the river, stopping for the night . . . having done about 25 miles from Assouan.' Such is the power of travelling downstream. 'The limit of our Nile journey has been reached, and beautiful Philae, its rocks, its palms, its mimosas & its temples are things of the past, and we are going northwards & homewards, but with much to think of and read about in the days to come.'

All was not well on the steamer: 'There has been a row on board, one of our passengers a wealthy and very clever & accomplished Austrian having said something offensive to one of the Hungarian counts; the former seems to have made himself disagreeable to most of the people, but today some apology had been offered through the mediation of an Italian on board & our English officer at Assouan, this latter having refused the Hungarian's wish that he should act as second in a duel.'

Twenty-four tourists on board a small steamer on a voyage up the Nile brought out the worst in many of the passengers. The next day, Clarence wrote: 'Everyone is ready at the slightest notice to fire up and then explode in some remark or other that would be better left unsaid.' And two days later, he complained: 'The squabbles on our boat continue, and someone or other is always in a bad temper, and using unparliamentary language. We have certainly some of the most vulgar, cross-grained, nasty-tempered people I have ever met. It may be the dry air, or the abounding dust, or the difficulty of fathoming the history of about 40 Egyptian dynasties which disturbs

Luxor by moonlight from the boat. 8/1/90.

their nerves . . . Our hair & claws are growing, our clothes wearing out, our nerves are getting twisted by the dry air & continual winds.'

On 8 January the boat had reached Luxor on its journey north, and the passengers had another opportunity to visit that great site. Clarence was reunited with his 'dear George Washington', whom he rode out to Karnak for a day of sketching and ambling around the great hall, admiring the sculptures.

By the 11th they had reached the jumping-off point for Abydos. The group set off at 7.45, after

the usual scrabble for mounts: 'Bad donkeys & a long ride of 1¼ hours, but a very pleasant one through the green corn & the sweet broad beans in full blossom, with thousands of pigeons flying about, & little woolly camels not yet looking conceited & cross.'

Clarence was captivated by the temple of Seti I:

I did not know anything was so beautiful, unlike all others in form, and more beautiful than all for its bas reliefs, exquisitely painted. The figures most

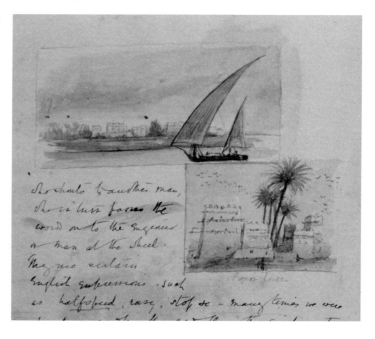

graceful, such an abundance of varied designs, such grace in the figure & such harmonious colouring. The stone a beautiful compact white limestone. Sethi offering a golden image of himself to a divinity, Sethi assisting his boy to lasso a wild bull, & similar subjects, with sculpture far finer than at Karnak, & colour better preserved than anywhere else.

How fitting to have such a satisfying experience in the final temple of the tour. At the end of the day, Clarence wrote: 'The sky is getting cloudier & the wind colder, and sitting on deck is getting more & more uncomfortable, while the saloon is always equally insupportable. Well, our excursions are over & we shall soon no more hear the continual cry of baksheesh, baksheesh, nor watch the queer figures huddled up in corners or squatting in rows like birds on the telegraph wires along the mud bank.'

At Karnak, Clarence had discovered a sculpture he found particularly interesting and worth describing to Burnat:

There was a sculpture on a wall of the flora of a country conquered by one of the kings which, in the hieroglyphs, is named 'the divine land.' This 'herbarium' was extremely pretty, nothing was symmetrical, but the plants were well depicted. One was clearly an Arum, another a tulip or Iris. Mons. Mariette [Auguste Mariette (1821–1881), French archaeologist and Egyptologist who published several guides to the monuments of Egypt] says in his guide that it is the only known example of this species. Therefore someone must have dried these plants? As for me, three thousand years later, I have taken all the plants I have seen, but they don't amount to much.[147]

Clarence was disappointed by the paucity of new specimens he found, but realistic; after all, he was travelling through a desert.

On Tuesday 14 January the steamer finally docked in Cairo in pouring rain, after becoming stuck on a sandbank the previous afternoon.

View from where we stuck on a sandbank.
2 pm. 13/1/90

'Just as we were finishing luncheon today about 2 p.m. came a succession of tremendous bumps and we knew at last we were well onto a sandbank, the long-threatened danger. The paddles paddled in vain.' The mishap was resolved by the entire crew and passengers heaving on a rope attached to the anchor and, after much effort, freeing the boat. The arrival in Cairo was less than inspiring:

> How miserable the villages looked & the slimy banks with the poor women slipping down them to fill their heavy jars with the muddy water, and struggle up the banks again with difficulty . . . Finally we reached the landing stage about 3.30 in worse rain than ever, and sent out for carriages, having bid goodbye to all our companions good & bad. Right sorry too we were to say adieu to the charming Italian on his way to Madagascar, & to the gentlemanly English architect & the charming French lady & her Italian husband & the German ladies – but there were the other sect, the vulgar, stingy quarrelsome ones we were thankful to leave behind.

Clarence and his companions went straight to the Hotel Royale in Cairo, they picked up tickets for their train ride to Alexandria and the boat to Athens, sorted themselves out and dined. Then it was off to the train station to catch the 11 p.m. train to Alexandria where they boarded their ship for Athens.

> At 10 in brilliant sunshine we started, sorry to leave Egypt glittering in the light & Alexandria's splendid harbour crowded with vessels of every kind. We soon had lunch & then sat on deck till feeling sleepy & land being well out of sight & went to lie down, but soon after the sea became a little rough and from that moment to Friday at noon I saw my companions no more, except D once the next day, who paid me a visit, gasping & groaning. That night the sea was rough, but all Thursday it was much worse, the waves swept over the deck, the wind howled, everything & nearly everybody too made ugly sounds, including some cats on board . . . But what had become of A, the 1st class, the able-bodied seawoman who was to have been our saviour on the sea? Did she hold up our heads, rub our feet, cheer us in our agonies, wipe our clammy hands, bring biscuits & soup & soda water to revive our fainting frames? No, not a bit of it. She turned out a broken reed in the house of distress, false & faithless, she who had found it so cold on the Nile boat that she could not stand the deck & so hot on shore that she couldn't walk & whom we had all tended with the greatest devotion, was now worse than all of us three B, C & D, not even putting in an appearance at dinner to which the rest of us sat down when we were nearing the Piraeus.

It sounds as though A, the weak Leach, had been struck off Clarence's list of good travellers, unlike her sister, the doughty B, who had bravely accompanied him when he ventured down into the interior of the Great Pyramid at Gizeh, an experience that even Giacomo avoided.

The weather improved by the time they neared their destination. 'Beautiful were the hours of our sea voyage as the Acropolis came in sight & Mount Hymettus slightly powdered with snow & the monastery behind Salamis & the port & the houses & ships stood out clear in the evening light.' They were greeted by a boat from the Hotel d'Angleterre, taken ashore, whisked through

Customs, and soon established 'in a very snug hotel in this most modern looking city, very dull & dreary looking after the East, with its common-looking shops & uniform people & empty streets.'

Clarence became less and less enamoured of modern Athens, but more and more entranced by the antiquities:

> There are singularly few trees anywhere, & no gardens with flowers. The palms & everything else in the public or royal gardens look dying of cold & winds. The evenings are deadly dull. There is not a creature in the streets, & no amusements, hardly any shops open & nobody in those that are. The town is indeed a depressing place. All the glory of Athens seemed centred in that undying Acropolis & the hills & islands & plains around made famous by great men & great deeds . . . The modern cathedral is ugly & gaudy inside & out.

On Sunday 10 January Clarence went to a service in a Greek orthodox church, and this found him reflecting on the uniformity of worship. 'I am always more and more impressed with the certainty that popular worship is the same, under different forms & that there is next to no difference between the Jewish & Egyptian temples or the Greek ones or the R. Catholics. They all have a mystery, with priests & sacrifices & hidden places & sacred objects, and gods [whether] they be called Jupiter, Osiris, St Joseph or any other name . . . still the apparent reverence of these Greek church people is pleasant to see, and making the cross hundreds of times & kissing pictures & all the rest of it may make them happy. Perhaps the simplicity of the Mahometan mosques impresses me most, if only the women were admitted too.'

The four spent the next few days visiting temples, attending the opera, taking a daunting carriage trip out to Eleusis, and trying out the local wines. At Eleusis, Clarence had his first taste of retsina, 'the horrible country beverage, something like the Italian Fernet, being a good red wine made disgusting by the addition of turpentine from the pine trees.' Later he assessed his samples: 'Today I tried a 4th kind of Greek wine. Attique rouge. I like the cheap white Santorini, much like the Sicilian Corvo; the mousey Parnes not at all. Attique is good, & the best white Oinos Aediforos.' This is a different Clarence from the man who had worked so ardently for the temperance movement at Stoke-upon-Tern.

Then began the last leg of the journey back to Bordighera. The group took a train to Patras where they boarded a very dirty ship for Brindisi; they were doomed to another rough passage. 'The waves swept over the deck; the water poured down into our cabins through the windows that would not fasten, and poor D had at least of a foot of it rolling about where he slept and all his clothes soaked. A truly fearful time of it. Of course we were hours late, & arrived on Saturday morning at 10 o'clock in a pitiable condition at cheerless, comfortless Brindisi, with its horrible hotel. Pitiless place, infernal wind and impudent gamins. To bed we went, but by 4 p.m. we were off in the train, A, B, & D home via Bologna, I to Rome.'

At Rome and then at Florence, Clarence met with fellow botanists. At Florence, he admits to 'enjoying Sr Groves' herbarium & despoiling his packets of duplicates of flowers for myself.' These duplicates, along with the rather small assortment of specimens he gathered in Egypt, meant that Clarence did not return home botanically empty-handed, in spite of his complaints to Burnat about the abysmal state of Henry Groves's herbarium:[148] 'Mr Groves takes care of his plants very badly, and his duplicates are not dated!' Groves (1835–1891) was an English pharmacist and botanist who settled in Florence in about 1862.

On Thursday, 30 January, his Egypt diary shouts its last entry: '9.30 a.m. reached HOME–'

## CHAPTER NINE

# FAMILY MATTERS

IN APRIL 1890, CLARENCE WROTE to Burnat, welcoming him to stay at the Villa Rosa, but with a caveat. If his son Jean accompanied him, they would have to stay in a hotel because there was only one free bed in the villa. Another was taken up by an ill nephew, while the ground floor was occupied by two female relatives. The nephew in question was Edward Elhanan Berry, who was not so ill that he could not spend time helping his uncle to dry plants to be used for exchanges. 'A tedious job', according to Clarence.

Clarence's beloved oldest sister Ada and her husband, Edward Berry, had produced two daughters and four sons: Maud, Edward Elhanan, James, Arthur, Grosvenor and Clara. Maud was an artist who lived with her mother, with whom she shares the same tombstone in the Stansted, Kent, cemetery; James, later Sir James, was born with a cleft palate and one leg shorter than the other, trained at St Bartholomew's hospital and became a well-regarded cleft palate and goitre surgeon at the Royal Free Hospital; Arthur was a professor of Mathematics at Kings College, Cambridge; Grosvenor bred Jersey cows in Essex; Clara attended University College, London, and led a life devoted to girls' education.

Having raised her children, Ada had thrown herself energetically into the work of the Froebel Society, an international forum dedicated to the spread of early-childhood education, and in 1874 she founded the Croydon High School for Girls.

Of all the six children, it was Edward Elhanan Berry who played the most important role in Clarence's life. In 1891, when he was 30, he left London and moved to Bordighera for health reasons. Soon after arriving in Bordighera, he set up and ran an agency for Thomas Cook, with whom he had prior connections. He also set up a bank, named after himself, and an agency which found housing for British visitors and took care of their freight. He was a problem solver for the English colony and quickly became the man to consult on any aspect of Bordighera life. His advertisements in the *Journal de Bordighera* made the following claims: 'Houses and flats to let – Villas and building sites for sale – Luggage forwarded to all Countries, and insured against loss by theft, etc. Excellent storage accommodation – Pianos on sale and hire – Wines and spirits specially selected for invalids, also India and China teas kept in stock – Houses and furniture insured against theft.'

Edward and Margaret Berry; their passport photos.

In addition to his industriousness in the business world, Edward was an indefatigable hill walker, and it must have delighted Clarence to have a blood relative at hand, the son of his sister Ada, who enjoyed wandering in the Maritime Alps as much as he did.

In 1897, Edward was appointed British Vice Consul for Bordighera and was thinking seriously about marriage. Clarence was shortly able to write to Burnat that his nephew was getting married at the end of August and he and his wife would spend the winter with Clarence in order to start off economically. The bride was Margaret Serocold, a regular visitor to Bordighera with her family since 1890. A large woman of great energy, she was a fine addition to Edward's life and work. Among many other endeavours, she formed an agency for servants, which she ran for ten years, to complement Edward's housing agency.[149]

Margaret became a great favourite with Clarence. She brought with her a fund of humour, warmth, generosity and a sense of family; and she loved her new uncle dearly. She was inclined to see him through rose-tinted glasses, but even so we learn a good deal about Clarence's character from her biographical sketch:

> He was truly 'all things to all men', yet always himself – a vivid personality, loveable, upright, sincere and modest and he gave with open hands to all who needed help, mate-rial or spiritual. His door was always open to the sick, the sad and the afflicted, and English and Italians alike went to him as to their best friend for sympathy, advice and assistance. Intensely affectionate and emotional, he was inclined to violent prejudices from which he could not always easily free himself, and the haste with which he flung himself into new intimacies was a standing joke amongst his old friends. He showed his disapproval by coldness and reserve rather than by actual anger, and no one who incurred his displeasure would easily forget the expression of his keen blue eyes. But his habitual cheery manner and his merry laughter endeared him to everyone, and his eccentricities and the vivid radiance of his imagination made him the most delight-ful of conversationalists. He delighted in puzzles, riddles and jokes, and saw humour everywhere. He was never idle for a moment, and got through more work in a day than another man would accomplish in a week.[150]

Shortly after she married Edward, Margaret was at Lorenzini's, an artists' supply shop in Siena, when she noticed some magnificent volumes of first-class drawing paper, bound in white vellum – the perfect gift for 'The Uncle' as she called Clarence and indeed, it was. Some months later he returned the album to her, but now it was filled with watercolours of wildflowers. Each time she went to Lorenzini's, Margaret bought another album for Clarence, returned to her once again filled with flower illustrations and this continued until 1914 when, presumably because of the war, it was difficult to acquire the volumes. The albums, of which a dozen are known today, represent Clarence's most creative art and they are described in detail in chapter 14.

In August 1891 Clarence went to see his brother Percy in Ireland and to England to visit his brother Sidney in Sussex. When recording Clarence's visit in his autobiography years later, Sidney noted the success of the visit: 'My brother Clarence came on a visit to us at Staplefield [Sussex] on August 8, and stayed till the 14th. He told me he had enjoyed himself very much, and I thought he had.' During the visit, he asked Clarence why he had suddenly given up being a clergyman, and received this response, 'Because I could not go on teaching such abominable lies any longer.' Sidney could not then refrain from commenting, 'That was plain speaking with a vengeance, but does not satisfactorily explain why he posed as a sort of saint, preached missions, and condemned marriage etc. for so many years, and did not discover what he now thinks the truth a good deal earlier, for he was at that present date 49 years old.'

Sidney went on to say that Clarence offered no apology or expression of regret for having cut him and his family all his life without any reason, and continued, 'Unfortunately for the value of this improved change of mind concerning me, he has not been to see me again in the last 18 years; so I fear he has relapsed into his original dislike of me, or whatever it was which kept him away.' Sidney, of course, does not see any fault in himself for never visiting Clarence at Cambridge, Walworth, Stoke-upon-Tern, or Bordighera.

What was it that kept Clarence away? For a start, his mildness of disposition would put him at odds with Sidney's censoriousness. In spite of Sidney's vaunted activity and achievements, Clarence would perceive his life as hollow because everything he wrote and achieved was mere advertisement for himself. Even his genealogical contributions to the historians and biographers of the Bicknell and Browne families served to puff himself up. He had a consuming desire to improve the families' social status. For instance, he decided that the Huguenot name of his Browne forefathers must be Le Brun, on no evidence whatsoever, but purely because it made a connection to Charles Le Brun, the great painter at the court of Louis XIV. The family name was actually Bruneau. As far as his own first name went, he added the Algernon to the existing Sidney 'partly because my brother Henry has also the initial S, and I thought it might create some confusion having brothers both S. Bicknell.' But that was not the only reason. The name Algernon added a veneer of classy Frenchness because 'Eustace, Count of Boulogne, who succeeded his father Eustace I in 1047, was distinguished by the sobriquet "Aux Gernons" or "Als Gernons" [with whiskers] and this was the origin of "Algernon,"' and was thus a suitable name for a young man with the kind of whiskers that Sidney sported.

Even Sidney's admittedly fascinating book, *In the Track of the Garibaldians Through Italy and Sicily*, a record of his adventures in Italy in 1860, can be seen as a paean to himself, his

A.S. BICKNELL.

*After a Daguerrotype, by Kilburn.*
*Circa 1850.*

bravery, adventurousness, and powers of observation. Indeed, these particular attributes cannot be denied, but flowing just below the narrative is always that undercurrent of hubris and self-satisfaction, attributes with which Clarence had no patience at all. Sidney felt empowered to criticise the world; Clarence was tolerant of its foibles. Sidney vaunted his achievements; Clarence went quietly about helping others less fortunate than himself. In spite of having turned away from the church, its dogma, and its 'abominable lies', Clarence remained a staunchly active, compassionate Christian, firmly believing in deeds, not words.

Sidney was not tolerant. 'The widow of my brother Herman called on Aug 9 [1893] to introduce her only son, Herman, aged 18 last April. I had heard nothing of her for

Algernon Sidney Bicknell in 1850.

Clarence with his bicycle outside the Villa Rosa, probably 1892.

about 15 years. After my brother died I naturally did not seek her company any more than was necessary for me to assist in winding up his affairs, finishing his Háfiz, selling his instruments etc. She was not a lady, utterly common, and uninteresting, and a sordid pervert of Catholicism . . . My dying Brother had begged me to be the child's guardian, but I could not accept that office, because his mother was to be appointed joint guardian with me.'

It is notable that Sidney's intolerance stood in the way of his granting his respected brother's dying wish because the widow was 'utterly common . . . and a sordid pervert of Catholicism.' That is exactly the sort of reaction that would have driven Clarence mad.

James Berry, Clarence's surgeon nephew, visited at Christmas 1891, and Clarence hiked with him to mountain villages where they visited people afflicted by gout. Telling Burnat about this, Clarence reminded him that gout was James's specialty. Perhaps it was that ardent cyclist James who influenced Clarence to buy a bicycle. Clarence had reservations about it, as he later explained to Burnat: 'I am learning to ride a bicycle, but it does not serve me well for shopping, up till now it tires me too much, and then after a long outing I prefer to return home resting in a carriage; my 92 kilos are enough to carry on the machine, without having packets of plants!'[151]

Clarence writes on the back of this photo 'Clarence Bicknell and his hat, as they appeared in A.D. 1894 or thereabouts, June 1897'. Photograph by Ezio Benigni.

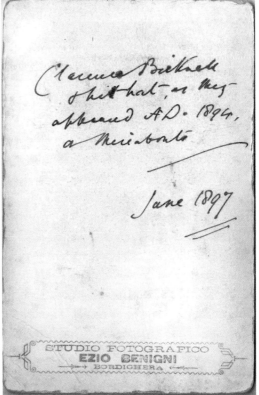

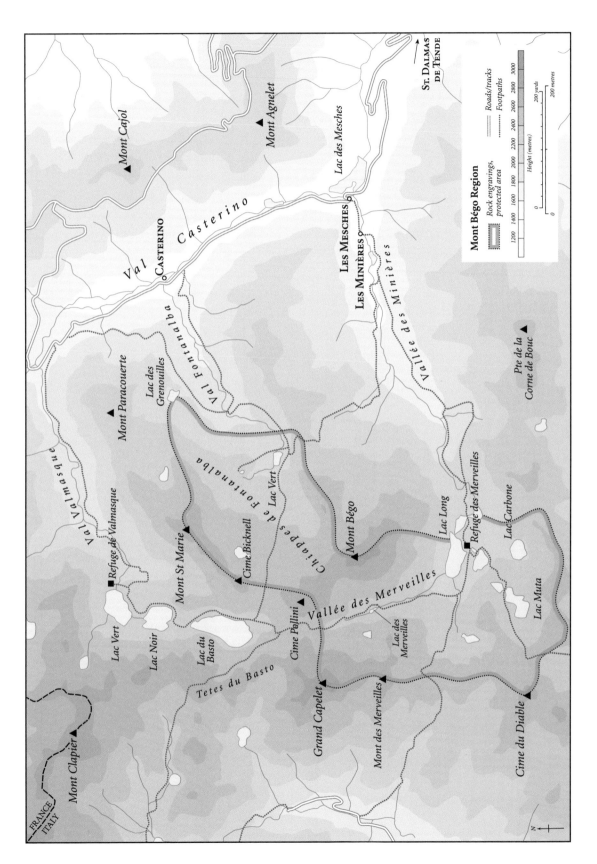

Mont Bégo Region

Rock engravings,
protected area

Roads/tracks
Footpaths

Height (metres)

1200 1400 1600 1800 2000 2200 2400 2600 2800 3000

0    200 yards
0    200 metres

St. Dalmas
de Tende

Mont Cajol

Mont Agnelet

Lac des Mesches

Val Casterino

CASTERINO

Les Mesches
Les Minières

Vallée des Minières

Pte de la
Corne de Bouc

Mont Paracouerte

Lac des
Grenouilles

Val Fontanalba

Val Valmasque

Refuge de Valmasque

Mont St Marie

Cime Bicknell

Chiappes de Fontanalba

Lac Vert

Mont Bégo

Lac Long

Refuge des Merveilles

Lac Carbone

Lac Vert

Lac Noir

Lac du
Basto

Cime Pollini

Vallée des Merveilles

Lac des
Merveilles

Lac Muta

Tetes du Basto

Grand Capelet

Mont des Merveilles

Cime du Diable

FRANCE
ITALY

Mont Clapier

N

CHAPTER TEN

# THE ROCK ENGRAVINGS

It is a hellish place, with figures of devils and a thousand demons engraved
everywhere on the rocks.

Pierre de Montfort[152]

Soon after coming to winter in the Riviera in 1879, I heard of the Meraviglie, and two
years later walked up there from San Dalmazzo with friends, returning the same evening.
It was in the early days of June, and as there was so much snow upon the rocks we saw very
little. In September of 1885 I went there again, having slept at the Miniera. [Mines near the
Lac des Mesches between St Dalmas and Casterino that produced zinc, silver and lead.]
This time I was able to explore more fully, saw figures on both sides of the Vallone and
lake, and made about 50 drawings in my sketch-book.

So wrote Clarence in Chapter III, 'The Story of Our Own Explorations', in his book *A Guide to
the Prehistoric Rock Engravings of the Italian Maritime Alps* (1913).[153]

The Vallée des Merveilles, the Valle delle Meraviglie of which Clarence had heard, was the
site of rock engravings in the region of Mont Bégo, higher up in the Maritime Alps than he had
so far been. Situated between the Col de la Madeleine and the Col de Tende, in the mountain-
ous border region between France and Italy, the region was covered by permanent ice in the
Quaternary period, but is now, in the lovely words of Gabriella Parodi, 'furrowed by deep valleys
and gorges, rich in grand circuses, and constellated with many, many lakes.'[154] Thirty-five thousand images engraved in the Bronze Age onto flat rocks in the open are only free of snow from
June to October; Clarence located and made copies of 12,000 of them.

To reach the carvings, Clarence had to travel to Ventimiglia by train, and then hire a coach
and horses to follow the Roya valley gorge, with its precipitous limestone cliffs, up to St Dalmas.

The Lac Long, Mont Bégo and Mont Clapier seen from the northwest, the Gelas pass.

Mont Bégo (2,872 metres high) dominates the Vallée des Merveilles, the Val Fontanalba and the Valmasque, where the rock engravings are found. Viewed southeast from the Chiappes de Fontanalba.

C.B., *Breil-sur-Roya, February 1882*, watercolour.

By mule or on foot, he travelled from St Dalmas up the steep path to Les Mesches (the lake at Les Minières) and then southwest until veering north into the Vallée des Merveilles, a deep defile in the shadow of Mont Bégo. (English-speakers today use the French name Vallée de Merveilles, rather than Valley of Marvels. The Italian name Valle delle Meraviglie was used in Clarence's time. The upper Roya valley, including Tende, La Brigue, Casterino and the Bégo mountain area, became part of France in 1947. San Dalmazzo is now St Dalmas.) There the valley opened up into the wild and desolate Val d'Inferno, the Valley of Hell. This valley was not alone in bearing a threatening name. The surrounding mountains also bore titles such as Devil's Mountain and Shaking Mountain, names given in the Middle Ages, when mountains were regarded as fearful objects. As late as 1878, Edmond Blanc wrote about the area: 'The summits of Monte Bego, of the Capelet and of the Cima del Diavolo, seem to be immense skeletons of an infernal divinity. Here reigns the silence of the tomb and if anyone speaks in a loud voice to give a little life to this horrible solitude, there is no responding echo.'[155] The area's reputation did not discourage Clarence, who had few limits when he had a goal in mind. Even though the walk from St Dalmas to the Merveilles was 20 kilometres up and 20 kilometres back down again, with an altitude gain of 1,400 metres, [156] he took it in his stride.

The rock carvings of the Vallée des Merveilles had been mentioned in print as early as 1690 by Pierre Gioffreddo (1629–1692) in his *Histoire des Alpes Maritimes,* but Gioffreddo had not seen the rocks himself. He had received information about them from Onorato Laurenti (born Honoré de Laurens), a parish priest at Belvedere, west of Mont Bégo. Laurenti may not have seen them either but heard about them from hunters or herdsmen. Gioffreddo claims that 'the authors of these spirited jokes were probably only shepherds and herdsmen who wished to while away their idle hours.' This claim was reasonable, but in 1821, in his *Voyage aux Alpes Maritimes,* François Emmanuel Fodéré speculated that the carvings had been made by Carthaginian soldiers, in the army of Hasdrubal, on their way back to Africa because 'the writing was neither Greek, nor Latin, nor Arabic, but one might conjecture was Punic.'[157] And in 1864, Elisée Reclus, in his *Villes d'Hiver,* wrote that the mountain people claimed the rocks were engraved by the soldiers of Hannibal.

It was not until 1868 that the botanist Matthew Moggridge – father of John Traherne Moggridge whose book on the wildflowers of the Riviera had impelled Clarence to produce his own volume on the subject – wrote about the carvings. Accompanied by a fellow naturalist and friend of Bismarck, Herr Dieck, Moggridge made a two-day trip up into the Vallée des Merveilles to see for himself the 'Marvels' about which they had heard so much from the local people. Unfortunately, the weather was too wet and they were unable to take any rubbings and casts, so Dieck made quick pencil sketches while Moggridge scouted out new subjects. Moggridge was sceptical about their being the work of Hannibal's soldiers because 'Hannibal, in that country, plays the same role as Caesar, Oliver Cromwell, and his Satanic Majesty in England.'[158] That is, he was everywhere but nowhere in particular.

Other explorers followed, having heard about the rock engravings, but they often failed to locate them. They spent far more time arguing about the provenance of the carvers than patiently examining the carvings, copying them, and collecting data.

Already fascinated by the alpine flora that flourished during the short summers in the mountains, Clarence's excursions took him higher and higher as he sought rare species that eluded him at lower levels. But his trip to the Vallée des Merveilles in June of 1881 was a disappointment because any flowers that had dared to raise their heads were covered by a spring snowfall, as were the rock carvings themselves. However, his return in September of 1885 was far more satisfactory. Snow had not yet fallen on the valley and the autumn light cast low shadows that made the incisions much more visible than they were in the flat light of high summer. He sketched about 50 of the figures, fascinated by what he saw. It would not be until 1897 that he saw them again.

In the meantime, he spent his summers between Italy, England, Ireland, Switzerland – and Germany in 1894, where he spent 16–19 August at Bayreuth wallowing in Wagner, attending *Lohengrin, Tannhäuser* and *Parsifal* on successive days. He had been captivated by Wagner, as is evident from certain books in his library, such as *How to Understand Wagner's Ring of the Nibelung* and the libretti of *Siegfried, The Twilight of the Gods, The Rhinegold* and *The Valkyries.*[159]

Clarence decided not to travel abroad in the summer of 1897, but instead to head back up the Roya Valley and into the Mont Bégo region to indulge in cool weather and the opportunity to botanise at ever greater heights. He knew he would find unusual Alpine plants flourishing among the acidic rocks, plants unlike those that prospered in the alkaline, calcareous rock of most of the

C.B., *Casterino looking North* 6.7.97, sketch, 1897.

Alpine chain. He told Burnat that he intended to occupy himself with the study of *Hieracium* (hawkweed) to annoy Saverio Belli, the specialist in this flower and with collecting plants for exchanges.[160]

He rented a house for the summer in the hamlet of Casterino – sometimes called la Maddalena because of the chapel located there – from Arturo Pellegrino of Tende, on the recommendation of Émile Burnat, who had previously stayed there. Signor Pellegrino's house must have been quite commodious because it could house Clarence, his house guests, and his domestic staff, who consisted of his cook Maddalena and Luigi Pollini.

On his arrival at Signor Pellegrino's, Clarence was accompanied by his nephew Arthur Berry, Edward's brother, and he was awaiting the arrival of his protégé, the tenor Pietro Zeni. The next visitors to arrive were another nephew, James Berry and his wife, Dr (Frances) May Dickinson, an anaesthetist. This couple had the reputation for having friendly altercations in the operating

Lafayette, *Sir James Berry*, half-plate nitrate negative, 1 September 1928.

Lafayette, *Frances May (née Dickinson), Lady Berry*, half-plate nitrate negative, 1 September 1928.

The staff at Pellegrino's house are on the stairs with Luigi Pollini at the top. Clarence is sitting on the bottom step next to Dr May Dickinson Berry, Sir James Berry, 'aunt Manin' with the sick chamois, and 'Luigi Cameriere' according to a pencil-written note on the back of the photo.

theatre of the Royal Free Hospital.

They brought with them ropes and ice axes and the intention to climb Mont Bégo and Mont Clapier. They may not have been the most relaxing of visitors, but gained Clarence's gratitude for the medical care they paid to a little chamois, orphaned when its mother was killed by someone whom Clarence scornfully called 'one of those so-called "sportsmen" for whom no life is sacred.'[161] One can hear the hiss as he utters the words 'so-called "sportsmen".' He continues the tale: 'A goat came three times a day to give it milk, but, even though the little creature appeared to be in good health for some time and was quite tame, playing and climbing and descending the stairs behind us, she suddenly fell ill.' At that point, the Doctors Berry called upon their combined professional skills in the hope of saving her, but she died within half an hour 'to our great sorrow.'

By 7 July, Clarence was able to write to Burnat that 'we are well settled here . . . we have everything necessary, and the air and water are very refreshing after the heat and dust of the Riviera . . . every day I jump into the river, and I eat like a wolf.' It is worth bearing in mind that the river water was snow melt. 'My nephew thought he would be roughing it in this place so far

C.B., *Saxifraga florulenta*, watercolour. UniGen.

*Saxifraga florulenta* like to hide among the rocks. 2017. Courtesy of Elisabetta Massardo.

from civilization, but [he found] that it was not a bad thing to have for a dinner in the mountains good soup, trout, cutlets, tomatoes, salad, cheese, fruit and tea ices (that Luigi made with snow and which were exceptionally good).'

In a letter written on 15 September 1897 to Arturo Issel, Clarence mentioned James and May Berry:

> My nephew, who together with his wife, were with me in Val Casterino, returned to England (by bicycle) via Ivrea, Aosta, il piccolo S. Bernardo ecc. If only I had known that you were staying near Ivrea! I would have asked you to meet him. This would not have been annoying for you because he is a truly distinguished young man, one of the best surgeons in London, and is much taken up with geology.'[162]

Arturo Issel (1842–1922), archaeologist at the University of Genoa.

The most arresting statement in this paragraph is that James and May travelled back to England by bicycle; they may well have arrived by bicycle too. Just imagine the mountains they rode up and down as they left Italy, a feat that James managed to accomplish in spite of having one leg shorter than the other. May was nothing if not a modern woman, dashing and brave. She would have taken well to bicycling bloomers, which were all the rage in the 1890s.

'I am very, very happy with my stay here', wrote Clarence to Burnat in August. He was thoroughly enjoying the fresh air, his plunges into the river, and his treks into the mountains, especially a long circuit from Casterino via the Minières to the Lac des Merveilles by the col to the Basto lake and a descent from Valmasque, finally returning to Casterino.

'We did so well, my nephew and I, in 11 hours with plenty of stops.' Nonetheless, the seemingly indestructible Clarence was not exempt from human frailty. As he told Burnat, 'In recent days I have had to stay at home, spending much time in bed, having really annoying haemorrhoids which prevent me from walking.'[163]

Clarence had one other complaint: the lack of interesting wildflowers in the area, and he confessed to Burnat that 'botanically I have done very little. It is much less rich here than at Val Pesio, and even when I climb up to the lakes of Valmasca, d'Agnel, the Meraviglie, and M. Bégo (where nothing escapes the goats!) I always find the same old plants.' And he had spent many fruitless, frustrating hours searching for the rare *Saxifraga florulenta*.

His persistence paid off. By the end of the summer he related to Burnat that he had finally found that elusive plant in bloom. Although Clarence does not describe the actual moment he saw it, the great plant collector Reginald Farrer (1880–1920) was extravagant in his description of his sighting of it in 1910 on the Col de Cerise: 'Grey obscurity enveloped all the slope, swirling and shifting, lightening and darkening. And now the sharp zigzags of the track brought me up against the buttress of Mercantour. For an instant the mist dissolved into a pearly shade. And in that momentary rending of the veil I found myself looking straight into the face of *Saxifraga florulenta*.

> For a moment I could not believe my eyes; for another moment I felt convinced, insanely, that some botanist must have put the rosette there as a practical joke . . . Then, when my reason had ceased rocking on its seat, I rent the welkin with a cry of triumph.' After his great yell, Farrer calmed down and 'in awe-stricken silence contemplated for the first time the Ancient King of his race, the most wonderful plant in all the ranges of the Alps.'[164]

The Ancient King is a large and rare succulent with a small range, found exclusively within the central section of the Maritime Alps between Tende and Argentera. Fussy about its location, it finds its preferred home in crevices of acidic rock, often hiding in hard-to-reach spots. Year by year, over decades, its fleshy leaves multiply into a perfect rosette until it is mature enough to flower. Then (the eloquent Farrer again); 'Up from its heart comes a stout glandular spike which develops into a stocky spire, of some eight or ten inches, very thickly set with nodding flowers of a purple rose, most wonderful to see.' Its 40 or more bell-shaped flowers are impossible to miss. But that's it; once having achieved its reproductive climax, it withers and dies. No wonder the Ancient King used to be the emblem of the modern-day Parc National du Mercantour, which includes the Vallée des Merveilles and the Val Fontanalba.

The rock on which the Ancient King flourishes is the same acidic rock – schist, sandstone, and granite – that presented such excellent purple, orange, green and yellow patinated faces on which to carve petroglyphs. As Christopher Chippindale points out, 'On these inviting surfaces are inscriptions of all periods: prehistoric figures totalling upwards of 50,000; an obscurely obscene Roman message (Gascou, 1976); renaissance names and blazons; shepherds' and highwaymen's marks; recent tourist graffiti; and even Provisional IRA slogans.'[165] Modern graffitists have tended to use metal tools to inflict their contributions, but the prehistoric artists used a different technique, namely repeatedly hammering into the rock to peck out little cupules, and with them forming lines. Chippindale suggests that their tools were made of quartz,[166] and Clarence suggests quartz too, or other hard stone, not metal, since no trace of metal had ever been found near the engravings. About the artists' technique, he says: 'The little round holes . . . vary in diameter from one to five millimetres, and are of about the same depth.'[167] He claims that for the majority of figures two tools were used, one as a chisel, one as a hammer.

C.B., *Farm and hay stooks in Val Casterino*, watercolour.

'The voices of our prehistoric friends were mingled with the marmot's whistle'.

To those Bronze Age people spending long summer days up in the mountains, what temptation those rock faces offered to create *something*, something whose mystery is still the subject of debate. Clarence sensed the presence of those carvers: 'Sometimes we have felt that the voices of our prehistoric friends were mingled with the marmot's whistle and the music of the falling streams, and almost expected to find some of them carving their figures and emblems, and to be able to ask them who they were, whence they came, and what was the meaning of their work.'[168]

Although Clarence had seen the rock carvings in the Vallée des Merveilles in 1885, it was not until he stayed in Val Casterino in the summer of 1897 that he became aware of another large collection in nearby Val Fontanalba. He had joined the Italian Alpine Club in 1890,[169] and in 1897 he wrote to the secretary of the club, asking for information about the Merveilles. Clarence describes what had happened: 'He referred me to Dr. Fritz Mader, an Associate who had a thorough knowledge of the Maritime Alps, and who spent his summers in Tenda. It was then, through the full and courteous reply to a letter that I wrote to Dr. Mader that we first heard of there being inscriptions in the valley near us, and we immediately went up to search for ourselves.'[170] Mader was a young German alpinist, writer of Baedeker guides, and natural historian.

By August, Clarence was able to write to Burnat: 'I'm very charmed again by the Meraviglie and more than ever absolutely convinced that the inscriptions – that is, the old ones – are prehistoric. I'm in correspondence with Dr Mader of Tenda (who speaks of you) and he has given me lots of information on the subject – he also tells me that similar inscriptions have recently been found in Val Fontanalba – that's what I thought when I saw the same kind of rocks there. In a few days I will begin a series of excursions – I would like to find them and draw them.'[171] He did just that, as Mader recounts: 'Recently a learned botanist, Monsieur Clarence Bicknell of Bordighera – where he founded a public museum with a free library and a conference hall – spent three summers (1897, 1898 et 1901) at the Pellegrino house in Val Casterino; when I told him there were inscriptions in the Val Fontanalba that he had not yet encountered, he set about studying them and ended up copying about 650.'[172]

Clarence greatly appreciated Mader's help and his industriousness – in 1900 Mader published a 450-page guide-book to the Riviera in German – but the young man had certain shortcomings, as Clarence explained to Burnat: 'He is very well-educated, intelligent, but so deaf. He does not wish to use an ear trumpet, and today I have a terrible sore throat.'[173]

C.B., *Lago Verde, August 11, 1897*, in pocket sketchbook.

The Val Fontanalba, secluded and far from the acknowledged path towards Mont Bégo, is nowhere mentioned in the literature until 1886, when Professor Emanuele Celesia of Genoa and his colleague, Professor Bacchialoni, plus the Tende schoolmaster and two guides, set off from Tende and made the long ascent. On the way, they encountered two goatherds who knew of the engravings and were willing to help locate them. The report that Celesia published of this excursion,[174] together with seventy drawings, was the first account of the rock engravings in the Val Fontanalba. Later, Clarence criticised some of the drawings and allowed that Celesia's paper was 'chiefly a treatise on the Phoenicians, whom he considers to have been the authors of the engravings.' He continued: 'This is all that has been written about Val Fontanalba till lately and the region was forgotten and unvisited till we ourselves in the summer of 1897, twelve years later, went to spend the summer in Val Casterino.'[175]

Clarence had already visited the Val Fontanalba earlier that summer, walking very close to the engravings without seeing them. As he says, '

I had, only a few weeks previously been up the Val Fontanalba for the first time with a nephew. The sight of some chamois on the snow slopes in the distance enticed us on and, when near the foot of Monte Bego, we decided to come back another way crossing over the rocks to the foot of M. Santa Maria. We passed over a number of smooth yellow rocks, and I remember observing that they were exactly like those at the Merveilles, but intent on looking for plants and choosing as far as possible the grassy strips rather than the rocks, I noticed no figures, though I now know that I must have passed quite close to many.[176]

Ezio Benigni (attributed), *Rock engravings 'near the upper margheria'*.

Armed with the advice of Fritz Mader, who had informed him of Celesia's report, Clarence sallied

Luigi Pollini rubs a rock engraving while Clarence and Mahdi relax. Possibly the photograph was taken by Alice Campbell.

forth again with Edward Berry, and at once came across a number of engravings just beyond the Lago Verde.

Thereafter, he and Luigi quickly established a working routine, leaving Casterino as early as 5 in the morning and making the hour-and-a-half trek up into the Val Fontanalba before they reached the area of the rock engravings. 'At first we made some 450 small draw-ings, but seeing that they were far from satisfactory, we procured large sheets of paper from Tenda and began to take pencil rubbings. We made about 211 of these in 13 long days.'[177] They invited Ezio Benigni, Bordighera's pre-eminent photographer, to join them and record the engravings, and he took some startlingly good photographs with his large, professional camera.

'What is a field naturalist to do? First, to search and find. Then, to record and describe. Then, to classify', writes Christopher Chippindale, a devoted student of and writer about Bicknell since the 1980s. 'All these things Bicknell did.'[178] Clarence's work that sum-mer was the beginning of his 12-year compulsion to describe the rock engravings using methods not unlike those used in his botany, noting place and date, copying and recording them.

Later Clarence commented on this compulsion.[179] 'I am only an amateur botanist, and have gone up into these neighbouring moun-tains in my summer holidays in order to study their Flora; but the fascination of the rocks has made me neglect my special hobby; and I have spent the greater part of my time in making draw-ings and taking notes of the rock figures'.

When he wrote to Burnat on returning to Bordighera in September, Clarence admitted that he had paid scant attention to wildflowers that summer in light of the discovery of so many interesting rock engravings. He allowed that, though beautiful, he did not find Casterino and the Valmasque botanically rich, although he and Luigi had often dined on wonderful *uva spina* [gooseberries], raspberries, bilberries – and mushrooms.

It may seem that by 1897 Clarence's summer life was focused entirely on rocks and flowers, but from his home in Bordighera during the rest of the year he took leave from his scientific obser-vation to attend social gatherings, lectures, the opera, and the theatre. For instance, in a letter to Arturo Issel, he writes that he had visited the botanists Gibelli and Belli in Turin, but that 'The Duse cheated us, announcing at the last moment to the Turinese public that she was remaining in Milan and not performing in Turin, which meant that I like many other people who had already bought tickets a few weeks ago lost out. Naturally the company returned our money, but not the cost of the trip nor our faith in the lady.'[180] The Duse was Eleanora Duse (1858–1924), the great Italian actress.

In the same letter, Clarence tells Issel that he tried out 'a few kinds of Camera Lucida . . . but I ended up buying a pantograph', a device which would have enabled Clarence to reduce in size copies of his drawings.

Clarence returned to Casterino in August 1898, having spent the previous three weeks in hectic London, followed by a few relaxing days in the bliss of Ada's garden in Kent doing nothing but reading and writing or walking in the woods and fields. Back in the mountains, he tried another method of recording the engravings, and recounted that with better paper and heelball, he and Luigi did better work.

Heelball is a mixture of lampblack and hard wax, manufactured for giving the dense black colour to the heels of shoes. He had also been convinced that photography was an extremely good method of recording the truth. Not wanting to own a camera as cumbersome as Benigni's, Clarence invested in two small versions, a Kodak and a Frena. Luigi took over as photographer and carried all the photographic equipment, along with much else, such as food, water, and paper on which to make rubbings of the engravings. By the end of the summer, Clarence crowed that they brought home 538 rubbings in their 12 visits and about a hundred photographs. They also carried away two small pieces of detached rock each with a horned figure on it, one of which Clarence kept for the Museo Bicknell, the other he sent to the British Museum.[181]

Here are excerpts from the accompanying letter:

Clarence mailed this rock with an engraving of a horned figure to the British Museum in 1897.

Bordighera, Italy
1 September 1897

Dear Sir,

I have been spending the summer in a valley of the Maritime Alps, about 4 hours walk from Tenda. In and above the Fontanalba, at 2 hours walk from us, the rocks are covered with figures, similar to the well-known ones by the neighbouring Laghi delle Meraviglie . . .

I have spent so far 11 long days up there, exploring and making some drawings and rubbings, and yesterday I and my servant managed to bring home a piece of rock, detached from a large rock surface on which we counted about 308 figures, with a figure on it of which I will send you a rubbing.

I write to ask you if you care to have this for the B. Museum? . . . The thing, whatever it be, figured on the rock, is one of the commonest types. It has always been taken for granted by the numerous writers . . . that they are heads of sheep, goats, cows, chamois, ibex, deer, elks &c &c. *Perhaps* some may be, but I am inclined to think they more probably represent insects . . .[182]

Clarence soon revised his opinion about insects being the subject matter, deciding that the drawings represented the horns of cattle, ploughs, and property boundaries. Chippindale writes 'Bicknell's key insight was to recognise the pictures of ploughs. In these two of the horned forms

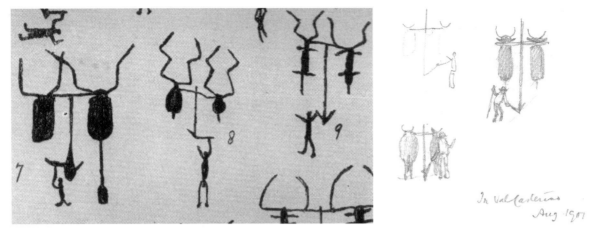

Clarence's key insight was to recognise the pictures of ploughs. On the left, some of many rock engravings of a plough drawn by two oxen, from Clarence Bicknell *A Guide to the Prehistoric Rock Engravings of the Italian Maritime Alps* (1913). On the right, a sketch of August 1901 in Val Casterino that demonstrates how clearly Clarence saw what the rock engravings were showing.

are joined together by a yoke linked to a shaft with a ploughshare. The ploughman is sometimes drawn in behind.'

Clarence's new career as an amateur archaeologist was off to a flying start. He was fascinated by the engravings. He applied the techniques he used when collecting flowers to document the engravings: he would list them, copy them, and describe where and on what date they were found. However, his methodology was simple and he realised its shortcomings, stating 'we are fully aware that if scientific men had had the opportunities we had, they probably would have made more important discoveries. They would have known where best to have looked for the traces of habitations or burial places of the prehistoric sculptors, and might have found what we have failed to do, and shed more light upon their mysterious work. We are only the collectors of facts, and must leave to others the task of studying them more profoundly.'[183] Nonetheless, the mere collector of facts wrote about the engravings that winter, and delivered his paper at the Società Linguistica in Genoa. The following year he wrote another paper for their bulletin. It is notable that he only ever wrote one article about the engravings for a British publication,[184] and did not join any British archaeological societies, having distanced himself from his roots and academic archaeology.

In claiming he was merely a collector of facts, Clarence was being far too modest. His painstaking documentation of the engravings is an enduring record of their existence and condition at the beginning of the twentieth century, a record that can forever be consulted. His recording of details is far more useful to modern-day scientists than any amount of wrong-headed speculation about their provenance by eminent archaeologists. Chippindale confirms 'Bicknell's efforts make his work the model for work a century later'.[185]

All the same, by the beginning of 1899, Clarence had begun to formulate his own theory about the people who carved the rocks. He told Burnat that he felt 'they were, at least in part, farmers and I believe they cultivated the ancient terraces of Fontanalba –between 1000 and 1500 years before J.C. – and I also believe, without doubt, that they went there for their religious festivals.'[186] Apparently the Sorcerer, the most mystical of the rock engravings, was having an effect on him.

'Happily we were always haunted by the thoughts of our prehistoric friends who seemed to be calling us back again,'[187] wrote Clarence about the gap of two years when he and Luigi did not revisit their discoveries. He did not resist their call; in 1901, he rented Signor Pellegrino's house again, where he anticipated a visit from Émile Burnat, telling him that a wonderful meal awaited him on arrival, made from everything delicious they could forage: sorrel soup, trout from the river, purée of Good King Henry [goosefoot], many varieties of mushroom – all exquisite and very good for the health – and a salad of dandelion and salad burnet.

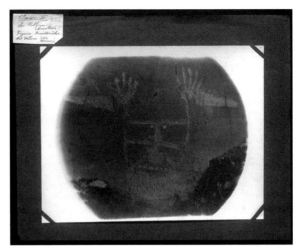

Luigi Pollini, *Le Sorcier* (The Sorcerer), photo IISL.

In a collection of letters[188] to Clarence's best friend, Rosa Fanshawe Walker, his niece Margaret Berry sheds light on everyday life at Signor Pellegrino's house in Casterino.

The first letter, written on 15 August 1901, describes how Clarence and Edward, her husband and two domestics, Maddalena and Libera, head off at 6.30 on a 'short' walk, returning for lunch at 11.30. Margaret admits to staying behind and lazing around in a deck chair, wrapped up in a rug and all her winter clothes, while Luigi keeps house. 'The Uncle is very well and fat and sunburnt and distinctly "good" . . . He seems thoroughly happy here, and enjoys every minute of the days, always "so busy there is not a minute to spare" and "no time to read."' She continues:

> Rob [Margaret's dog] is very happy here and is much interested in and rather afraid of 6 rabbits which are loose about the house and yard and which are to be killed shortly to feast Mr and Mrs Pellegrino's daughter and son-in-law and family who are arriving on Friday, tomorrow.
>
> The utter peacefulness of this is perfect. No rings at the bell . . . Nothing to do but to eat. Sleep. Vegetate. Read, write, work as one's fancy prompts or wander about in the grass and the rocks or by the rushing river side.
>
> You will be glad to hear that the smell in the WC is not so bad as it was and that it has been cleaned and whitewashed and is really respectable outwardly. What it is inwardly I do not know . . . I am going to make minute enquiries about the cleaning out of the horrible pit, but perhaps it is best to leave it while we are here and not rake up horrors of smells in the effort to clean it out . . .
>
> No sign of lack of food here as yet. *Far* too much to eat at every meal.[189]

For Margaret to complain that there was too much food tells us that Maddalena was overproviding and that Clarence himself was putting on weight.

She wrote again to Rosa on 23 August, describing the pattern of the days in Casterino. Clarence and Edward consumed a breakfast of coffee and 'large wedges of toast and butter' at

6.30. Margaret indulged her 'natural laziness' for another half hour. 'The Uncle continues to think me lazy and ignorant and a "fine lady" into the bargain, and despises me accordingly. But I am bearing up nevertheless, and continue to darn socks, and make the beds and pick gooseberries for dinner in the most approved domestic style.' Clarence and Edward went for long walks every other day, alternating them with short walks. But one day Margaret stirred herself enough to join the entire household – Clarence, Edward, Luigi, Maddalena, Libera and Celestino (Luigi's brother) – on an expedition to Lago Verde and the rocks beyond it. Margaret was deeply stirred by the experience:

> I saw the wonderful drawings and sat by and watched the squeezes and rubbings being taken ... Quite the finest scenery I have seen yet is in Val Masca at the head of this valley and at right angles to it, where the mountains tower above one, and the torrent roars beneath, while the gorge narrows and heightens till one realises one's littleness amid all that grandeur and ruggedness, and one wonders at the centuries that have passed and left their traces only in glacier slides and wrecks of trees brought down by avalanches. It is a wonderful sight certainly, and when one turned a corner, out of the darkness and gloom of the rugged valley, to see the distant peaks of the French mountains with the glory of the sunset behind them, and felt the glow of the red and yellow rays one one's face, it was like the opening of the gates of Paradise after the long dark valley was past.

Margaret again talks about food in a letter on 3 September:

> I have seen no signs of starvation as yet tho' I am constantly being told that we are on the verge of it. However, some kind providence always seems to step in and supply the special want; either a sporting shepherd brings in a chamois (very tough and nasty!! ...) when we have no other meat left, or a neighbour 'lends' us some bread, when ours runs short ... We eat many funghi, wild raspberries, wild green gooseberries and wild spinach.

And then she describes an 'enormous' outing they had taken that day, starting at 6.20 a.m., 'I on a large and stalwart mule.'

> We went over what seemed to me miles of Uncle C.s red inscribed rocks and very marvellous and interesting they are ... We lunched up at the top at 10.30 and did not get home till 5.20 so I was almost faint with hunger. E had to give me whisky at 3 to keep me going, but 4 ½ hours on a mule's back and 3 ½ on foot over *very* rough ground, not to mention being out in this very strong air for the whole day, are calculated to take it out of one. Since dinner I have recovered and feel almost myself again except for stiff legs and very shaky knees, so it shows it was only want of food.

Margaret writes again two days later.

> The Uncle and E. have again gone up to their beloved rocks for the day and will return, I suppose, as usual, about 5 o'clock, famished and thirsty and very hot and sticky, but nevertheless triumphant with their day's work. Each new rubbing always seems to me remarkably like the last, but I do not dare say so, for there is such intense pride and satisfaction in the 'new' ones that I cannot betray my ignorance and want of perception in thinking

Edward Berry, Capi, Clarence Bicknell and Margaret Berry on the balcony of the Casa Fontanalba.

them all alike. Once you have seen a plough and oxen's heads and horns and a weapon and a plan of a 'property' and a skin, you have seen it all, and the differences are only to ring the changes in size and shape of these. However, they are as happy as happy can be over it, and Rob enjoys these long days on the rocks as much as they do, for he cheerfully and diligently hunts marmots all day long but needless to say, never catches one.

For the first time during Margaret and Edward's stay in Casterino, they had to dine indoors that night because it was wet and cold outside, but Margaret consoled herself, saying: 'but we are indeed lucky to have had three weeks of such splendid weather', and then she continues, 'I am still contentedly lazy, and have not written so much as one article for that haunting and terrifying "Journal."' Here she is referring to the *Journal de Bordighera,* the very proper 'voice' of the English colony.

Meanwhile, Clarence was keeping up his correspondence with Burnat, and on 26 August described the various expeditions he had taken during the summer: 'I went many times up to Val Fontanalba, once up Monte Bego, and then to the Col del Vej del Bouc, passing by some horrible places at Lac d'Agnel.' He was disappointed to find nothing at Mont Bégo, but happy to find

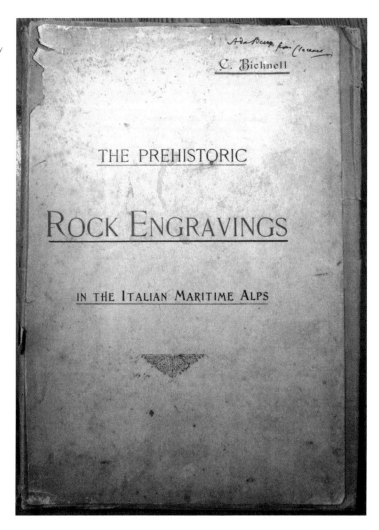

*The Prehistoric Rock Engravings in the Italian Maritime Alps.* This 1902 first edition is dedicated by Clarence to his dear sister Ada.

prehistoric figures when descending through rough rocks to Val Valauretta. Clarence's remark that he went many times up to Val Fontanalba sounds rather casual, but he and Luigi were, in fact, working hard to catalogue, photograph and make rubbings of the extensive collection of rock engravings they had discovered there.

At the end of the same letter to Burnat, Clarence mentioned that love was in the air and was infecting his staff. He had been obliged to send Luigi off to his home at Lake Maggiore to visit his fiancée, a young woman whom Luigi had not seen for a year. In addition, his cook Maddalena was getting married at the end of October. His 'family' was expanding.

In an undated note – probably 1902 – to his new friend, Lieutenant Alberto Pelloux, a career soldier and mineralogist, Clarence cried out: 'My Luigi is in love! Me too.'[190] Luigi's love object was twenty-year-old Mercede Varesi, whom he brought back with him from Lake Maggiore to Bordighera on their marriage. Plainly, Clarence was taken with her too, and she certainly seems to have thrown

Mercede Pollini, born Varesi, in about 1910.

Chef du Tribu (Head of the Tribe), a celebrated rock engraving logged by Clarence. IISL.

Clarence Bicknell, *Weapons and implements*, a plate from Clarence's *The Prehistoric Rock Engravings in the Italian Maritime Alps*.

herself into life in Bordighera in a creative manner of which he approved. On 5 February 1903, he wrote to Pelloux telling him that Mercede was working day and night making 500 paper roses for a ballet to be performed as a fund raiser for the tennis club.[191]

'Me too' in this note could mean that Clarence was in love with Mercede. Or perhaps he had someone else in mind.

Clarence's first account in English of his archaeological work was published in 1902 with the title *The Prehistoric Rock Engravings in the Italian Maritime Alps* (74 pages). He published the book in English but not in England, using the Bordighera publisher, Pietro Gibelli. The paper he gave in Italian at the Società Ligustica in 1897 had already been published in 1898 with the title *Le figure incise sulle rocce di Val Fontanalba* (23 pages).

His finds had also been reported in 1901 by Arturo Issel, his friend the paleontologist from Genoa, who had visited him in Casterino and had climbed with him up into the mountains. In 'Le rupi scolpite nelle alte valli delle Alpi Marittime',[192] Issel, the professional, is clearly speaking to his tribe, those men working the same field as he, but in other locations. He plunders Clarence's work on the engravings in the Mont Bégo region, and uses his photographs and dozens of rather odd negative reproductions of his rubbings – giving tribute, to be sure, where tribute is due.

For Clarence to lead the agreeable Professor Issel up into the Val Fontanalba and show him his discoveries was a great pleasure. It would have felt wonderful to discuss knotty issues such as the age of the engravings, their subject matter, and the question of who created them. They tried to solve these problems together, and came to much the same conclusions: the engravings represented, for the most part, ploughs, oxen and weapons, while a few appeared to have some religious, but absolutely no funerary, significance.

In his book, Clarence defined the engravings further, paying tribute to Issel in turn, but not always agreeing with his assessments. He writes clearly, concisely and authoritatively, describing the region, the rocks and the routes to take to find them. He talks about his own experience and, in his own clear manner, he (ever the list maker) further enumerates the engravings:

1. Horned figures
2. Ploughs
3. Weapons and tools
4. Men
5. Huts and properties
6. Skins
7. Geometrical forms
8. Miscellaneous and indeterminable figures.[193]

Both Issel and Bicknell found it difficult to draw conclusions about the artists – 'It is a great mystery', Issel would complain.[194] Clarence continued to study the engravings and to write about them for another ten years. In 1903 he published *Further Explorations in the Regions of the Prehistoric Rock Engravings in the Italian Maritime Alps* (39 pages) and in 1911 a second edition of *The Prehistoric Rock Engravings in the Italian Maritime Alps* came out. Then in 1913 he published his classic work, *A Guide to the Prehistoric Engravings in the Italian Maritime Alps* (136 pages), which was the summation of his research. In 1971 it was published in French and Italian, and in 2016 republished in English by Cambridge University Press. This book is still the authority on the engravings of the Mont Bégo region.

In 1913, Clarence wrote: 'For the present then we can only say that the authors of the engravings were at least in part an agricultural people who possessed weapons some of which are believed to be those of the early bronze period, perhaps 1000–1500 B.C.'[195] He pointed out that the rocky valleys in which the engravings were found were not suitable for pasturage, and then stated: 'We are inclined to think that many people must have gone there together and even then during a long series of years, but only for a very short time, and that they were not engaged when there in any other occupation, but went for the express purpose of cutting the figures.'[196]

As Clarence's friend Émile Cartailhac said, 'His techniques and his choices of rubbings show that he behaved like a naturalist of the terrain, trying to create thematic and analytic plates, in the way he knew best as a botanist . . . This way of working does not allow us to classify him in the category of archaeologists of his time, who were generally more historians and antiquarians, but were not as knowledgeable about the terrain as he was.'[197]

Clarence learned the landscape through his feet, by walking the mountains over many years.

# CHAPTER ELEVEN

# WANDERLUST

IN 1898, WILDFLOWERS TOOK HOLD of Clarence's imagination again, and he was deeply engaged in sharing his finds with other collectors. Early in 1898, he had made plans to visit Malta but cancelled them in favour of a trip to Sicily and the Egadi islands. 'I have decided to go first to Palermo, hoping to find the famous *Centurea* in flower', he wrote to Burnat on 17 April. 'My friend in Palermo is S. Leopoldo Jung, well-known in commerce. He is a very good friend of the rich millionaire M. Florio – so perhaps M. Florio will invite me to go on his yacht to Marettimo [one of the Egadi islands]. At the least I would like to see Marsala and Trapani [on the mainland] although travelling in Sicily is so awful, the trains are horrible, it is a purgatory.'[198]

When Leopoldo Jung was not in Sicily, he spent time in Bordighera, where he and Clarence became good friends, often supporting the same philanthropic causes. In Sicily, he worked for Fratelli Jung, the Palermo family firm that exported dried fruit, citrus and sumac. A postcard to Burnat on 2 May 1898 from the Palazzo Jung, a magnificent building and oasis of greenery in the centre of Palermo, complete with yet another monstrous *Ficus macrophylla,* expresses Clarence's delight at the idea of botanising in the Egadi islands: 'Today I received a letter from M. Florio, king of the Egadi islands, asking his administrator to extend every possible courtesy to C.B. . . . We (Luigi and I) will leave next week for the island of Favignana, where there will be at our disposition a palace, a flotilla of boats, and I don't know what else!' Not as much as he expected. Boats were indeed provided but the flowers on the Egadi islands were few and far between; they had arrived too early. A violent scirocco imprisoned them on Marettimo for several days, an island that Clarence described as picturesque, rocky, precipitous, very primitive, short of water and home to 1,000 fishermen, where they ate poorly – no vegetables, no fruit, everything cooked in abominable oil – and the wine was too strong and the water too warm. After seven days, the wind finally dropped and they took off in a little sailboat back to Favignana.

Clarence's wanderlust was unabated. In December he made a 12-day trip to Algeria with Luigi, spending time in the city of Algiers and in the region of Kabylia, in the coastal mountains. He was clearly drawn to the city because of the famous Botanical Garden of Hamma, also known as the Test Garden, founded in 1832 and still highly regarded. He found the Hamma garden charming, with its huge variety of palms and giant bamboos. He also enjoyed the mountains and villages of Kabylia, but apart from seeing *Clematis cirrhosa* in bloom for the first time, and lots of yellow narcissi, the trip was disappointing in terms of wildflowers. What seems to have struck him most forcibly was the deeply-rooted chauvinism of the French. 'I found horrible the universal sentiment against everyone, not just against the Jews but against anyone who was not French born', he told Burnat.[199] 'I have never seen such newspapers, and every day I expected the renewal of last year's riots.' Those riots had been directed against the naturalization of Jews. The French weekly newspaper, *L'Antijuif,* was inflammatory in its particularly virulent Algerian edition. Clarence would have found this bigotry exceptionally nauseating.

Clarence was keen to seek out his *Pimpinella bicknellii* again. He and Luigi set off for Majorca at the beginning of May 1899, but the visit was doomed. Shortly after their arrival both men fell ill with what Clarence refers to as malaria. 'It's not pretty being ill in Pollensa', he confided to Burnat, 'always night fevers, thirst, bad food, etc. Nonetheless we went to Ariant where I found my Pimpinella again, looking very fit, the fruits quite well developed, magnificent plants of 70–100c.' This expedition was extraordinary for a 52-year-old man with a fever as the hike included some actual rock-climbing. The effort made Clarence's condition worse because he broke down and called a doctor. 'I hope we will get better', he told Burnat. 'I fear that we won't

*Cypripedium calceolus*, the Lady's Slipper orchid.

be able to do much here since I find myself quite weak after these fevers, but at least I have seen l'Ariant again – that ideal spot – and the marvellous precipices and pointed rocks.' Nothing had stopped Clarence from finding his flower again; not the fevers, nor the abysmal condition of the ancient paths, nor the exuberant springtime vegetation hiding those paths, nor the uneven terrain he traversed.

After the challenge of Majorca, returning to the florally well-endowed region of Val Pesio that summer of 1899 must have felt like going to heaven, with its comfortable accommodation, good food, lack of mosquitoes and nearby thermal baths. But, best of all, Clarence and Luigi made a notable find on 6 July: *Cypripedium calceolus,* the rare plant known in English as Lady's Slipper orchid and in Italian as *La Scarpetta di Venere.* Barely controlling his emotion, Clarence wrote to Burnat immediately and enclosed a specimen.

The work of Burnat and Bicknell, collecting and recording wildflowers in the Val Pesio region is not forgotten. In the Marguareis Natural Park, in the province of Cuneo, visitors will find the E. Burnat/C. Bicknell Nature Reserve,[200] which commemorates their contributions to the natural history of the area. The reserve occupies an area of about a hectare, at a height of between 1,970 and 2,000 feet, and contains rare, threatened and endemic plants in the wetland section of the reserve. Clarence alone added 73 new species to the known flora of the Ligurian Alps, and defined the precise areas in which the various species were distributed.

He and Luigi clearly regained their strength in Val Pesio, and by September they were ready to set off to visit Émile Burnat in Nant-sur-Vevey.

❧

At the beginning of 1900, Clarence was busy with indoor work. He had found a new hobby: poker work, that is, a method of decorating wood with a red-hot poker. By February, he had amassed enough bowls and platters to show them at the museum and to sell them in aid of the war effort,[201] the Boer War.

Still making use of his very convenient museum, in March he organised a series of five concerts to be performed by the San Remo Opera Orchestra. Unfortunately, this venture was not a financial success.[202]

Clarence's desire to see ever more wildflowers remained undiminished, but his plans to go to Portugal were scuppered by Rosa Fanshawe Walker's illness. She was suffering from a recurrence of a dangerous aneurism that was causing her great pain. On Good Friday, she had nearly died, but since then her condition had improved.

Clarence decorated this slightly oval bowl, 33.5 x 37 cm, with images from the rock engravings using a red-hot poker. The bowl was probably given by Clarence to his friend the prehistorian Professor Issel in Genoa. It was found 100 years later in an antique market by its present owner Fabio Negrino, also of the Antiquities Department of the University of Genoa.

She recovered slowly but well – and eventually lived to be 79 years old. In a letter to Burnat on 27 April, Clarence described Rosa as his best friend in Bordighera. This is not surprising because of the many months they spent together at the Villa Rosa when Clarence first arrived in Bordighera.

Once Rosa's health had stabilised, Clarence was free to pursue his travel plans. He organised his trip to Spain around a visit to Elche, near Alicante. Elche was on the meridian of a total eclipse that would occur on 28 May 1900. He did not have grand botanising plans, and did not take along a lot of drawing paper. On arrival, Clarence described to Burnat the huge influx of foreigners into the little Moorish town, all fluttering with excitement about the eclipse, all anxious about the weather. Even the famous French astronomer, Camille Flammarion, showed up. As it happened, the weather was clear on the 28th, and Flammarion later wrote that the sky was black at the moment of totality (seventy-nine seconds) and that the corona was oblong. The great man was known not just for his astronomy but for his mysticism and science fiction; it is possible that he and Clarence were already friends as both men belonged to the Society for Psychical Research in London.

Elche provided another lure for Clarence – its historic palm forest, now a UNESCO World Heritage site. The entire forest, which is said to contain 200,000 date palms was laid out in orchards, of which the Huerto del Cura was the most famous because it contained the astonishing Imperial Palm, dating from before 1850, a specimen that has sported seven trunks and looks for all the world like a giant candelabrum.

Like the leaves of the date palms of Bordighera, the leaves of Elche's palms were – and still are – harvested, dried and whitened for use in Palm Sunday celebrations. The fruit of the palms is no longer harvested in either town.

~

On his way to visit his family in England and Ireland during July and August of 1900, he stopped in Paris for the *Exposition Universelle*. It was 22 years since his first visit, and much progress had been made in those years. Clarence wrote to Burnat about moving pictures of animals and birds; the music he listened to on Edison's phonograph; and his ascent of the Eiffel tower, adding that if anyone were to ask him what astonished him most, he would reply that it was the price he had to pay for two potatoes in a restaurant!

Once in London, he complained about the number of social calls he had to make, but described a wonderful trip to Kew Gardens – possibly intended as a purely scientific visit but ending up as a pleasure trip. This being the great era of botanical exchanges, Clarence may have been presenting a specimen or two to Kew's herbarium. To this day, Kew owns four species collected by Clarence, one of which bears his name: *Euphrasia bicknellii*. Writing to Burnat about the visit, he exclaimed, 'It truly is a paradise in this great park, walking on the lawn amidst trees and flowers, and what masses of beautiful plants I saw! Everything is so tidy and so well cared for.'

Two days later, he arrived at his sister Ada's newly acquired house in Much Hadham, 'a charming old house, with pretty rooms, low but beautiful, two great fireplaces, long corridors, a formal garden between brick walls where one can imagine ladies from the Middle Ages arriving, like in the paintings . . . lots of animals and many flowers.' Now there was a place where Clarence could relax and enjoy visits from his nephews and nieces.

∾

At the end of 1900, he was travelling again. Taking Luigi with him, he set out on 29 November from Marseilles to Alexandria on one of the Messageries packet boats, whose ultimate destination was Yokohama. 'I yearn to see Cairo again, the desert and the pyramids', he told Burnat before setting off, but revisiting a place can destroy one's beautiful memories. 'I find Cairo horribly changed; the tourists no longer consider the monuments and all the beautiful things of the East, but think only of the luxurious modern life in the grand hotels. Fortunately, the desert, the pyramids, and the Arabs do not change.'

Clarence's plans included visiting Jerusalem, Damascus, and Constantinople, but the plague in Alexandria forced them to spend two days in quarantine in Beirut which used up the time allotted to Constantinople. The trip was clearly taxing, physically and emotionally, and Clarence said nothing about its religious impact in his letters to Burnat. He merely commented that Damascus pleased him and, damning with faint praise, that Jerusalem pleased him more than he had expected; his particular thrill was in finding wonderful spring flowers around Jericho.

Clearly wildflowers played a more important role in his visit to the Holy Land than did religious matters.

He was exhausted and suffering from bronchitis on returning home, after a long and rather painful trip, with rough seas. He told Burnat that the East had been all very well for a few weeks, but he had tired of the continual noise, the dirt and the lies, the corruption and the thieving.

Clarence did not have much time to recover before his two nieces, Linda and Nora Bicknell, Percy's daughters, arrived

Linda (*left*, 1871–1960) and Nora (*right*, 1873–1929) were Clarence's nieces, daughters of his brother Percy. 5 May 1901.

to stay, bringing with them a lady's maid – who promptly died. She had been the chief bread-winner of her family, but neither Linda nor Nora knew her home address nor how to reach the other family members. Clarence reported to Burnat that they were all very sad, before remarking that it was also very sad for Luigi and the cook, who had appreciated the help of an English maid.

On 12 April 1901, Clarence wrote a letter of sympathy to Burnat about the death of his brother, and went on to say that Bordighera was full of maladies, deaths, and bad weather that spring. He added that his own brother in England, Sidney, had almost died of an intestinal tumour, but the tumour had been absorbed.

In May, he took off again for Corsica with Luigi, finding the island even more charming than before, and he was happy to find many plants he had not previously seen and to have succeeded in travelling along the swampy coastline without falling prey to malaria.

By the summer of 1901, he was ready for a change from botany.

~

Natural curiosity led Clarence to reflect on the world and the universe around him, and he was well aware of climate change long before it became a twenty-first century concern. Writing to Burnat in November 1903, he complained that Italy was under water, and he asked whether blame for this should be placed on maximum flare activity at the beginning of the 11-year solar cycle, or on marconigrams, or on whatever else was wreaking havoc with the atmosphere. Marconigrams were messages or telegrams sent by radio, thanks to Guglielmo Marconi (1874–1937) who made the first cross-Channel transmission in 1899 and the first transatlantic communication in 1901.

Clarence loved to travel in the spring, before the summer heat, and on his arrival in Sardinia in the spring of 1904 he was delighted to find so many flowers in bloom – and many costumes too. The main purpose of this trip was not botanical but a tour of Sardinia's *nuraghi,* the megalithic conical towers and walls that are scattered all over the island. Needless to say, the botany of the island was irresistible, and as soon as he returned to Bordighera, he wrote to Sommier, admitting that he botanised every day and made a 'fairly complete' list of the flowering plants he saw. He then proposed to Sommier that he (Clarence) write a brief account of his trip for the bulletin of the *Società Botanica Italiana,* an account that might be a useful aid in compiling a complete list of the flora of the island. 'Tell me frankly, yes or no.'[203] Sommier said, frankly, yes, and Clarence lost no time in writing the article, which was snapped up and published in the society's bulletin in May 1904.[204] As for the *nuraghi,* he is mute on the topic.

In June, still thinking about building a house up at Casterino, he could not resist taking a trip into the mountains to look for a site. It was cold and rainy during the week but he recognised what a benefit the rain was to the mountain pasturage after the long drought.

He and Luigi cooled off in the Dolomites, at Cortina, but even there it was unusually warm. In August, they set off on another trip to Sardinia, hot on the trail of the elusive and, to him, extremely desirable *Kalbfussia.* 'We look for it day and night, and do not find it',

C.B., *Monte Cristallo, Cortina d'Ampezzo, 30 July 1904,* watercolour.

Clarence and mineralogist
Alberto Pelloux resting
on the high mountains.
IISL.

moaned Clarence to Burnat, 'and the chief gardener [presumably of the botanical gardens] who comes from Milan but knows the plants of Sardinia very well says that it has not been seen for [many] years . . . Perhaps, with so much progress in cultivation, it has disappeared.'[205] They found the botanical gardens 'fort curieux' [very strange], although not without interest. 'It's the best place on the island to collect plants, being full of weeds, and I have seen poppies, *medicago* [medick] and *Adonis* [crowfoot].' But as for works of reference on Sardinia, Clarence was out of luck: 'There's nothing in the bookshops – nothing – not even a map of the town. A few bad novels, but of history, of travel, of antiquities, only rubbish. The only thing I can find is a little brochure of Sardinian tales.'

In spite of all his other foreign travels, Clarence did not forget his family and friends in England, and was regularly surprised by the changes he found there. His letters to his young friend Alberto Pelloux reveal how shocked he was by the hustle and bustle of London.

In one letter he writes:

The buses are full, the streets a heap of automobiles, bicycles, etc. Yesterday a young man was squashed between two buses and taken to the hospital where my nephew works, his cranium cracked, and all the bones in his face broken. I believe that he died today. . . . And am seeing many women on bicycles in the middle of omnibuses, and it's a wonder that there's not a calamity all the time.[206]

In another letter, he writes:

I have worked very hard, rushing about in trains aboveground and underground, paying calls and short visits to relations and friends, and I am always tired. It has rained or been foggy every day since I arrived, and one day there was a thick London fog, the very worst, when even the lamps were invisible and people were lost in the complete darkness, but happily that day I was in the country with a blue sky. I have had no time to go to any amusements, except once to the theatre and with my brother to the Zoological Gardens, nor have I been able to do much shopping.

It is so difficult to arrange all my visits. There is in London a post *every hour* from 8 a.m. to 10 p.m. and every time I come in, I find a lot of letters, upsetting my plans, and have to write and make new ones.[207]

However, Clarence did manage to get to Oxford, where he saw 'very interesting things from the Cretan palace of Knossos and also a magnificent collection of things lately discovered in *prehistoric* Egyptian tombs.' In 1897, Clarence had corresponded with Sir Arthur Evans,[208] the discoverer of the site at Knossos, about similarities between the rock carvings in Crete and those in the Maritime Alps.

In spring 1905 Clarence and Luigi set off on a little jaunt to Corsica. 'I was so fed up with the season in Bordighera . . . and after the burnt and dried-up Riviera, this verdant island is more charming than ever', he exulted to Burnat, even as he lamented that it was too early to see many wildflowers in bloom. 'How I love Corsica. If the ferry service weren't so infrequent and so bad,

I would go again and again to see its forests and its rocks. I am always enchanted by the island.'

Clarence made a reconnaissance trip to Casterino in May. His friend Harry Buddicom had recently acquired an automobile and drove him as far as Tende, a surprisingly enjoyable two-hour journey. 'I had always sworn that I would never go in an auto, but now I am enchanted!', Clarence told Burnat. Unfortunately, the weather was not as kind as his friend. The rain streamed down on Tende and snow fell on the mountains, preventing him from making the hike up to Casterino to determine the site for the house. 'If the weather doesn't improve by tomorrow, we shall descend because I have absolutely nothing to do here.' Clarence was incapable of sitting still, but his mind was spinning along, already planning travel arrangements to Boulogne for the first international Esperanto congress and thence to Switzerland to see Burnat, who had included Luigi in his invitation to stay. 'You are very kind to invite us both . . . and Luigi sends a thousand thanks for your most amiable invitation', wrote Clarence, who was always delighted when people were courteous to Luigi and did not treat him as a servant. Having known his employer since he was five years old and Clarence was 36, Luigi thought of him as a second father, and Clarence treated Luigi as the son he never had. They supported each other without fail, and had the ability to work together harmoniously on whatever they turned their hands to. Luigi was just what Clarence needed in an assistant. In his preface to *A Guide to the Prehistoric Engravings in the Italian Maritime Alps,* Clarence pays due tribute to his companion: 'In our explorations and discoveries, I have nearly always been accompanied by my Italian friend Signor Luigi Pollini, for very many years my faithful assistant at home, and my helpful companion when travelling and botanising in Europe, Africa and Asia.

Without his quicker eyes, nimbler feet and indefatigable assistance, very many of the rocks most difficult of access, and of the figures cut upon them, would not have been discovered. He has climbed steep and slippery places where I was loth to go, and taken copies and made photographs of the figures there, and has never been weary when I could walk or work no more.[209]

Luigi Pollini in 1912, from the programme of the Esperanto Congress in Cracow.

Émile Cartailhac (1845–1921), French prehistorian. Museum of Toulouse

~

Clarence met Émile Cartailhac (1845–1921) at the Congress of Prehistoric Anthropology and Archaeology in Monaco in April 1905. They immediately struck up a friendship, even though Clarence's prime interest lay in rock engravings *en plein air* while Cartailhac's lay deep in the caves at Altamira and in the Dordogne and Pyrenees. Both men were consumed by the idea of conserving and cataloguing their miraculous findings – and talking and writing to each other about them.[210]

Cartailhac had gained notoriety for ridiculing the claim that the cave paintings at Altamira, near Santander on the north coast

Front cover of 1884 issue of *La Guêpe*, satirical journal of Toulouse illustrating *Émile Cartailhac*.

of Spain, were paleolithic in origin. He simply could not believe they had been painted as early as the Stone Age, and denied the proposition vehemently. The images in question were of bison on the ceiling of the cave, and had been discovered in 1879 by nine-year-old Maria de Sautuola who pointed them out to her father, Marcelino Sanz de Sautuola, an amateur archaeologist and the owner of the land on which the caves were located.

In 1880, Sautuola and Juan Vilanova y Piera wrote up the findings, which were highly acclaimed by the Spanish, but the French scientific community scoffed at the Spanish claims, even going so far as to accuse Sautuola of forging the images. By 1902, however, closer analysis of the paintings and the finding of more painted caves nearby led the sceptics, with Cartailhac at their head, to reconsider their early judgment. That year Cartailhac published his famous apology, 'Mea culpa d'un sceptique'.[211]

By the time Cartailhac and Abbé Henri Breuil (1877–1951), a young archaeologist and prehistorian with an extraordinary career ahead of him, met Clarence at the 1905 Monaco congress, they were full of stories of the wonders of the caves near Les Eyzies-de-Tayac-Sireuil in the Dordogne and the newly discovered cave at Niaux in the Pyrénées. Cartailhac even went so far as to slip a brochure about them into Clarence's photograph album while at the conference, an act which prompted Clarence to promise that in return he would make rubbings for him of the rock engravings above Casterino.

By 1907, Cartailhac had stirred up Clarence's interest in the cave drawings to such an extent that Clarence determined to visit the Combarelles and Font-de-Gaume caves near Les Eyzies as well as the cave at Niaux in the Tarascon valley in the foothills of the Pyrenees. In a letter to Cartailhac at his home in Toulouse, Clarence asked his friend to find a simple, clean hotel in Toulouse, not one for tourists, to accommodate him and his 'botanical aide-de-camp', who would be accompanying him on the trip to France.[213] In the event, because of sickness and snow, it was not until the beginning of March that Clarence and Luigi finally left for Toulouse, a city that was fortunately equidistant between Les Eyzies and Niaux. After visiting Cartailhac, they made their way north to Les Eyzies, armed with his instructions.

Clarence later related the experience to Cartailhac: 'A very agreeable stay at Les Eyzies, in spite of the fog and rain . . . but most of the time we spent in the two grottoes, Combarelles and Font-de-Gaume. Combarelles is truly astonishing, but one needs a lot of time to visit it properly and to rest from time to time, because it is painful to walk almost always bent over in this gallery . . . We went right to the end where the figures in black are. But holding the candle and the guidebook, while drops of water are falling everywhere, along with sweat from my head, while discovering all the marvellous beasts in their zoological assemblages was not easy . . . how much time it must have taken those artists to do the work, and do it so well.'[214] Clarence then described their guide, a charming, funny, little man, 'but not very intelligent.' He was, however, able to reveal several items that, without him, Clarence and Luigi would have missed. The paintings of animals at Combarelles depicted mostly horses and reindeer, but also included a few mammoths, cave bears and cave lions.

Émile Cartailhac, *Image of a bison in the Niaux cave*, photo.

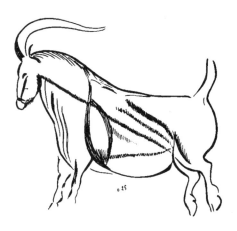

Image of an ibex deep in the Niaux cave discovered by Cartailhac. Breuil, *Cartailhac* (1907).

From their base at Les Eyzies, they also visited the cave at Font-de-Gaume, recently discovered by Denis Peyrony. (Denis Peyrony, 1869–1954, had studied archaeology with Cartailhac; along with Abbé Breuil and Louis Capitan he was one of the discoverers of the caves at Combarelles and Font-de-Gaume.) Clarence was disappointed that the walls had been defaced by earlier tourists. On the bright side, the guide was both kind and intelligent, and pointed out many polychrome paintings of bison, horses and mammoths that might otherwise have escaped their notice. Even though the weather in the Dordogne at the beginning of March is notoriously cold and wet enough to frighten many a visitor away – and sadly for Clarence it was too early for wildflowers – there was still enough business at the time to keep guides working. Tourists were fascinated by the discovery of cave paintings, and speleology had become the new extreme sport.

What neither Cartailhac, nor Abbé Breuil, nor Clarence, nor Luigi could know at the time was that just 25 kilometres from Les Eyzies were located the greatest painted caves of all, those of Lascaux. These would not be discovered until 1940.

Clarence and Luigi then headed south to Ariège in the foothills of the Pyrénées, where they were joined by Cartailhac. From Ariège they scrambled up a long, steep, narrow track to reach the Niaux cave at 678 metres above sea level. The very entrance resembled a cathedral, 50 metres wide and 55 metres high. From there they began their walk into the kilometres of galleries and gazed at paintings of bison, horses, and ibex from the Magdalenian period (20,000–13,000 years ago). This cave had been visited since the 1600s, but it was not until 1906 that Commandant Mollard and his two sons discovered the 'Salon Noir', deep in its furthest recesses. To reach it, 'It is necessary to climb almost constantly, hills of very fine, dry sand up to the entrance to a large rotunda, with a high dome and walls which are creased to form multiple shell-shaped flattened apses, wide and shallow. Here, spread out over a length of 40 metres, the black frescoes of Niaux may be found.'[215]

Cartailhac led Clarence and Luigi to the Salon Noir, about which Clarence had this to say in his letter of thanks to Cartailhac: 'No doubt, the grotto of Niaux, with its vast rooms and its Sancta Sanctorum in the most distant corners, its magnificent, well-conserved paintings and its layers of sand with engravings on which no one has ever walked in hundreds of centuries, impressed me most. Several times, it all seemed a dream. In all my life, I have never taken a more satisfying journey, completely new and unexpected. From this moment on, I will maintain the greatest interest in all your excavations and explorations.' And then he concluded: 'My thoughts will be with you … in your Pyrénéan churches. The time will arrive, will it not, when the sanctuary at Niaux will be more moving than that of Lourdes? And the paintings of these true, unknown artists will be more appreciated than all those religious canvases that the world admires because it is told to admire them … My Luigi thanks you for your warm welcome. You have no doubt lit in him more than ever devotion to the truth.'[216] Much later, in 1920, Cartailhac also remembered that day in a letter he wrote to Salomon Reinach: 'I had the satisfaction of making [Bicknell] visit our caverns, and this promenade in our Pyrénées gave him much pleasure. To thank me, he offered me a choice of prints, around 50 [of the rock engravings] which I have often displayed.'[217]

On the fragile paper band that holds together the letters from Bicknell to Cartailhac is written the words: 'Souvenir à Bicknell – mon ami et des meilleurs archéologues, il fut des plus utiles.' ['In memory of Bicknell – my friend and of the best archaeologists, he was among the most useful.']

'We had scarcely arrived when I received the sad news of the death of Mr. Hanbury of La Mortola and, as an old friend of the family, I had to leave immediately to attend a ceremony at his home,'[218] wrote Clarence to Cartailhac in March 1907 after his visit to the caves. 'Then to an Esperanto concert in Alassio, followed by two days in which I was fully occupied in choosing and arranging between two and three hundred watercolours for a show that will begin tomorrow. But I have thought about you a great deal, and spoken of you too, and in spirit I am still more or less in your grottoes.' Clarence included with his letter a cheque for 250 francs, to which Luigi had contributed what he could, in support of Cartailhac's future excavations.

By the beginning of April, Clarence and Luigi were on the road again – or rather at sea, on a smooth voyage from Genoa to Gibraltar. Clarence hated the town, but in two days on the Rock, they managed to collect many new plants, in spite of prohibitions on where they might go. 'Today we managed to spend an hour in defended sites without being seen. What luck!'[219] he crowed to Burnat.

From Gibraltar, they travelled to Ronda, Seville, Cordoba and Granada, and on returning home Clarence wrote contentedly to Burnat on 26 April: 'Here we are back again after a second superb voyage; the sea was like a lake. The view of the Sierra Nevada from the sea, like that of Granada was magnificent. We did everything we possibly could during such a short trip … We didn't find any rarities, but many plants we had never seen before.'[220] It is strange, but perhaps unsurprising, that Clarence makes no mention of the Spanish trains nor of the great sights he saw: the El Tajo canyon in Ronda, the Alhambra in Granada, the Great Mosque of Córdoba, the Alcázar in Seville. Flowers always came first.

CHAPTER TWELVE

# WOMEN!

WE HAVE FOUND NO EVIDENCE that Clarence ever enjoyed a full-blown, body and soul relationship with a man or woman. Brother Parrett, that 'naked Apollo', could be a candidate, but the ease with which Clarence bade him farewell and took up with Rosa Fanshawe Walker seems to rule him out. Like many men of his generation, particularly those of the Anglo-Catholic priesthood, he apparently preferred the single life, although he cared deeply about his friends and relatives, developed crushes on individuals both male and female, and adored his domestics, whom he called his Italian 'family.' But what about the human need for touch?

Rosa Ellen Fanshawe Walker is the likeliest female candidate for a relationship. There is hardly a day in which Clarence does not mention her in his 1878/9 diary. They go everywhere together, on endless walks, shopping, services in the parish church, moonlight strolls, and occasions like this: 'Took Mrs W. to the Paradise in the Nervia valley where we were caught in a storm & got a good wetting.' and 'Mrs W. unfortunately hurt her knee somewhat in a fall coming down the loosely rocky path.' It would have been hard not to touch each other.

They remained close friends. After she sold the Villa Rosa to Clarence in 1880, Rosa Ellen lived just a few steps away in the Casa Fanshawe on the Via Romana. In 1885, she converted part of the house into a Casa di Salute – a clinic for poor women and children – in memory of her mother.[221] It is easy to wonder why they did not marry; Rosa Ellen was an eligible widow and Clarence an eligible bachelor, thrown together by circumstances. Perhaps he was daunted by her nine-year seniority and, if she was anything like her mother, her rather dominant personality. And perhaps she could not envision returning to live in the Villa Rosa, by then stuffed full of pressed flowers, with watercolours drying on clotheslines all over the house.

By 1902, Clarence's life was full of women: his sisters Ada and Lucinda; his nieces Nora and Linda; Margaret Berry, his niece by marriage; Ellen Willmott, the famous horticulturalist; Rosa Junck, the Esperantist; his avowed best friend, Rosa Fanshawe Walker; the mysterious Scottish lady, possibly Alice Campbell, with whom he spent time during the winter of 1883 in Finalmarina and again in 1897; and later on, starting in 1909, the Baroness Helene von Taube, with whom he had what was probably the last deeply felt relationship of his life.

'Laying of the Foundation Stone of Monte Verde 1904', ink inscription next to the photo. Edward Berry holding the plans of the house, next to Margaret and her dog Robber. Clarence is half way up the right side in a bowler hat and with a full beard.

Clarence's oldest sister Ada Berry remained the favourite of all his siblings. After the death of his mother when he was seven years old, Ada, then 21, assumed the role of parent to her little brother and they formed a close, lasting bond. He made sure to visit her on all his trips back to England. After his visit there in October 1903, he brought her back to Bordighera, where she, in turn, relaxed in Clarence's garden and consulted with her son Edward and his wife Margaret about their plans to build the Villa Monte Verde. Ada had been a widow since 1875, and a busy widow at that, with her strong commitment to education.

In February 1902, Clarence received news of the sudden death at the Grand Hotel in Montreux of Henry Maxwell Egan Desmond, his much-disliked brother-in-law, husband of his sister Lucinda. (Egan acquired the additional name of Desmond late in life.) 'I wrote to my sister to leave the hotel and to come and be tranquil with me', said Clarence to Burnat. 'My brother-in-law was very old, about 80 I believe, but he possessed an extraordinary vitality . . . I never liked him much, but it's very sad for my sister, and I believe that he was a good husband and father.' Egan Desmond's death allowed Clarence to spend time with Lucinda again, although she did not take advantage of his offer of tranquility. She chose instead to go to Terme d'Acqui and later to meet up with him in Turin.

Nora and Linda Bicknell, daughters of Clarence's brother Percy, began showing up at the Villa Rosa on a regular basis. Nora evidently thought highly of Bordighera, and made her home and her living there for several years, working as a clerk in Edward Berry's bank, and she had her own business as a photographer and maker of greeting cards and calendars, often donating the profits from her sales to charity. She and Clarence later travelled together.

Clarence loved spending time with Margaret Berry. Her ebullience was catching, and she committed herself wholeheartedly to the town and its inhabitants. In 1904, she and Edward laid the foundation stone for the magnificent Villa Monte Verde, the home they would build on the hill above the Via Romana, where they reigned like the king and queen of Bordighera.

Clarence had been hunting high and low for the perfect botanical pin with which to skewer his specimens when he first met Ellen Willmott, probably in 1901 at La Mortola, the home of Sir Thomas Hanbury whose impressive gardens cascaded down a cliff just outside Ventimiglia. Miss Willmott later bought property two miles away at Boccanegra, where she, too, created a spectacular garden, also cascading down the cliff. Clarence corresponded with her for years,[222] and watched the development of this garden, providing plants and seeds

Ellen Willmott (1858–1934) created the Boccanegra Gardens between Ventimiglia and the Hanbury Gardens.

for it, but his first letter revolved around the thorny topic of the aforementioned botanical pins. He also sought her advice about which fungicidal medicines he could use to destroy the disease that was attacking the cardboard on which he mounted his drawings.

Sixteen years younger than Clarence, slim, rich, good-looking with curly, ginger hair, devoted to gardening, always in a hurry, bossy like his beloved sister Ada, Ellen Willmott was bound to appeal to Clarence, even as he appealed to her. As Audrey Le Lièvre points out in her biography, 'Ellen Willmott valued above all things companionship with a man of intellect and stature who shared her own interests.'[223] Unlike others, Clarence was not daunted by her, even though her horticultural credentials could have intimidated a lesser man. She had become a member of the Royal Horticultural Society in 1894, and only three years later received its Victoria Medal of Honour, inaugurated that year to celebrate the Queen's Diamond Jubilee. Along with Gertrude Jekyll, she was one of only two women out of sixty recipients to get the award. She was also elected to the coveted RHS Narcissus Committee, and over the years won numerous RHS Orders of Merit and gold medals, particularly for her groups of rare daffodils. In 1904, she was one of the very first women elected as a fellow of the Linnean Society.

In spite of her status as a horticulturalist, Clarence did not hesitate to castigate her for not thanking Luigi for his gifts of seeds, and pestered her to inform him whether the seeds had germinated. He did not live to see Miss Willmott's downfall at the point when she had to sell off her overseas properties and say goodbye to Boccanegra. She had been extravagant to a fault, and at one point employed 104 gardeners[224] at Warley, her magnificent estate in Essex, where, in its heyday, it is estimated she grew 100,000 varieties of trees, plants and shrubs. Over sixty species were named after her or after Warley. 'Miss Willmott's Ghost' (*Eryngium giganteum,* the giant

*Eryngium giganteum* is known as 'Miss Willmott's Ghost' after the nineteenth-century gardener Ellen Willmott, who liked to scatter seeds of the plant in other people's gardens.

sea holly) is the plant most identified with her, and she delighted in secretly spreading its seeds in her friends' gardens so they would not forget her, the subsequent plants gleaming silvery grey-green and spectral in the twilight.

Esperanto caused Clarence to spend more and more time in the company of Rosa Junck. Born in 1850 in the town of Tabor in Bohemia (now in the Czech Republic), Mrs Junck, née Bilek or Bilekova, had arrived in Bordighera in 1890. A widow and an exceptional linguist, she set herself up in business as a language teacher. She and Clarence translated works into Esperanto and wrote

Rosa Junck (1850–1929) set herself up as a language teacher in Bordighera. Photo 1906. From *Albumo de Konataj Esperantistoj*.

articles for magazines, and they both played important roles at the Boulogne congress in 1905. But sometimes their Esperanto work took a different turn. In a letter to Alberto Pelloux in 1906, Clarence relates: 'The other day Mahdi [his dog] and I have sat in the garden translating into Esperanto. Mrs. Junck wants me to act with her in the next Geneva Esp. Congress, in a comedietta of De Amicis, *La floro de l'pasinto*,[225] which she has translated, but as she is the heroine I am not invited to take the lover's part (who is, she does not tell me). I have declined.'[226]

In the same letter, Clarence exults: 'Bordighera is lovely, a wilderness of roses from the ground to the house tops and tree tops and down again. Hotels nearly empty. O *gioa, gioa*, and I shall soon be able to parade about in Zulu costume.' This mad joy was the result of the departure of the winter visitors.

Mystery surrounds the Scottish lady whom Clarence first met in 1883 and saw again in 1897. Hard as we try, we cannot identify her, but it is possible that she is the Alice Campbell, whose

Clarence with two women, possibly Alice Campbell and her mother, in front of the Museo Bicknell. IISL.

Clarence, Mahdi and Alice Campbell up on the Chiappes de Fontanalba. IISL.

relationship with Clarence is still much whispered about in Bordighera, without any hard evidence. In one reproduction of the photograph on the lower left of the facing page, she is identified with him in front of the Museo Bicknell.[227] The wisteria is looking fit and well grown, so the photograph probably dates from the late 1880s or early 1900s. In the photograph on the right, she is identified with him and Mahdi up in the mountains.

When Enzo Bernardini was writing about Alice Campbell, he interviewed the redoubtable 'Miss Muriel', that is, Muriel de Burgh Daly, who was old enough have known Alice. She responded indignantly to his questions: 'About that woman I do not intend to speak.'[228] It sounds as though Bordighera, at least the tea-drinking gossips, did not approve of her liaison, or whatever it was, with Clarence.

The mystery of Alice Campbell persists to this day, and our research continues.[229]

≈

No mystery surrounds Baroness Helene von Taube, thanks to a lengthy and loving correspondence. Clarence met the amateur botanist Helene von Taube in late 1908 or early 1909, when she came to Bordighera from Weimar seeking warmth and sunshine for her ailing husband, Baron Otto von Taube (1833–1911). Born in 1845, she was three years younger than Clarence. Her father was Count Alexander Friedrich Lebrecht Michael Arthur Nikolaus von Keyserling (1815–1891), a geologist, paleontologist, botanist and zoologist of Baltic German descent, and her mother was Gräfin Zenaida Cancrin, of Russian descent. Helene had three children, Otto, Marie and Helene, the last of whom died of tuberculosis during the course of Clarence and the baroness's correspondence.

They never called each other by their first names, and their letters, while ostensibly about botany, are a lode of information about their lives, their joys and sorrows and their philosophies. The collection, written between 1909 and 1915, was donated by the baroness's son to the Natural History Museum in London, the majority of the letters being from Clarence, but they include a few of Helene's drafts in response. She did not write to Clarence in her native German, but in a rather flowery, expressive English. Clarence always wrote in English, except for his last two letters, dated 1914 and 1915, which were in Italian, presumably because it was a less dangerous language than English in which to communicate with Helene in Weimar during World War I.

When one digests the sum total of their letters, the writers' deep devotion to each other is apparent. Clarence wrote to Helene in a manner in which he never revealed himself to anyone else, and Helene poured out her feelings of joy and sorrow to a man whose ability to listen and comfort had no equal. They became soul mates, and there was even an undeniable ripple of attraction between them.

Clarence's first note, from January 1909, possibly written before he had even met Helene, reads: 'Madame, The wild plant you sent me is *Globularia Alypum L*, common in our dry hills, a characteristic Mediterranean plant . . . I shall be very pleased to tell you at any time what little I know about flora and show you my herbaria and drawings or dried specimens.'

After that first 'Madame', Helene was always 'Dear Baroness', and Clarence was 'Dear Mr. Bicknell!'

They set up meetings, either at the Villa Rosa or at the museum . . . 'I hope you will often come to the museum, or into my garden.' 'As the weather is bad you probably will not expect me; but

Clarence Bicknell in about 1905 photographed by Ezio Benigni of Bordighera. BibCiv

anyhow I cannot come . . . as I have a touch of bronchitis. Perhaps tomorrow or the next day.' 'Please settle whether you will dine with me today or tomorrow.' 'I could see you pm (but only for a few minutes) before dinner. I say a few minutes because I give an Esperanto lesson to 4 people at 5.30. I am glad that you will come again to lunch. Next time we will make proper preparation.' 'Come & sit in my garden when you like, but now one has to come in by the back gate.'

Helene wrote in similar fashion: 'Could I see you to-morrow Wednesday at 9 ½ o'clock in the morning. If not, leave me at your door a message, when I could see you to-morrow Wednesday ne fut-ce que pour un quart d'heure. I would come except at 12 till 1 o'clock, when I have an appointment already. Or were it possible to come to our hotel for you? between 2 and 4 o'clock? From 4 to 5 I am going to Mrs. Berry reception. I pass your door in every case at 9 ½ hour to-morrow and I shall enter if you are at home.'

The von Taubes' winter visit to Bordighera 1909 was helpful enough to the baron's health for them to decide to return in 1910. Clarence certainly had something to do with this decision, even going so far as to recommend a hotel. On 22 November 1909, he wrote to Helene from Kent, where he was staying with Ada, saying: 'I dare say the winter in the south will do [your husband] good. I think he will be very happy in the level garden of the Iles Britanniques hotel.'

Shortly after the von Taubes returned to Bordighera, Clarence spent New Year's Eve with them, and his thank-you note reads: 'Once more "a Happy New Year to you and yours." I thank you for the pleasant evening which I spent with you. Here are the two Daisy Books containing all the best things and also much rubbish.' His next note reads: 'Pray look at my herbarium while I am away.' Being 'away' refers to the trip that he and Luigi were about to take to Tunis and Malta. Just four days later he sent a postcard to Helene: 'Tunis. 5.1.10. We had an excellent journey, arrived here *before time* yesterday, and have spent today in the bazaars and among the ruins of Carthage . . . There are very few flowers. I have seen one which I do not know, a little *Compositae*. The only common thing is that terribly ubiquitous *Oxalis libyca*.' That same day he told Burnat what easy voyage it had been and expressed surprise that people did not leave Europe more often.

As for Malta, Clarence made the mistake of going there too early in the year to see many wildflowers, but was delighted to encounter Esperantists in full bloom, delight that he expressed in a letter to Stefano Sommier on 5 February 1910: 'I could have made more excursions, but my Maltese Esperantist friends took me out to lunch, tea, etc.! and in the countryside it was dreadful, we walked and walked without seeing even a *Fumaria* or other "weed", only endless *Oxalis*.'[230] *Oxalis, Oxalis* everywhere. Sometimes referred to as wood sorrel, *Oxyalis* is a family of nearly 1,000 species, found worldwide, except in the polar regions.

WOMEN!

By April 1910 Clarence was back in England, visiting Ada, about whom he wrote to Helene on the 30th, saying:

> I find my sister very well; she looks younger and more beautiful, and is much as she was some years before her paralytic stroke. She is 78, but remembers everything and takes the keenest interest in politics and social questions and in her garden, and is wheeled out every day to see the Daffodils and Tulips and all the spring flowers. The woods here are most lovely – masses of primrose, anemone and carpeted with Scilla nutans (bluebells) – our poet Tennyson said they were like the heavens upbreaking through the earth. I had not seen England in the spring or these wildflowers for more than 30 perhaps 35 years, and the sight fills me with wonder and joy.

Clarence suffered health problems during July. He wrote on 6 July from Casterino: 'Four weeks ago I was taken ill and could not move for 3 weeks. I had an illness called *herpes* in English, something caused by inflammation of the sheaths of the nerves in the head and neck. I could not sleep at all on account of the pain for a long time: then followed some breakdown in stomach which quite finished me off, and I became very weak. I came up here on a mule with my niece Margaret Berry . . . and I am now rapidly feeling better . . . I can sleep and eat and walk about the gardens and pull up weeds but alas I may not go up higher to see all the gentians and anemones and the rhododendrons and other lovely flowers. So I have to send Luigi and I draw and read at home; but I hope soon to be allowed to take more exercise and work at the rock engravings.' Clarence refers elsewhere to his condition as erysipelas, a more likely diagnosis. Shingles, too, would have many of the same symptoms.

At the same time, he wrote to Alberto Pelloux, saying he was getting better,

> but have horrible neuralgia in the head which comes on at night and keeps me awake till morning. . . Mountain air is the cure for most things. I think Dr Odello has quite enjoyed my illness. 1. It is a rare one. He has never seen it in Bordighera. 2. It lasted one week as he said it ought to do. 3. He stopped it from spreading into the brain and giving me meningitis, etc. etc. *meno male* (thank heavens). As far as the far as the *dolori atroci* [terrible pains] which I have now: they are quite common and not interesting.

While Clarence had these issues, Helene's anxieties concerned both her husband's health and that of her daughter. Things had gone from bad to worse by the end of July. She took her husband to enjoy the baths at Gastein, but returned home on account of his worsening condition, and all the while her daughter's health was deteriorating. She commiserated with Clarence about his illness, advising him that a visit to Bad Gastein might do him good. He thanked her for her account of the 'blue water' but insisted he was feeling better, although still weakened by the illness. His main complaints that summer were the dry weather, flies and soldiers. On 30 July, he wrote:

> How I wish Italy would spend all the money now spent on military purposes in replanting the denuded hills with trees . . . We have had three batteries of artillery here for nearly 3 weeks, and the soldiers chopped the lines, trampled down our garden, and have left the meadows near covered with paper, rags, tins and messes. Soldiers as individuals are very nice, but collectively they are an abomination.

145

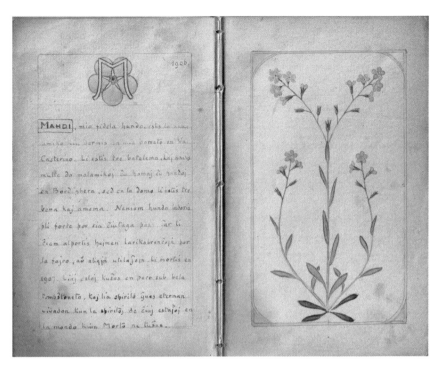

'Mahdi, my faithful dog, was the first friend that slept in my cottage in Val Casterino'. The first line of Clarence's epitaph for Mahdi in his illustrated *Book of Guests in Esperanto*. Bicknell Collection.

By 6 October, Clarence was fit. Writing to Helene, he said: 'I came home on Friday night, walking down the Roia valley till the evening with my dog, and then getting a carriage to Ventimigla. Luigi with his wife and all the luggage, huge packets of plants, rolls of drawing of the rocks, some pieces of rock with inscriptions on them, and all our other summer treasures, came the next day: and now we are busy settling down at home, enjoying the autumn fruit and lovely weather, but sorry to have left the free life, the mountain air and the quiet of Val Casterino, in exchange for crowds of people, and shops and the microbes of the lowlands.' Mahdi had died in 1907, and was celebrated in the *Book of Guests in Esperanto*, so the dog was Capi, Nora's dog, whom Clarence seems to have taken over.

Clarence celebrated his 68th birthday *en famille*. Giacomo Pollini had acquired a large trout from Lake Maggiore, and Clarence told Helene that he enjoyed 'a democratic dinner party, [with] him, Luigi & wife, my cook and 2 gardeners.' He continued: 'I know many people [think] that it is all wrong to follow Xst's words literally even occasionally, and bid others than the rich &c to a feast, but I do not think so. I find everyone behaves very well, and do not do their duties any the less. And *Communion* in church seems to me to be no longer a mark of brotherhood and unity but rather a sign of separation.' This is strong criticism of the church to which Clarence had been so bound in earlier years.

He was overjoyed to be walking long distances again. In his letter to Helene of 12 November, he wrote:

> Yesterday – after years – I again went on foot from Ventimiglia to Menton – slowly I looked into the gardens – at the sea – at the olives – the weeds – at everything. No carriage, omnibus, motor or bicycle rush – a quiet walk on my own legs, and oh! how much there was to see. I thought how much I should like to walk always. *Nobody sees anything nowadays.*

# CHAPTER THIRTEEN

# BOTANICAL EXCHANGES

CLARENCE'S NATURAL INSTINCT TO SHARE his botanical findings with others was the starting point for his role in helping to create and maintain a network of experts in museums and universities around Europe. His mailings of large quantities of botanical samples, pressed flowers mostly, encouraged other specialists to share their finds and knowledge too.

With *The Prehistoric Rock Engravings in the Italian Maritime Alps* safely published and a display of fifty of his and Luigi's photographs of the engravings presented at the museum in February 1903,[231] he naturally reverted to the study of botany, in part because of a minor disaster. 'We heard with dismay that Signor Pellegrino had sold his house, and as there was no other abode in the valley where it would be possible to make a lengthy stay with any sort of comfort, we feared that our work was over' by which he meant archaeological work. In this he was completely wrong. Three years later he built his own summer retreat at Casterino and returned to his work on the rock engravings.

In the meantime, irritated by his inability to go there in the summer of 1903, Clarence went with Luigi in June to Capraia, one of the little, rocky islands in the Tuscan archipelago, of which Elba is another. He described the journey from Livorno to Burnat: 'Bad crossing, storms, rain, wind etc.' Matters did not improve once they had arrived. 'Horrible weather here for several days . . . I don't think we will find any rare plants . . . the mountains are very difficult, brush, rocks, no paths.'[232] What he did come across, however, was the Agricultural Penal Colony. Founded in 1873 it was one of several 'open-air' prisons located on the islands. Both the director of the prison and the head postmaster of Capraia told Clarence that a famous Florentine botanist, Stefano Sommier, had already visited the island twice. Clarence then learned that Sommier was working on a book about the wildflowers of the Tuscan archipelago. Ever wanting to share his knowledge and his finds, Clarence offered to exchange his list of Capraian plants for Sommier's list of the same. Thus began a correspondence, an exchange of specimens and a friendship

Stefano Sommier (1848–1922), botanist.

147

with Sommier that lasted until the end of Clarence's life.[233] Sommier was a leading member of the *Società Botanica Italiana*, and he was so impressed by Clarence that he recommended he be admitted as a member to the society, the equivalent of London's Linnean Society.

While he was in Capraia, Clarence had picked up a nasty gastro-intestinal disease that lasted for two weeks. Once recovered, he started making plans to go to Alagna in Valsesia in northern Piemonte, at the base of Monte Rosa, hoping to find a quiet inn there because he could not abide the life in grand hotels. After a long, hot journey, he and Luigi were indeed able to find a pleasant hotel that fitted their needs. His gastric problems flared up again, but he recovered and was able to hike out to some glaciers, where he was delighted to find the rare *Potentilla grammopetala*. But the greatest pleasure of his stay was meeting the charming botanist, Abbot Antonio Carestia. Carestia had assembled an immense herbarium of about 25,000 species, including 600 lichens, and he too was a generous exchanger of specimens. The two began a correspondence that was naturally botanical but also contained some interesting personal facts; Clarence informed Carestia in 1903 regretfully that he could not study lichens, even under the microscope, because his sight had begun to fail as a result of too much drawing.[235]

Abbot Antonio Carestia (1825–1908), botanist.

In the same letter, he told Carestia he was about to go to England. Ada had written to him, begging him to come. He also mentioned that one of his close relatives, in whom he had total confidence, had stolen from him, and he was reluctant to go where he might run into him. The close relative who springs to mind is brother Percy, but Clarence never seemed to hold his profligacy against him. Then Clarence commented on the consolation of natural history: '[I]t does not treat us ill – yes, certain *Ortica* or *Rubus* or *Cirsium* sting . . . but the wounds do not last long, while those given to us by friends leave at the heart an indelible scar.'

When winter arrived in Bordighera with its rain and cold, and snow on the nearby mountains, Clarence was concerned about Abbot Carestia's health, and found himself lecturing him. 'Now I preach at you. In my opinion, priests should listen to what the laity has to say. I say to you simply to take care of your health and do not be imprudent during the cold months because there are so many people who love you.'[236]

Clarence continued to acquire more botanist friends, and during winters in Bordighera much of his and Luigi's time was spent in packaging up specimens to exchange with colleagues. He was always a generous giver and the care with which he – and Luigi – prepared the specimens for shipment was far greater than the effort expended by his recipients. Clarence was philosophical about this but Luigi was often irritable about the lack of response from other botanists. The gift of a large package of specimens from Abbot Carestia in December was a pleasant surprise, and Clarence responded enthusiastically:

> What a packet! I do not know how to thank you, not ever before having received such a rich botanical gift . . . you have certainly lifted my Luigi's spirits – because he, being younger than I and always more impatient, often declares that we do nothing but hunt for flowers and dry them and pack them up for others while we receive almost nothing. He had almost lost faith in the honesty of botanists! But now he believes in them again.[237]

Clarence spread his botanical net wider and wider.[238] Specimens collected by him are to be found in at least 21 herbaria in Europe and the USA – in Italy (Genoa, Florence, Torino, Sassari, Ventimiglia), Britain (Oxford, Kew), Belgium (Meise), the Netherlands (Leiden), Germany (Berlin, Frankfurt, Stuttgart), Sweden (Göteborg), France (Montpellier), Switzerland (Geneva), Austria (Vienna) and the United States (New York NY, Boston MA). However, although they were collected by Clarence himself, not all of these specimens were donated directly by him to the institutions in which they are held; in some cases, he gave them to a collector, who in turn donated them to an institution.

Many clubs and societies for the exchange of botanical specimens were founded in the nineteenth and early twentieth century in Europe and in Britain, but Clarence seems to have had little patience with them, even going so far as to call them annoying and to complain about their lack of diligence. In winter 1899, he lamented that he had received almost nothing from those dilatory exchange societies. He preferred to communicate directly with botanists of his acquaintance, even though he made scathing comments about them. When asking Burnat if he had ever corresponded or exchanged plants with Monsieur Eugen Klek of Vienna, he let slip that he suspected Klek was a thief. However, he praised the renowned Viennese botanist and collector Ignaz Dörfler for sending him an attractive selection of plants, in return for the large packet of specimen – 600 examples – that Clarence had sent him the previous year.[239] He also reported that a Mr Käser of Zurich had sent him some really peculiar *Hieracium* [hawkweed].

While not averse to exchanging plants with British collectors such as J. Walter White and Cedric Bucknall, Clarence did not join any of the British exchange clubs; his name does not even appear in the list of members of the Botanical Society and Exchange Club of the British Isles, the largest and most prestigious of them. His interest was centred in the wildflowers of Liguria, not those of Northampton or Norfolk. Nevertheless, he was well enough known and respected as a botanist that J. Walter White, the 'Distributor' of the club, co-wrote a glowing obituary for him in the club's annual report of 1918.

At the end of the day on 19 July 1910, Clarence must have sunk down with a sigh of relief in one of his American deck chairs on the verandah of the Casa Fontanalba. Edward and Margaret Berry were there to take care of him because he was still easily exhausted from his 'erysipelas', and his skin continued to itch.

Clarence Elliott
(1881–1969), alpine
plant specialist.

Suddenly, two English botanists appeared, tired and thirsty, making their way up to the house. One was Reginald Farrer, who like Clarence had been in Ceylon a few years earlier, and the other was Clarence Elliott.[240] Farrer was on a six-week tour in the Alps of France and Italy, and Elliott had joined him at Terme di Valdieri. From there they walked over the mountains to Boreon and Saint Martin Vesubie, and then travelled by bus, train and horse-carriage to St Dalmas, where they stayed for some days to botanise. After an excursion to nearby cliffs in search of *Primula Allioni* they walked up Val Casterino to arrive, unannounced, at Casa Fontanalba.

Reginald Farrer (1880–1920),
botanist and plant collector.

Curiously, we have two versions of this enigmatic encounter – both from the hand of Farrer – while there is no mention of it in Clarence's correspondence.

In 1910, Reginald Farrer was thirty years old, a man of multiple talents. The elder son of an affluent family with an estate at Ingleborough, Yorkshire, he studied at Oxford and travelled extensively in China, Japan and Ceylon and in the mountains of France, Austria, Switzerland and Italy. He hoped to make his name as a playwright and novelist, but had no success; he tried his hand at national politics, but failed to be elected to Parliament. His abiding passion was botany; in his youth he collected flowers in the Yorkshire hills, and already by the age of 14 had published a note in the *Journal of Botany*, and as an adult he made regular summer excursions in the Alps.

During these tours Farrer collected plants to send home to his nursery at Clapham in Yorkshire. The rock garden craze was sweeping Britain, and Farrer provided not only a supply of alpine plants but also books and magazine articles on how to look after them. Commentators later described him as 'virtually the patron saint of rock gardening for much of the twentieth century' and 'a Messianic figure in this branch of gardening.' Elliott, for his part, was a gardener and horticulturalist with a nursery near Stevenage.

Farrer was in many ways unconventional, and in society he could be disconcerting. He had a speech defect, was misogynistic, and had converted to Buddhism in Ceylon. Osbert Sitwell, his second cousin, gives this description of him: 'his eyes shone with that particular and urgent light that is only to be noticed in the eyes of the deaf or of those who encounter some physical difficulty in utterance. Yet this in his case was unaccountable, for he possessed no hesitation in his speech, which, at its worst, sounded like one of those early gramophones fitted with a tin trumpet. He was vain, it must be admitted, in several directions, and liked to air the contents of a well-stored and observant mind.'

Farrer's prose style was florid. A reviewer of one of his gardening books wrote that it had 'what to some will appear a defect and to others an added charm, namely, a copious discursiveness.' Another said that he was 'prone to unpardonable exaggeration and to an overwhelming torrent of epithet, which at times quite obscured his meaning.' Farrer's description of his meeting with Clarence is an example of his mischievous exaggeration and embellishment. In the version of the encounter that he published in 1911, he wrote:

> We were told that it took two hours of easy sauntering, up in that divergence of the Miniera which leads to the right, and is called the Val Casterino; and we found that it took three and a half hours of solid stodging. I draw a veil over the feelings with which we viewed our informant and the Miniera generally. Nor did our welcome at La Maddalena [the old name for the village of Casterino] quite correspond with our heat and our weariness, our hunger and our thirst. Not to put too fine a point upon it, our hosts were scantily pleased to have two total strangers dropping in on domestic bliss 'en villegiature' among the wild mountains. They eyed us with frigidity as we climbed over the garden-railing, and indicated that tea might be obtained, perhaps; but that the meal was over, and the fire gone out, and the bottom of the kettle fallen through. And, pray, what would you say, then, or I, or any normal person, if we retired into the remotest Alps for solitude, and then saw two strange figures toiling up into our garden, armed with trowels and collecting tins?[241]

This text resonates with frustration and embarrassment. Clearly, the two visitors had not informed Clarence of their visit in advance, which was contrary to the norms of polite behaviour, so naturally he was surprised. Are we supposed to believe the story about the kettle, or consider it a pretext for not offering tea? Was Farrer's concealment of Clarence's name motivated by a wish to avoid further embarrassment? As a matter of fact, his book is full of concealment: he misleads the reader about the location of rare plants, and omits to mention the name of his companion Clarence Elliott.

In a letter to his mother on 22 July, written just three days after the visit to Casa Fontanalba, Farrer gave a somewhat different account:

> We were sent up [from San Dalmazzo] to see a Mr Bicknell, a botanist, in a remote glen, which we were told was a two hour's stroll. Unfortunately the stroll turned out a trudge of 3½ hours, at the end of which old Bicknell merely offered us Vermouth (which I hate) and no information that I didn't know before. His nephew was there, the Consul of Bordighera [Berry] whose fat wife, the fattest woman to be found here, in a country of fat women, discovered in me a violent likeness to someone of my name, who afterwards on enquiry and analysis, proved to be Minna! [Daughter of Sir Thomas Farrer, a relation.]

Here we see Farrer in venomous mood, finding fault with Clarence for offering a hospitable drink, grumbling that he gave no new information, and disparaging Margaret Berry. But clearly the two visitors were not turned away; they were offered refreshment, and engaged in conversation, probably on botanical matters and possibly about Ceylon, and before they left were duly invited to sign their names in the Casa Fontanalba visitors' book. Farrer's signature is bold and backward-slanting, with a large, dipping capital R and capital F, underscored with a long slash. It is by far the fiercest signature in the book.

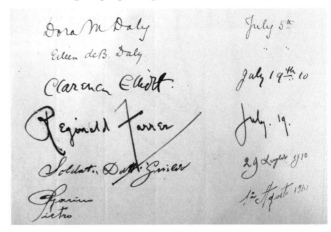

Farrer and Elliott signed the *Casa Fontanalba Visitors' Book* on 19 July 1910.

Several years later, Farrer mentioned Clarence again in another book, *The English Rock-Garden*, his *magnum opus* in two volumes, in which he described every species of Alpine plant. He wrote of *Primula marginata*:

> In nature, this loveliest blue Primula of our Alps is a rare species; extremely abundant, indeed, but only in a small limited district ... [the gardener] is particularly recommended to go the valley of La Maddalena, above San Dalmazzo de Tenda, not only because there *P. Marginata* exists in the most rampant profusion and the most riotous and lovely degree of variation, but also because that valley is further occupied by a famous English botanist, one Mr Bicknell, who has there a house and spends long summers, in the course of which

Casa Fontanalba. Clarence sent this postcard view of the house to his botanist friend Émile Burnat on 14 June 1909, ending his message 'J'espère donc de vous voir chez nous en juillet, votre affectueux, C.B.' Burnat and his companions duly arrived; they signed the Visitors' Book on 27 July that year.

he asks nothing better than to show the treasures of his hills to all such fellow-collectors as desire to see them. Therefore, in asking him for guidance, the gardener will not only be gaining profit but giving pleasure also – a holy and pleasing thought.[242]

Farrer's reputation for malice was such that later botanists interpreted this passage as a barbed invitation to disturb Clarence, who supposedly hated visitors to his valley. But Farrer's statement that Clarence 'asks nothing better than to show the treasures of his hills to all such fellow-collectors as desire to see them' would seem to be a statement of fact rather than a malevolent fabrication. One could even interpret it as a wish by Farrer to set the record straight after his exaggerated report of the 'frigid' reception in 1910.

CHAPTER FOURTEEN

# CASA FONTANALBA AND THE VELLUM-BOUND ALBUMS

Whatever you have in your rooms, think first of the walls;
for they are that which makes your house and home.

William Morris [243]

Wall painting is very amusing.

Clarence Bicknell [244]

THE IDEA OF BEING GROUNDED and having his own cottage up in the cool of the mountains was appealing to Clarence, a place where he could stay put for the summer and return to the study of those rock engravings he found so intriguing. He leased a plot of land above the village of Casterino from Count Guido d'Alberti della Briga, and during the winter of 1904, he turned his mind to building his dream. Fortunately, an architect friend was staying right next door – none other than George and Louisa MacDonald's son, the architect Robert Falconer MacDonald. When the plans were complete, Clarence hired Signor Lanteri of Tende as the builder, assisted by Arturo Pellegrino, who by selling his house at Casterino had left Clarence hot and houseless during the summer months. Work on Casa Fontanalba began in the spring of 1905.

In his 'Notes on Casa Fontanalba,'[245] Clarence declares: 'The house has been furnished as simply and as inexpensively as possible, with wooden bedsteads, plain wooden tables, made by the Tenda carpenter, common chairs and American folding ones, without wardrobes, carpets, or hangings, the only exception being some cushions given by a friend for a sofa-bed, and some small mats (7 in number) made by ourselves with *horn* patterns, 64 horns in all.' Clarence's horn patterns were inspired by the rock engravings, the most widespread of which showed a plough drawn by two oxen. Physical comfort was not a high priority, although he made sure that the house was equipped with a fireplace in the sitting room and in the dining room. Even during the summer, evenings could be nippy up at Casterino.

By May 1906, Clarence was despairing that his house would ever be completed, and complained to Burnat: 'I expect a letter every day from Pellegrino telling me that the carpenter and the painter have gone to Casterino, but as I have paid for almost everything, I think that no one is bothered about finishing my cottage, and that it will be not habitable before???' On 15 June he wrote to Pelloux: 'If I do not go up, my cottage will never be finished, and now I don't even know if the beds and blankets have been taken up. Can you tell me if *sleeping bags* are to be bought at Turin?'[246]

Evidently Clarence heard from Pellegrino because the very next day, accompanied by Luigi and Mercede, he made it to Casterino, and all three proudly signed their names in *The Casa Fontanalba Visitors' Book*.

In his notes on Casa Fontanalba, Clarence proudly described Luigi's enormous contribution to the territory surrounding the house. 'A woodshed was put up by my factotum Luigi Pollini, and garden paths, bridges & the watercourse etc. arranged by him. He also planted mountain ash, alpine laburnum, firs and pines, & made beds for currants, strawberries and vegetables.' He and Luigi transplanted interesting local plants from the neighbourhood, and by the end of the summer, Clarence was able to count about 450 different flowering plants and ferns growing on the property. However, he later wrote that many had disappeared while others were choked out by larger plants, so that 'the numbers well established and likely to remain is about 350', an amazing total even so.

When not working on the house and garden, Clarence and Luigi made rubbings for Émile Cartailhac, the eminent prehistorian and specialist in cave art, with whom Clarence had a close friendship. By 12 August, Clarence could write to Burnat that they were doing very well in their little house, much occupied with the garden, and enjoying 'stalks of *Rumex alpina* cooked with sugar, like rhubarb, very good.'[247] And on the 18th he wrote to Pelloux, 'What with guests, and excursions, and hard work at home in the garden, I write very little and read less. I am becoming a perfect *vegetable* . . . I have had my museo gardener Ampeglio here for a week and he has been most useful.' Less agreeably, he was plagued by a lack of rain and biting flies.

Following the Geneva Esperanto conference in August 1906, Clarence, Luigi and Mercede returned to Casterino, taking with them Bingham Crowther, Clarence's Tasmanian doctor friend, with whom he had travelled to Bayreuth in August 1896. No record exists about when and where they met. The journey back to Casterino was a nightmare of missed trains and lost baggage. What a relief for Clarence to arrive at St Dalmas de Tende and settle his friend on a mule for the last leg of the journey, and then to hurry ahead, achieving the 13.5 kilometre (8 ½ miles) climb in a mere 2 hours and 20 minutes, a record he proudly announced to Burnat.

Clarence and Bingham had much to talk about – the botany of the area, the rock carvings, and the local ants, for this was the same Bingham Crowther who had probably provided Clarence with the specimens of the Australian ant named for him: *Iridomyrmex bicknelli*.[248] Clarence gave specimens of this ant and others to his friend Oreste Mattirolo (1856–1947), Professor of Botany and Director of the Botanical Garden at Bologna from 1894 to 1900, who in turn handed them on to Carlo Emery (1848–1925), Professor of Zoology at the University of Bologna, who wrote up the ant and named it after Clarence in gratitude for the gift.

On the trails and over dinner in the evenings, conversation with Bingham must have been fascinating. The son of William Crowther, a well-known Tasmanian doctor and collector, Bingham grew up in Hobart. In 1869, when he was 19 years old, he accompanied his father on a skull-snatching expedition. William wanted to acquire the skull of the newly-dead William Lanney, said to be the last Tasmanian aborigine, whose bones were thus highly collectible and much sought after by scientists and museums. William removed the skull of a white man, Thomas Ross, from its body which had been lying the dissecting room of the hospital, and took it to the morgue, where Lanney's body was lying. He then flayed Lanney's face, removed his skull and replaced it with Ross's, which he then covered with Lanney's facial skin. All this was witnessed by the young Bingham. The theft was discovered, and the case became a *cause célèbre* in Tasmania.

Bingham Crowther (1850–1924).

His father's behaviour put ideas into Bingham's mind, and in November of the same year he somehow acquired the corpse of a native of the Pacific Savage Islands, which he cleaned and sent to William Flower at the Hunterian museum at the Royal College of Surgeons in London.[249] Then he left for medical school at Guy's hospital in London. On finishing his studies, Bingham returned to Tasmania, where he took up the practice of surgery. But he took his surgery too far, and in March 1891 was charged with having 'unlawfully attempted to procure the miscarriage of one Annie Jordan Cope.'[250] On 26 December 1891, the *Launceston Examiner* shouted: ARREST OF DR. BINGHAM CROWTHER. CAUGHT AT COLOMBO. Rather than face his charges, and after leaving false trails, Bingham had fled to Ceylon, where the police caught up with him and repatriated him. His health was in tatters; in fact, his health was often precarious, caused, his father thought, by his nervous disposition. Bingham may have chosen to recuperate in Europe because he accompanied Clarence to Bayreuth in 1896, before returning to Tasmania.

In 1901, Bingham had served in the Boer War in South Africa as an army surgeon, returning exhausted to Hobart a year later. Hobart's newspaper, *The Mercury,* published an interview with him on 28 March 1902, in which he described his harrowing experiences 'in his expressive, inimitable style (for he is a brilliant conversationalist).'[251] 'A brilliant conversationalist.' Yes, conversing with Bingham Crowther was a provocative experience and a particularly intriguing kind of conversation compared to the tameness of Bordighera's tea-party gossip.

                            ~

Listen to the sounds that accompanied Clarence throughout his days at Casa Fontanalba: the crystalline water as the snowmelt stream beside the house tumbled and gushed over the boulders of its stony bed; domestic clatter; the hiss of boiling water in kettles and pans; the chink of china being set out on tables; the sharpening of knives; the scrubbing, stirring, and whisking of ingredients; the beating and shaking out of rugs; the airing of bed linen; the sweeping of wooden floors and hard surfaces; and the chopping and stacking of firewood to feed the cast iron stoves. Every week clothes were washed in a steaming iron boiler and then carried out in wicker baskets to flap in the alpine air; mountain hiking boots had to be scraped of mud; and when evening drew on candles were set in place and lamps trimmed.

During the day, the distant bleat of mountain chamois and ibex reached the balcony of Casa Fontanalba, as did the high, thin cry of royal eagles, falcons, bearded vultures and kestrels. In

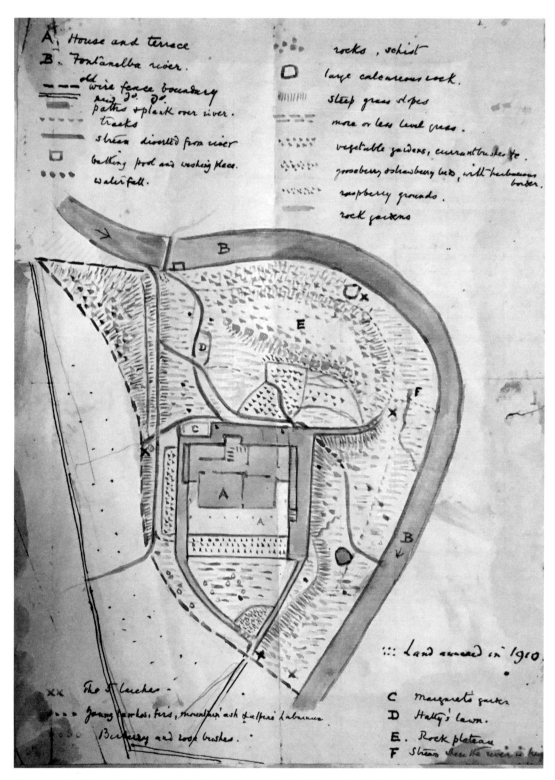

Clarence made this map of the garden at Casa Fontanalba showing the different soils, the diverted streams and the washing place. From his list of plants in *Wild Flowers*. IISL.

spring, the songs of nesting field birds filled the air; summer nights echoed with the call of hunting owls; in autumn, the sharp bark of foxes and the rasping bark of deer were interspersed with the whistling cry of marmots returning to their burrows as the light faded.

From the cluster of buildings that constituted the hamlet of Casterino, sounds drifted upwards: the clanking of cow bells; the braying of heavily laden mules and the clatter of hooves as they made their way up to Casterino; the sounds of revelry during nights of celebration. Below ground there were tectonic movements destabilising the rocks and triggering noisy landslides, while overhead frequent storm clouds built up, followed by rolling thunder and great forks of lightning exploding over Mont Bégo.

On their expeditions into the mountains, Clarence and Luigi were aware of the distant sound of encroaching human activity: regular dynamite blasts from the silver, zinc and lead mine in the nearby Val des Minières; the clanking and tang of metal as gangs of men constructed new roads, laid railway tracks, and constructed bridges, viaducts and tunnels. Once inaugurated, the railway lines generated new noises as the trains chuffed up the valleys and whistled before entering tunnels and arriving at newly built stations.

At Christmas 1906, Clarence received the gift of Volume 4 of Burnat's magisterial work, *Flore des Alpes Maritimes* (1906). He was thrilled with the gift, especially when he saw how many times the pages were 'hérisées' [pricked like a hedgehog] with his name. Burnat mentioned him 207 times.

A few days later, on 28 December, two signatures appear in the *Casa Fontanalba Visitors' Book*. As far as we know, this is the only time Clarence went up to Casterino in the dead of winter. He took with him Desirée and Percy Peake, new friends met while hiking over the Monte Mora Pass on the border between Switzerland and Italy. They spent Christmas with Clarence, before leaving for Casterino, where they spent three days and two nights. 'It was rather difficult to get there because of the ice that covered the path here and there', wrote Clarence to Burnat, 'and we did not have the alpine ice axe with which to cut steps. For quarter of an hour we feared that we would have to abandon the expedition. But it was so beautiful up there in the solitude of winter.'[252]

Once the walls of the Casa Fontanalba had been painted white with distemper, they resembled nothing more than a giant canvas and a giant temptation. It was on that wide canvas that Clarence succumbed to the fullest expression of his art.

'Nearly every year some part of the house has been decorated with rough or conventional representations of wild plants', he wrote in 1916. But he did not limit himself to botanical subjects. He also created visual representations of his other great passions: archaeology and Esperanto. 'As the house was built to enable us to continue our studies of the prehistoric rock figures in the valleys near, the half of which, some 6000 or more, represent horns of various forms and signs, and which without doubt had to the sculptors a special religious or symbolical meaning, horns have been painted in all parts of the house (106 in all), inside and out, and especially over doors and windows to prevent the entrance of evil spirits, goblins, witches &c. . . . with proverbs and sentences mostly written in Esperanto.'[253]

The original inspiration to paint the walls of his house may have been lurking in his mind ever since his visit to the caves at Les Eyzies and Niaux, but the influence of the Arts and Crafts movement also played its part. It might be easy to think of Clarence, tucked away in Liguria, being unaware of the upheaval going on in the world of design, but this would be misguided. On his visits to England, he would have noticed the influence of the movement everywhere; Ada's house may well have been papered with William Morris or Charles Voysey's designs. His library in Bordighera contained two of Walter Crane's books on design, *Bases of Design* and *Life & Form;* Frank Sanford's *The Art Crafts for Beginners;* Charles Holme's *Modern British Domestic Architecture and Decoration;* and just for good measure, Flinders Petrie's *The Arts and Crafts of Ancient Egypt*. And in conversation with his architect Robert MacDonald, if not with Robert's brother Greville himself, he would have become aware of the Peasant Arts Society, founded in Haslemere, Surrey in 1897. Greville MacDonald, eldest son of George MacDonald, Clarence's illustrious next-door neighbour, was one of its founders. The society rejected the industrialization of goods and committed itself to reviving lost country crafts, crafts with which Clarence was familiar, such as rug-weaving and woodwork.

Once he had started decorating the first wall, there was no stopping him. Over the entrance door he painted the name of the house, Casa Fontanalba, and added an image of the seven streams into which the River Fontanalba divided just below the house. Facing the entrance door, he painted the lines 'Welcome be to every guest/Come he north, south, east or west', while someone leaving would read 'Go he north, south, east or west/God speed every parting guest.'

Every room, including hallways and even the photographic dark room and larder was embellished with paintings of flowers and trees, butterflies and horns, some painted freehand and some stencilled, and everywhere the visitor felt welcomed and inspired by sayings in Esperanto and English. The background colour of the downstairs rooms was terracotta or yellow, while that of the bedrooms was pale blue. Clarence tried to tailor the subject matter of each bedroom to its occupant. For instance, the cook's room was decorated with comestibles – a frieze of raspberries, gooseberries, strawberries, wild spinach, dandelion, caraway, monks' rhubarb, chives and mushrooms!

Clarence used oil paint for the bright green shutters, each of which had its own flower and inspirational saying in Esperanto, such as 'Ne laŭdu la tagon antaŭ vespero' [Don't praise the day before the evening.] And listmaker Clarence did not fail to paint on the dining room walls the initials of guests who spent a night at the Casa Fontanalba – and then wrote a mini-biography of his favourites in the *Book of Guests in Esperanto*.

After his visit to the Casa Fontanalba in August 1913, Alberto Pelloux wrote excitedly to his mother: 'Bicknell's house is a thing really worth seeing. You've no idea how he's fitted it out with drawings and pictures, all made by himself on rainy days! It's wonderful to think that he did all this himself . . . It gives an idea of the prodigious activity of this man, who is full of a sense of poetry and art . . . In one room, on the walls, are all the initials of his guests, within an ornamental design. We left in the morning at six, and our initials were already in place.'

Another recollection[254] came from Luciano Minozzi, son of a friend of Bicknell, who wrote that:

> In the morning the guests and their host got up very early and dived into the cold water of a nearby stream, even if the weather was cold and they didn't wish to bathe; then everyone was free until lunch, but had to do to something useful not only for himself but for the community, and report on it at the meal. After eating (vegetarian food, since Bicknell was a crusader for animal protection) guests had to wash their own dishes because it did not

seem fair that Luigi, a man like any other, should do it for everyone else. In the afternoon there was a compulsory excursion until dinner-time. The place was like a boarding school, or a house of correction, for meals were strictly regulated; only vegetarian food, no fish, no eggs, not even milk or butter, but instead salad, roots and broth made from vegetables or fruit. As for a certain kind of convenience, Bicknell was quite stubborn; he had banned the renowned English toilet, so famous in those times, and preached that it was immoral for a man to keep waste matter in his house; to go out in the open air was not only poetic, healthy and decent, but useful for the plants.[255]

H. Stuart Thompson
(1870–1940), botanist
from Bristol, in 1896.

Nora Bicknell, Clarence's niece, accompanied him to Casterino in June 1907. With her ability to draw, paint and photograph, she would have been an asset to Clarence. Just three days later, H. Stuart Thompson (1870–1940), one of the Bristol botanists, hiked up from St Dalmas, and stayed for three days. Thompson was an alpinist as well as a botanist and archaeologist, and his philosophy seems stirringly like Clarence's. In the preface to his *Alpine Plants of Europe* (1911), Thompson quotes the mountaineer Alfred Mummery: 'Above, in the clear sky and searching sunlight, we are afoot with the quiet gods, and men know each other and themselves for what they are.'[256] This could be Clarence speaking.

The two men stayed in touch, and seven years later collaborated on Thompson's handbook, *Flowering Plants of the Riviera* (1914). In his preface, Thompson says: 'I am greatly indebted to Mr. Clarence Bicknell, of Bordighera, for kindly lending me a number of his water-colour drawings of flowers in the reproduction of the book.' It sounds from this as though Clarence provided just a few watercolours. In fact, the total was 112 different flowers, printed on 24 plates. As Thompson points out, they naturally suffer from being reduced in size, while adding much charm to his book. Clarence agreed about the reduction in size, but felt they were well printed, although he admitted to Burnat on 29 April 1914 that the book itself had no value because Thompson knew little about the mountains and precious little about the coast.

Clarence, now 65, was clearly fighting fit during the summer of 1907, so fit that he hiked to the crest of Mont Bégo and botanised up there. His letter to Burnat of 10 September summarizing the summer's activities gives an idea of how much he accomplished in one short season: 'I have once again copied many of the rocks of V. Fontanalba, always finding engravings never before observed, and last week Luigi and I camped up at the Laghi Lunghi, and made a quantity of copies in the environs of the Lacs des Merveilles . . . Always new figures, always rock engravings everywhere. We are doing very well here, our "garden"(!) according to me is superb. Lots of potatoes, lettuce, turnips, carrots, onions, etc. in the little cultivated patch, and lots of flowers among the rocks. I have made an album of pictures, drawn very quickly, of everything that grows, flowers and ferns – not everything, because I haven't had enough time – but I have drawn 301 of them, and 20 or more remain for next year. I have greatly decorated the rooms [of Casa Fontanalba], and at present I occupy myself every day spoiling good paper, trying to paint water colours.'[257]

Clarence did not confine his artistic endeavours to Casa Fontanalba. The Villa Rosa also felt the effect of his domestic decoration, although the floral and archaeological themes had stiff competition from Esperanto. A writer in the magazine *Esperanto* describes the experience of

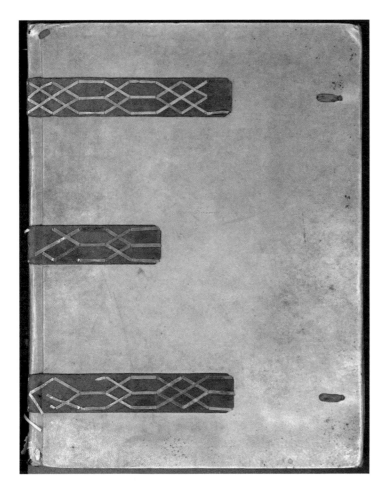

The *Casa Fontanalba Visitors' Book*: the front cover in vellum with leather spine straps.

visiting the house: 'His home in Bordighera remains an indelible memory for many of us who spent time there, next to the azure sea, surrounded by December roses . . . What a surprise when they entered that garden, forever in bloom, and went into the house: Esperanto through and through from cellar to roof. Our language was the only one to be heard there; everywhere were artefacts adorned with Esperanto symbols on vases, embroidery or cushions. It was life in an Esperanto paradise, with the external world excluded.'[258]

It was not only in interior decoration but also in the design of the albums that Clarence reveals the influence of the Arts and Crafts movement, and develops for himself a style which approaches it. *The Casa Fontanalba Visitors' Book*, one of his masterpieces,[259] is among the dozen or so albums bought for him by Margaret Berry; he must have worked on it throughout the winter of 1905/6 in order to have it ready by the time the house was habitable in June. It is an album of forty cartridge-paper sheets, bound in vellum with leather decorative stitch work, and it measures 265 mm x 340mm (10½ x 13½ inches). Clarence illustrated every page on the right with watercolours of flora of the region; the left pages remained blank for guests to sign their names and add the date.

The *Casa Fontanalba Visitors' Book*: the logo on the first page, designed by Clarence.

*Overleaf:* The *Casa Fontanalba Visitors' Book*: the first page of signatures and C.B.'s watercolour of *Athragene alpina L.* (clematis) facing it.

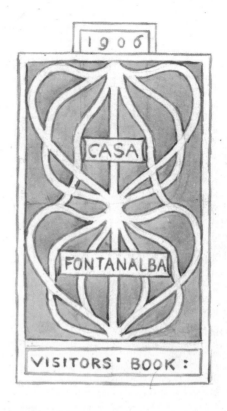

Clarence then created another visitors' book: *The Book of Guests in Esperanto*. Smaller than *The Casa Fontanalba Visitors' Book*, it was the vehicle for Clarence to combine his artistic talents with a bit of humour while promoting Esperanto. He wrote descriptions of selected friends, family and visitors in Esperanto on the left page and painted watercolours of flowers on the right. Individuals range from eminent botanists and archaeologists to three dogs: Leo, Capi, and Clarence's much loved Mahdi. The page for Emile Cartailhac (see p. 165) shows how proud Clarence was that the eminent archaeologist visited the rock engravings of the Val Fontanalba. Cartailhac's initials 'E.C.' are illuminated with features from the rock art including the plough and oxen.

Forty-four individuals signed between 16 June and 16 September 1906. Many have Italian names, so they would have been neighbours paying their respects. The first overnight visitors to arrive were Edward and Margaret Berry, followed by two more of Clarence's nephews from England, James and Arthur and their wives, all of whom pitched in to clear the property of builders' rubbish and fill the vacant patches with earth and turf. Clarence's cook Maddalena did not sign the book but she was certainly present because on 19 July Clarence complained to Alberto Pelloux that there were soldiers all over the place: 'if they were English they would be watching us over the fence all day and chaffing Maddalena & Mercede.'[260]

Clarence Bicknell. 16th June 1906.

Luigi Pollini 16 Giugno 1906

Meriade Pollini ,, ,, ,, ,,

Margaret Berry July 6th 1906 — July 23 —

Edward E Berry July 6, 1906 — July 2.

Elizabeth B. Churchman July 23d 1906.

J. L. Churchman "

Achille Isnard. Juilla 23. 1906. Menton.

Angèle Isnard Juillet 23 - 1906 - Menton.

Emilie Bosshart July 23d 1906.

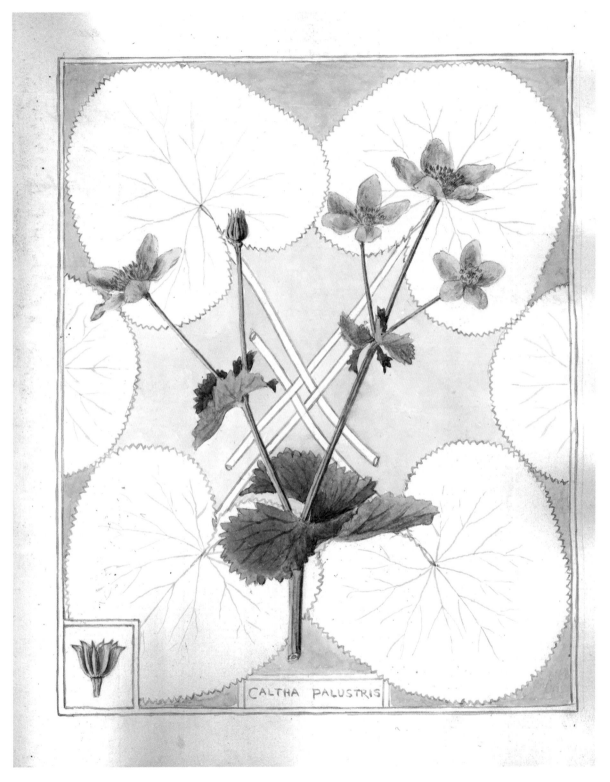

CALTHA PALUSTRIS

C.B., watercolour of *Caltha palustris*, in the *Casa Fontanalba Visitors' Book*.

The vellum albums provided by Margaret Berry became an outlet for Clarence's creativity. Each album contained a theme that had special meaning for Margaret, or in some cases for the person he dedicated it to. For instance, Clarence named one of the albums *A Book of Berries*, a play on Margaret and Edward Berry's name. *The Posy*, a book of poems (*la poésie* in French) decorated with appropriate flowers had several 'marguerites', a play on the name Margaret.

In 1911, to celebrate the coronation of King George V the previous year, he created a coronation procession of flowers. Another album, dated 1914, is an elaborate fantasy, *The Triumph of the Dandelion,* in which flowers compete to win The Order of the Golden Lion. Page by page each flower is illustrated presenting its claim in enchanting if somewhat sentimental prose and verse, and the common wild dandelion, rated by Clarence as his favourite flower, is the winner.

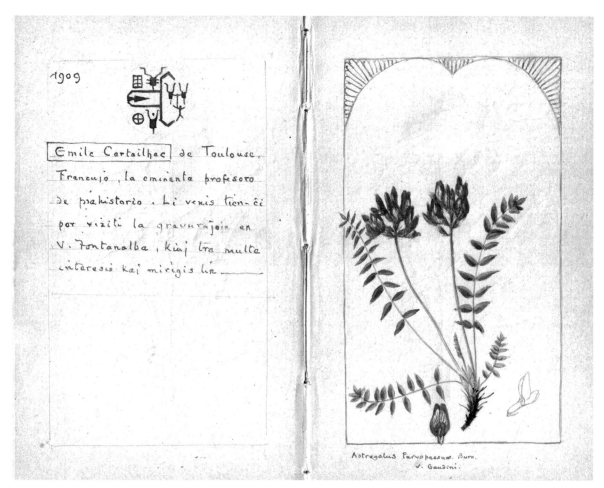

Clarence's words in Esperanto salute 'Emile Cartailhac of Toulouse, France, the eminent professor of prehistory'. From the *Book of Guests in Esperanto* by C.B.

*Next spread:* The *Children's Picture Book of Wild Plants* features four plants in watercolour on the right; on the left a description of each plant. Created by C.B.

ECHIUM ·VULGARE L.

From *echis*. a viper. Its seed like the head of a viper, was supposed to cure its bite. "In the Echium, a herb very celebrated for curing viper's bite, nature has created its seed like the viper's head" Matthioli.

Boraginieae. Viper's Bugloss.

Corolla of irregular shape (regular in other genera of this order) red at first, then turning blue. Flowers numerous in lateral branches, each one with a bract. Leaves with only one prominent nerve. Stamens protruding. The whole plant very rough and hispid, with bristles on a white or brown tubercular base. Common.

 QUILEGIA ALPINA L.

Alpine Columbine.

Flowers much larger than *A. vulgare* spurs of the petals less hooked; petals longer than the stamens. Anthers som purplish.

*A. Reuteri* Boiss. which grows abun below the Miniera is more branched, w fewer stem leaves. the leaves smaller less divided and the anthers are always yellow.

"The Columbine is pleasing to the eye, as respect of the beauty and not vulgar sha in regard to the azury colour thereof a holden to be very medicinal" (Guillim)

 ENTAUREA MONTANA L.

Pliny says that the Centaur Chiron cured himself from a wound he had received from an arrow poisoned by the blood of the hydra.

Compositae. Knapweed.

Scales of the involucre dark green with fringed brown border, the fringe not exceeding the breadth of the border. Flowers of the circumference blue, radiant those of the centre purple. leaves decurrent, lanceolate soft, more or less cottony.

Common.

The Centaurea is called in German Tausend Gulden, the word having been changed into centum aureos, a hundred gold pieces.

 ALVIA PRATENSIS L.

Salvia, the herb sage. Pliny: from salv safe. sound, in allusion to the medicinal

Labiatae. Salvia, sage.

Corolla with 2 lips, and 3 times as long the calyx. Calyx with 2 lips. the up one with 3 short teeth.

Stamens 2, the filament with a curved bar across the top, like the arms of a lev on a fulcrum, the longer arm bearing th anther.

Meadows. common. Flowers rarely whi or pink.

*Taraxacum vulgare Lamk.*

Another album, dated 1914, is an elaborate fantasy, *The Triumph of the Dandelion*, in which flowers compete to win The Order of the Golden Lion. Note the heraldic dandelion in the shape of a lion, bottom right.

Clarence's albums are carefully designed and colour coordinated. *The Children's Picture Book of Wild Plants* features four plants in water-colour on the right, often with a frame of style and colours derived from the flower shown, and on the left a description of each plant. Clarence, in this and many of the albums, delighted in taking the colours and details of flowers as motifs for the frame and for decorative capital letters.

All his albums are full of decorative letters that reflect the plants and people to which they refer. He had particular fun with capital letters. The *Book of Guests in Esperanto* has many good examples: paleontologist Emile Cartailhac's initials are surrounded by engravings; farmer Grosvenor Berry's 'GB' is embellished with cattle; in the *Children's Book* album, Clarence's illustrious literary neighbour in Bordighera, George MacDonald, has one of his poems initialled with an ornate 'B'. The vellum albums challenged Clarence's creativity; until then, his floral watercolours had been strictly botanical rather than artistic. Now, influenced by the Arts and Crafts movement, he began to see design everywhere. He painted his own fantasies, playing with the flowers and designing them within beautiful frames. Margaret had led him into a world where he could incorporate plants into designs however he wished. It is extraordinary that Clarence had time to create these fastidiously executed works alongside all his other occupations, but with these albums he found a way of relaxing while at the same time letting loose his imagination and taking great pleasure in their creation.

Seven of the albums dedicated to Margaret Berry are now in the Fitzwilliam Museum, Cambridge University; three others are in the Bicknell Collection and two in private hands on the Italian Riviera. Creating such books was very much in the Victorian tradition. Illustrated poetry books were popular gifts to be treasured and prominently displayed in the drawing-room whether in London or Bordighera.

Perhaps the most striking and successful images from the albums in the Fitzwilliam are those in the tradition of Arts and Crafts leaders like Walter Crane, Charles Voysey and William Morris. These patterns have a symmetrical square form rather than a repeat motif, and Clarence may well

Farmer Grosvenor Berry's 'GB' is embellished with cattle. From the *Book of Guests in Esperanto* by Clarence Bicknell.

Clarence's illustrious literary neighbour in Bordighera, George Macdonald, has one of his poems initialled with an ornate 'B'. Fitzwilliam Museum, University of Cambridge.

have used a 2- or 4-mirror kaleidoscope to achieve these symmetrical effects. Such optical instruments were very popular in the Victorian period.

The snow at Casterino had melted by May, allowing Clarence and Luigi to make a quick trip up to the Casa Fontanalba to plant potatoes. By 12 June, they were up in the mountains again, installed in the new house, ecstatic to be there, with Clarence writing to Burnat: 'My rocky little garden is superb (according to me) . . . Oh how ravishing the slopes are beneath the larches because of thousands of *Aquilegia alpina*.'[261]

The symmetrical floral patterns in the Fitzwilliam albums are arguably Clarence's most creative watercolours. Gentian, left, and Fritillary, right. Fitzwilliam Museum, University of Cambridge.

Clarence's watercolour of the *Aquilegia alpina* in the *Casa Fontanalba Visitors' Book.*

CHAPTER FIFTEEN

# ESPERANTO

Clarence was intrigued by the idea of a universal language, and in 1897, after a foray into Volapük, an earlier planned language, he began the study of Esperanto. It became one of the great passions of his later years. Its inventor, Ludovik Lazarus Zamenhof (1859–1917) was a Russian Jewish ophthalmologist, born in the multi-ethnic, seventy-per cent Jewish, manufacturing town of Bialystock, then located in Russia but now in northeast Poland. His mother tongue was Russian, but because of Bialystock's shifting borders and his ethnicity, he also spoke Yiddish, German and Polish while he was growing up. Later, at school in Warsaw, he mastered Latin, Greek and French. As he noted: 'In Bialystok, the population consisted of four diverse elements: Russians, Poles, Germans and Jews; each spoke a different language and was hostile to the other elements . . . [but] I was brought up an idealist.'[262] While remaining loyal to his Jewish beliefs and identifying himself as a Russian Jew, Zamenhof wanted to find a means by which all people could communicate. In a search for this ideal, he started working on an invented language when still in his teens. Because of their grammatical difficulty, he stayed away from basing his invention on dead languages like Latin and Greek and from living ones like those he spoke already. When he started studying English and found how easy its grammar was, he became determined that his invented language would be easy to learn, would have straightforward grammar and, unlike English, no exceptions. He came up with the idea of using recognizable root words, taken mostly from Romance and Germanic languages, which he could then supplement with prefixes and suffixes. Using this method, he found that it was possible with just three-thousand root words to create a twenty-thousand-word vocabulary. Esperanto has 22 letters that come from the Latin alphabet (leaving out q, w, x and y) and adds six new accented letters, Ĉĉ, Ĝĝ, Ĥĥ, Ĵĵ, Ŝŝ, Ŭŭ.

On 5 December 1878, he invited some school friends to dinner at the Zamenhof home, by now in Warsaw, to celebrate what he called the canonization of the language. He managed to teach them enough of what he then called the *Lingue Uniwersala* to be able to converse a little and to sing the anthem:

Malamikete de las nacjes
Kadó, kadó, jam temp'está!
La tot'homoze in familje
Konunigare so debá.

[Hostile barriers between peoples,/Fall, fall, it is time!/The whole of humanity/Must come together as one family.][263]

Investing the language with spirit, thus celebrating not just a language but a movement, was fundamental to Zamenhof's intent. But his invention still needed work, and he desperately needed time, of which he had precious little because he had just started his medical studies. Progress with the language was slow, and it was not until he began practicing ophthalmology in 1887 that he could publish his completed textbook, the so-called *Unua Libro,* with financial backing from his new father-in-law. The book was written under the pseudonym Doktoro Esperanto (Doctor Hopeful) and thus was the name of the language born. Zamenhof stated in the introduction to his book that Esperanto should not be the fruit of a single person's labours, but the rather the result of the combined efforts of the whole educated world. He invited others

to join him in adding to and refining Esperanto's vocabulary. In this he anticipated the same technique of adding to and refining employed by today's Wikipedia.

When Clarence discovered Esperanto in 1897 – how and where remain a mystery – Bordighera was a vibrant, international community. Visitors from Britain, France, Germany and Russia made the town their winter residence, or even their permanent residence. He saw at first hand the need for a universal language in which foreigners could communicate freely with each other and with the local Italian-speaking population. He realised how such a language could be useful for corresponding with botanists in different countries. And quite apart from the language itself, Zamenhof's ideals were Clarence's ideals: justice, fraternity, democracy, pacificism, religious tolerance and international cooperation. Both men fervently believed that disparate people had the capacity, without divine assistance, to communicate, even to forge peace, by using a common language.

Clarence's interest in Esperanto continued to escalate, and he became an ardent proselytiser for the movement – in his own quiet way. His letter of 15 March 1900 in the *Journal de Bordighera* bears witness to his sincerity and commitment.

Dear Sir,

I shall be grateful if you will make known to your readers that I greatly desire to interest my fellow-countrymen in the new international language called 'Esperanto'. . . I have endeavoured to satisfy a jury of competent Esperantists by submitting to a long examination in writing, the result of which I have just heard, and now find myself a certificated teacher and a holder of the Society's diploma . . . With very little study and with very great care I have been able to read and translate into 'Esperanto' some of the works of Shakespeare, Goethe, Poushkin, Tolstoi and others, and have corresponded with persons of four nationalities . . .

Clarence wears his Esperanto star with a distant and idealistic look in his eyes.

If therefore as many as a dozen persons care to hear what I have to say, and will kindly send me their names, I shall be glad to fix a day hour and place (the Museo or my own house) for bringing the subject to their notice . . . nothing can help more than the possibility of intercommunication in the same tongue.

Along with Rosa Junck, Bordighera claimed another eager proselytiser for Esperanto, the vivacious and witty Eileen de Burgh Daly, the editor of the *Journal de Bordighera* and proprietor of Bordighera's tea rooms.[264] Miss Daly had chosen the perfect site for the tea rooms, adjacent to the tennis club, where she set aside two rooms for bridge, and opened her doors for business in 1900. The tea rooms soon became the 'in' place, and set Miss Daly in a strong position to promote Esperanto and to pick up all the news and gossip of the day, which she could then relate in the *Journal*. The tea rooms served a proper English tea, prepared pastries and picnics to go, and at Christmastime did a roaring trade in plum puddings.

In a letter to Burnat in November 1903, Clarence mentioned he was overwhelmed by how much work his involvement with Esperanto demanded. 'Too much to do. Always correspondence, and now I must contribute to a new English journal.' (The journal was *The Esperantist*, launched in London in November 1903.) But six weeks later he wrote a delighted letter to Cedric Bucknall, who along with James W. White and Harold Stuart Thompson were Bristol botanists with whom Clarence communicated.[265] 'Esperanto is looking up here, we had a dinner with speeches etc. last Wednesday, & some French, 1 Russian & 2 Bohemians from outside joined us English & Italians here.'[266] One of those Bohemians was Rosa Junck.

Clarence's interest in Esperanto had developed into a full-blown passion, and he insisted that the language was the key to world peace. Like anything he set his mind to, he entered into the experience with a combination of enthusiasm and doggedness. By 1903, his face had already appeared on a postcard containing images of six Italian Esperantists, images not much to his liking. Sending a copy of the postcard to Burnat, he announced: 'I have no other postcards, and these Italian Esperanto cards are horrible. No one needs these six ugly portraits. They do something completely other than propagating sympathy for Esperanto.'

The Esperanto postcard that Bicknell sent to Burnat.

Clarence sent the same postcard to Stefano Sommier a few days later, commenting sadly, 'I don't know if the Esperanto language is making progress in Florence, here I have never been able to find converts . . . I regret that people don't dedicate a week to learning it – it's so easy and useful for every kind of correspondence.'[267]

Luigi had taken to Esperanto like a duck to water – as had his wife Mercede – and was studying hard in preparation for the first International Esperanto Congress in Boulogne in the summer of 1905. What a

heady time it was! Men and women from all over
Europe were arriving by the trainload, and the city
was buzzing with Esperanto. Clarence Bicknell,
Luigi Pollini and Rosa Junck would have travelled
from Bordighera to Boulogne together, taking
the train to Marseilles and changing at Paris for
Boulogne. Clarence, who loathed big hotels, and
Luigi secured lodgings at 26, rue Dutertre, while
Rosa Junck chose instead to stay at the Institution
Perdreaux.

The previous summer in Calais, English,
Austrian, Belgian, German and French Esperantists
had discussed the importance of holding a truly
international congress. They decided that Boulogne
was an ideal spot for it, being easily accessible by
train from Paris, and from Calais, just 30 kilometres
away. They contacted the Esperantists of Boulogne,
who immediately invited Ludwig Zamenhof to
preside over the congress. He accepted; he had
long yearned for a meeting where all the Esperanto
groups of the world could convene.[268]

Quite apart from the pleasures of the congress
itself, Boulogne offered many attractions: the beach,
the grand Casino, golf, racing, regattas, clay-pigeon
shooting and horseback riding. Situated in the Pas
de Calais, in northwest France, near the narrowest
point of the English Channel, it was an important
centre for the export of fish, fabric, leather, game
and eggs. Members of the new wealthy French middle class could hop on the train in Paris and arrive
in Boulogne in just three and a half hours, where
they could enjoy a stay in one of the excellent hotels
lined up along the beach. Although the air temperature rarely rose above 18 degrees (65 degrees
Fahrenheit), they could rent bathing machines –
wooden changing rooms on wheels that could be
rolled into the sea – and take shivering dips in the
sea, or could stroll to the harbour and watch as fish-
ermen hauled in immense catches of herring. And then lose a few francs at the Palais de Neptune
– the casino.

However, on that Thursday in 1905, Boulogne had become an international city in which
French lost its grip and the chatter and hum of a new language filled the air. Even the local

Clarence Bicknell and Luigi Pollini leave a meeting of the first
International Esperanto Congress in Boulogne on 6 August 1905.
Clarence is behind the lady with the dark skirt and white hat. Luigi is
further right in the photo, in a peaked cap, between the man with a
top hat and the man with a boater.

Photo by Ezio Benigni. Clarence is dressed up and
sporting the Esperanto star on his lapel, c. 1905. BibCiv.

Ludwig and Clara Zamenhof at Boulogne, 'de la unua congreso', the first congress.

shopkeepers learned the language, and proudly displayed signs saying 'Oni parolas en Esperanto' in their windows. The congress attendees represented all the nations of Europe except Turkey, and the influx of guests was reported to number nearly 1,500, although those listed in the official program amounted to 688. Boulogne's hotels were stretched to their limits and local residents were required to open their houses to paying guests. Clever merchants ranged all over town, touting a wide variety of Esperanto souvenirs, and local photographic studios were making a killing taking portraits of the attendees, all of whom proudly sported the Esperanto star on their lapels. When Ludwig and Clara Zamenhof arrived on the evening of 3 August, the whole town was flying the Esperanto flag, a white star on a green background. For Zamenhof, it was a dream come true.

The congress consisted mainly of grand meetings, planning sessions, concerts, plays, banquets, an outing to England and a huge exhibition of local produce, all of which provided great publicity for Boulogne, its manufacturers and its craftspeople. Most of the events were held in the highly decorated Municipal Theatre. At the opening ceremony, those attendees who had never before laid eyes on the great Zamenhof, were astonished to see before them a diminutive fellow whose towering achievement was not matched by his stature. Forty-five years old, he had a broad forehead and soft grey eyes behind thick spectacles; he sported a large, twirled moustache and a small beard. A polyglot, he made a point of speaking nothing but Esperanto during all ten days of the congress, even when giving speeches to English audiences in Folkestone and Dover and to French audiences in Calais and Boulogne. His speeches were immediately translated for the benefit of those who could not understand Esperanto.

Rosa Junck became something of a sensation, performing in various ways in almost all the entertainments. Her high point came when she was cast as Dorimène in Molière's one-act play, *Le Mariage forcé,* newly translated into Esperanto by Victor Dufeutrel. The cast members, from five different countries, met for the first time two days before the performance; they nonetheless managed to learn their lines and to perform admirably after a mere two rehearsals. Reports in the newspapers tell of their ease in performing and their perfect knowledge of Esperanto – and of the audience's complete comprehension and appreciation.

Later the same evening, Rosa sang a song composed by Clarence entitled 'Sainte-Lucie.' And when Zamenhof held a session on how to speak Esperanto perfectly, demonstrating where stresses occurred in the words, he called on Rosa Junck, whose Esperanto pronunciation he deemed perfect. She recited one of Zamenhof's poems, 'La vojo' ['The Way'], and outdid herself. Clarence's profile was lower than Rosa's, but his talent and enthusiasm were apparent, and by the end of the congress he was voted a member of the Esperanto Language Committee.

Zamenhof was committed to perfecting the language, and had published *Fundamento de Esperanto* in the spring of 1905. Based on his earlier works, this book fixed in place forever the basic principles of the language, and during the congress, at a meeting on 9 August, in the fourth article of 'La Bulonja Deklaracio' ['The Declaration of Boulogne'] *Fundamento de Esperanto* was

declared to be the unchangeable official source for
Esperanto – although it did leave room for future
official additions.

As a result of the congress and the attention it
brought to France and to Esperanto, Zamenhof
was made a Chevalier of the Legion of Honour by
the French government.

Clarence was so invigorated by the congress
that he became an even more ardent Esperantist.
With Luigi and Mercede, he took a break from
heavy labour and left Casterino to attend the second Esperanto congress in Geneva in August 1906.
The congress included a boat trip from Geneva to
Vevey that allowed enough time for them all to
make a quick visit to Émile Burnat, who welcomed
them warmly. Clarence was deeply grateful; he was
always happy when his friends treated the Pollinis
with kindness and respect.

Clarence found the congress exhausting, and
had trouble sleeping. He was obliged to attend large meetings for all the Esperantists and
smaller meetings for focus groups like the Language Committee, some of which sound crush-
ingly boring. He and the Pollinis left the congress early, after the final Language Committee
meeting. But that same year, together with Rosa Junck, he founded the *Gruppo Milanese per
l'Esperanto,* a centre in Milan where interested people could take courses in the language. That
centre still thrives today. And in 1910, again with Rosa Junck, and with Luigi as treasurer,
he formed Bordighera's own Esperanto group, named 'Antaŭen', an Esperanto word meaning
'Forward.' In addition, not wanting young children to miss out on the opportunity of learning
the language, Clarence started Esperanto classes in the Museum especially for them.[269]

As his skill with the language flourished, so did his writing and translating. He translated
prose and poems from English and Italian into Esperanto, and he wrote original poems in
Esperanto, although they were often closely based on an English original. For instance, his
poem 'Aŭtuno' is heavily influenced by Keats's 'To Autumn.' Soon he was publishing work
in British and Italian periodicals, most often in *La Revuo,* the Esperanto literary journal. He
also wrote hymns, and according to the distinguished modern-day Esperantist, Humphrey
Tonkin, 'He contributed translated and original hymns to the Order of Service According to
the Prayer Book of the English Church, published on the occasion of the Esperanto Congress
in Cambridge in 1907. Nine of his hymns are included in the ecumenical prayer book *Adoru*
(2001), the most widely used collection of Esperanto hymns today.'[270]

Clarence took both Luigi and Mercede to the 1907 Cambridge congress, held from 10 to
17 August. They were joined by Linda Bicknell who arrived from Ireland, and all lodged in
Grantchester. Apart from the stimulation of the congress itself, it must have been delightful
for Clarence to show the Pollinis and Linda around his old stamping grounds.

Esperantista Grupo "Antauen" - Bordighera.

A meeting of the Esperanto group in Bordighera, in front of the Museo Bicknell, probably in 1910 at its creation. IISL.

Before the conference, Cambridge as a whole had been sceptical about the invasion of the Esperantists, but ended swept up in the enthusiasm and goodwill of the attendees, 1,400 from 30 nations, all speaking the same language. One of the Cambridge policemen learned Esperanto to be able to communicate with visitors and point them in the right direction. The hard work of the conference was completed during morning sessions, while afternoons were given over to various pleasures, such as a garden party at Newnham, a military tournament, an excursion to Ely and, of course, punting on the Cam. Evenings consisted of entertainment in Esperanto, including a scene from *She Stoops to Conquer*, a Punch and Judy show, *Box and Cox* (*Boks kaj Koks*), and a dramatised version of 'Bardell vs. Pickwick', the trial scene from *Pickwick Papers*, with the irrepressible Rosa Junck playing Mrs Betsy Cluppins. The *Cambridge Daily News* of 15 August 1907 reports: 'If there was one character which attained to greater excellence than another, it was the Mrs. Cluppins of Sra Rosa Junck, the delegate from Milan . . . [who] ranks among the best exponents, professional or armateur [sic], ever seen in the Cambridge Theatre.'[271]

The Language Committee of the 1907 International Esperanto Congress in Cambridge, England, included Rosa Junck (seated, 3rd from right) and Clarence Bicknell (1st standing row, 4th from right).

At Cracow in 1912, the Esperanto Congress album shows that Clarence still described himself as a botanist even after his twelve summers of archaeology. The corresponding photos of Clarence and Luigi are on the next page.

Another delightful evening diversion, albeit extremely crowded, was the costume ball in the Guildhall – not to be confused with a fancy-dress ball. Attendees were encouraged to wear their national costumes, and it was a remarkable sight to see kaftans and kilts, kimonos and jebbas, swirling together around the dance floor, and the dancers communicating with each other in one common language. One wonders what Clarence wore . . . his Zulu costume?

Dragging their feet as usual about leaving Casterino, Clarence, Luigi and Mercede nonetheless enjoyed the splendours of the Esperanto congress in Barcelona (5–11 September 1909). Clarence found the cumulative effect of all the work and parties quite exhausting, but he glowingly described the events to Burnat: 'We heard beautiful Catalan music and saw the peasants dancing. There was also a magnificent play performed in Esperanto by professional actors. And I had the pleasure of receiving 4 first prizes [for poetry] in the "Jeux Floraux" . . . A first prize given by the Esperanto Society of Japan is beautiful and valuable, two very artistic vases.' It was probably in Barcelona that Clarence became friendly with Dr Kimishima, who subsequently spent time with him at the Villa Rosa in 1910, neither man having any trouble communicating with the other because of Esperanto, their shared language.

Although Clarence was delighted at winning the prizes, he was ambivalent about the value of poetry in Esperanto, telling Cartailhac on 4 October 1909 that the lack of synonyms and the regularity of the accent on the penultimate syllable were obstacles to writing really good poetry in the language. 'I only won the first prizes in Barcelona because my verse and prose were more worthy of recompense than those of other competitors, but that's not saying much, and I am not at all proud of my success. At least my compatriots were happy, because there was a man (a Frenchman, I believe), who received 3 first prizes, that is to say one fewer than I did.'

Yet again dragging their feet about leaving Casa Fontanalba during their summer idyll, Clarence and Luigi set off for the Esperanto Congress in Cracow on 8 August 1912. Writing to the Berrys, Clarence complained: 'What a journey & to be away a fortnight. I've always hoped I'd

be able to make up my mind *not* to go, but I can't; . . . I dread the journey, hotels, crowds, meetings, excursions & am so sorry to leave this life of peace.'[272] On his return, he admitted he had had a wonderful time.

Clarence decided to attend one more Esperanto congress in 1914. 'It is my own doing', he told Helene von Taube. He had offered to accompany two blind Esperantists to Paris, where they would join 50–60 other blind international Esperantists at a special section of the congress. He would meet them in Turin and take them to Paris, where they would be lodged gratis. He prepared for this task by copying out Esperanto verses for them and by corresponding with other blind Esperantists. 'I have a nice German machine for Braille writing and can now do this work pretty fast.'

CHAPTER SIXTEEN

# SPLENDOURS AND LOSSES

CLARENCE HAD LONG YEARNED to see true tropical vegetation, and was planning to spend five weeks in Ceylon, but first he made a quick trip to England in November 1907. A year had passed since Ada's stroke and he wished to check on her recovery. Also, he hoped to meet with Sir David Prain, Director of the Royal Botanic Gardens at Kew, who might be invaluable in providing names of botanists in Ceylon.[273] Unfortunately, while still at Ada's house, he himself was felled by a severe attack of lumbago which immobilised him, so the list of botanists failed to materialise.

Once back in Italy he and Luigi set off for Ceylon – for convenience, I shall use the word Ceylon, the common usage in Clarence's day – on 18 December 1907, but, and irritatingly, no diary survives from this time. All that exists is a couple of short descriptions in letters to Burnat. But where Clarence is wanting, Reginald Farrer is forthcoming. Farrer (1880–1920), then a 27-year-old world traveller and plant collector, also visited the island in early 1908,[274] and his book, *In Old Ceylon,* was published later that year. Thus Clarence's first view of Ceylon from the sea would have been the same as Farrer's, who begins his book with these lines: 'Hull down, hull down, lies Lanka, sleeping island of the saints . . . Faint breezes of perfume hover and linger round the ship as she dreams her way across the surface of a flawless opal sea . . . Everything heralds the approach of fairyland.' Farrer softens up his reader; then comes the dagger:

> Colombo is a modern ugly mushroom, a convenience, an invention of modern ugly races that were ravening in blue woad when Asoka ruled the East . . . Flat, flat is the land here, and the town that squatters along its shore – flat as an old stale story that was never interesting . . . big hotels upon its frontage extend their uncompromising European facades. Within them there is a perpetual twilight, and meek puss-faced Cinhalese take perpetually the drink orders of prosperous planters and white-whiskered old fat gentlemen in sun-hats lined with green.[275]

Clarence is kinder. On 11 January, he wrote to Burnat that a week had already passed in a paradise of vegetation. He did mention that Colombo was hot, but found the heat could be mitigated by going out early in the morning and again in the evening. He and Luigi made several excursions from the city, some by car, some on foot, and some on Ceylon's admirable train system.

The two men had enjoyed a splendid, calm voyage via the Suez Canal, with a stop at Aden, about which Clarence wrote: 'Aden interested me a great deal and I saw more than 78 species of flowers on the promontory, but not the famous *Adenia*.'[276] Like everyone arriving in Ceylon, he was immediately struck by the magnificence and omnipresence of palm trees, commenting to Burnat that the *Cocos nucifera* everywhere were truly superb. Clarence's 'everywhere' is borne out in a 1907 handbook of Ceylon by J.C. Willis which states that Ceylon's coconut palms were thought to produce 800,000,000 nuts annually.[277] Willis was the director of the Royal Botanic Garden at Peradeniya from 1896 to 1912.

After a week spent in Colombo and along the east coast of the island, Clarence and Luigi took the train to Kandy. In the first part of the journey, they travelled past paddy-fields, banana groves, palm forests and acres of waterlilies and lotus before beginning the climb up terraced hills, followed by ridge after ridge into the hill country. At last, the train entered a narrow gorge before it reached the final pass, and then, after all the uphill chugging and puffing, it ran merrily down into Kandy.

From the station, Clarence and Luigi ascended a steep 100 feet to the town, where they had their first view of its lake and the famous Queen's Hotel nestled on its shore. He expressed his delight to Burnat: 'How wonderful it is to see *Convolvulus* and *Thunbergia* everywhere, and an infinity of plants that I know only in our greenhouses, and then ferns and *Nymphaea* [water lilies] . . . After a week we hope to climb the Pic d'Adam, visit the high, cold [hill station] Newera Ellya [Nuwara Eliya] and after that the ruins of ancient cities.'[278]

The Pic d'Adam, or Sri Pada, is an astonishing 2,243-metre cone, the fourth highest mountain in Ceylon. It is famous for a rock formation referred to as the sacred footprint, claimed by Buddhists to be that of the Buddha, by Hindus as Shiva's, and by Muslims and Christians as Adam's. However, the Pic d'Adam is not as high as Pidurutalagala or Mount Pedro (2,524 metres), the highest mountain in Ceylon, which means Sidney Bicknell climbed higher in Ceylon than Clarence by 281 metres, a fact that would have pleased him mightily. This is assuming that Clarence fulfilled his plan, and it is hard to imagine that he did not.

Reginald Farrer visited the Tooth Relic, the holiest of holies, said to be the Buddha's canine tooth, housed in the magnificent temple at Dalada Maligawa, just outside Kandy. Clarence may well have done so too if he had been interested enough to tear himself away from the glories of the Peradeniya Garden to visit the temple. Clarence was much affected by Buddhism, although not to the extent Farrer was. He read about it

Sri Pada (Adam's Peak) 2,243 m.

– books on Buddhism were found in his library – but Farrer converted and remained a Buddhist for the rest of his life.

The distance between Kandy and the Peradeniya garden is 5.3 kilometres, a journey that Farrer made by rickshaw. Clarence and Luigi probably walked the short distance because it was cool in Kandy, and they would think nothing of such a stroll. Francis Ramaley, an American professor visiting Peradeniya in 1908, stated that the climate was such that the botanist could live there in comfort and work regularly as it was not extreme in either rainfall or temperature.[279] Just imagine the vegetation and creatures Clarence and Luigi would have seen as they strolled along close to Ceylon's greatest river, the Mahaweli Ganga, which on reaching Peradeniya loops around to surround the garden: brilliant butterflies, elephants being washed in the river, and perhaps a crocodile or two.

The Peradeniya Garden is vast, and fulfilled Clarence's dreams of tropical vegetation: acres of towering bamboos, palms and yet more palms, banyans, spices, cataracts of allamandass and bignonias flowing down from the tallest trees, and wisteria winding their way up. The scientist in Clarence appreciated the research facilities and the experimental station and its leaf insect breeding programme.[280] The director and author, J. C. Willis, made every facility available to visiting men of science, including the herbarium with its competent curators and the library of botanical books and periodicals. Clarence had hoped to meet Willis, but was unable to do so, because he was away. Clarence would, however, have made use of his handbook on Ceylon.

Clarence and Luigi took another glorious train ride through the mountains from Kandy to Nuwara Eliya. There they met John Ferguson, a long-time Ceylon resident and editor of the *Ceylon Observer* for many years, a man instrumental in the development of the railway system and deeply committed to the politics and agriculture of the country, and thus a mine of information. Ferguson and Clarence struck up a strong friendship and were still corresponding three years later. Clarence's letter of 23 August 1911 throws some light on his visit to Nuwara Eliya.

'I often think of your place in the mountains, ferns &c . . . your offer is very tempting as an exchange of houses for the winter, but I fear it is not possible . . . I suspect that NE [Nuwara Eliya] would be rather too civilised for me, rather too exclusively English & proper and that I could only be a black sheep there, but it is an enchanting place . . . Please give my regards to your wife and tell her that the necklace was just what I wanted and gave great pleasure to my man's wife – my man, if you remember, who figured as Mrs Bicknell in the Ceylon newspapers & ships' lists of passengers!'[281]

The Peradeniya Garden in Ceylon

The Maori jade pendants on Clarence's watch strap, with the silver medal of the Societas Sancti Spiritus.

Ceylon is known for its gems, especially rubies and sapphires – Farrer goes on for pages about them – and Mrs Ferguson would have helped Clarence pick out a truly gorgeous necklace. He owed it to Mercede for having taken her husband away for ten weeks.

It seems likely that the Fergusons sealed their friendship with Clarence by giving him the Maori jade pendants of which he was so fond. As the Fergusons had travelled to New Zealand on leave from Ceylon,[282] a gift of jade pendants to rock-mad Clarence seems quite natural. Margaret Berry, who inherited them, attached a note to the pendants saying that he acquired them in Ceylon; but if Margaret were mistaken about their provenance, they become a shred of evidence to justify Peter Bicknell's mention – often repeated by others without evidence – that Clarence himself had travelled to New Zealand. However, the team researching this biography has for years been scouring ships' records and botanical records in New Zealand for mention of his name but have yielded nothing, nor did Clarence ever refer to such a journey.

On 9 February 1908, Clarence and Luigi boarded the steamship *Zieten* and sailed home in second class with a motley company of Swiss, French, Italian, Japanese, Germans, Dutch, Americans and English returning from business or missions in Japan, China and India. By 20 February they had reached Port Said, from where Clarence wrote to Burnat: 'Up until now we have had a magnificent sea, absolutely tranquil, beautiful sunsets, and nights illuminated by a superb moon. Everything has gone well. We were totally enchanted by Ceylon. How many times I thought of you when I was admiring the great ferns, the *Rhododendron arboretum* with its great bouquets of flowers, or the superb *Gloriosa* in the hedges.'[283]

Finally he writes, with a palpable sigh of relief, 'Well, I shall be very happy to be back home and to recommence my tranquil life after all this travelling, the trains, the hotels, &c.'

Fritz Mader gave the name Cima Bicknell to a peak of 2686m (now shown as 2641m) just east of the Lac du Basto. Postcard in the Bicknell Collection.

'You have arrived back from Ceylon, the isle of wonders, and you are climbing back up to the alpine peaks! It is a dream to be thus able to pass from splendour to splendour', wrote Cartailhac in an undated letter on Clarence's return from Ceylon.[284] Indeed, Clarence's life was filled with splendours of one kind or another, the most important of which were discoveries of further rock engravings and the evolution of the Casa Fontanalba into his ideal home.

On 5 May 1908, he told Burnat that Fritz Mader had named a peak above Val Fontanalba 'Cima Bicknell' in his honour. In 1908 Fritz Mader published in the *Rivista Mensile* of the Club Alpino Italiano an article describing his excursions in the Maritime Alps in 1906; these included finding a minor summit of about 2,600 m. above Val Fontanalba, which he decided to name after Clarence Bicknell 'who with much patience for several years has explored, copied and illustrated the many prehistoric rock inscriptions in the surrounding area.' Situated between Mont St Marie and Mont Bégo, at 2,600 metres, the little peak was, according to Clarence 'très peu de chose', commenting to Burnat: 'I believe (between you and me) that it's hardly worthy of a name, and will not render me more illustrious, but at least I'm happy that you're not the only one in the Maritime Alps to have your own peak.'

In May, he found what he called pearls, or at least 'pierced objects', when excavating at Taggia, 26 kilometres northeast of Bordighera, with an English friend, the famous textile archaeologist, Grace M. Crowfoot.[285] Clarence pointed out to Cartailhac that she was very conscientious and had 'already recovered some human bones, etc.'[286]

Émile Burnat, his son Jean, his assistants Cavillier and Briquet, and other members of his entourage were among the 44 people who signed the *Casa Fontanalba Visitors' Book* in 1909. How splendid for Clarence to have a chance to show the wonders of his valley to his dear friend. Then, in August, Émile Cartailhac paid a visit, another splendour. Overjoyed to welcome him, Clarence and Luigi escorted the great scholar up into the Val Fontanalba and showed him their discoveries. The visit was a success, and subsequently Clarence wrote to his friend describing further new discoveries, adding: 'Every day I see E.C. on the wall of our little dining room, and I think about your

Émile Burnat (1828–1920) c. 1908. Six hundred and ninety letters and cards from Bicknell to Burnat are archived at the Botanical Garden of Geneva.

visit which gave me so much pleasure and instruction.' After each overnight visitor left, Clarence painted his or her initials on the dining room walls.

In celebration of Burnat's 80th birthday, Clarence was among 105 European botanists who signed a circular that was bound into a presentation album, along with photographs of them all. Although Clarence did not attend the party on 21 October 1908 at the Hotel du Lac, Vevey – all the guests were local Swiss – Burnat took care to send Clarence newspaper articles describing the event, and Clarence, in turn, wrote to say that he had been in Ireland on the day, at a great distance from a post office, and thus unable to join others in telegraphing his best wishes.

The final major splendour of 1908 was natural splendour in its most terrifying manifestation. On 28 December, Messina in Sicily and Reggio in Calabria were hit by a tremendous earthquake – 7.1 on today's Richter scale – the worst earthquake to occur in Europe in recorded history; its epicentre was in the Straits of Messina, the mythological home of Scylla and Charybdis. Estimates at the numbers of lives lost range from 75,000 to 200,000, and the devastation was appalling. Ninety per cent of the city of Messina was obliterated, and many of those who had escaped the quake itself were either drowned in the subsequent tsunami or perished during aftershocks.

The earthquake had the ability to destroy within a 300-kilometre radius, but its after-effects rippled throughout all Italy. As far away as Bordighera, which received a mere jolt, inhabitants prepared to help. On 16 January, Clarence wrote to Burnat: 'We are awaiting 50 refugees from Messina, in a state of convalescence. We have taken over an unfurnished hotel and are busy preparing it for them. Everyone gives what they can, beds, furniture, etc. This is difficult to arrange in a flash . . . I can't do very much but I want to be useful, and not just give money.'[287]

Clarence would continue to worry about earthquakes for the rest of his life. 'I fear we shall have a bad earthquake within a few years', he told Baroness von Taube in 1909, 'and then probably my house will suffer, for the walls were a good deal shaken by the one of 1887 and its constitution must be permanently injured.' Again, at the time of the Senboku earthquake in 1914, he wrote to her about his fear: 'The Japanese catastrophe does not seem so terrible as at first reported, but the loss of life is terrible enough . . . I have written to my friend [the Esperantist Dr Kimishima] who is on that island but far off in the north at his University, so he is quite safe. I think we shall soon have an earthquake here. I hope it will not come in the winter. I am not ready for it, having no big summerhouse in which to live as I did in 1887.'

~

At the end of September 1906, Clarence received distressing news. Sidney describes what happened: 'My sister Ada had a paralytic stroke, Sept. 27, in the middle of the day, without any warning, and it was for some weeks uncertain if she would live. One side was rendered useless, and speech and sight for a time was affected. This happened at her residence in the village or hamlet of Fairseat, near Wrotham, Kent.' Clarence wanted to rush to England, but was frustrated in doing so, being ill himself. Once recovered, he immediately set off, later writing to Burnat about Ada's condition: 'After 5 weeks, she speaks well, but the paralysis remains the same and from time to time she suffers terribly from sciatica. I don't know, no one knows, what will happen. I spent three very sad weeks with her.' Having Clarence around to encourage her as she struggled to recover must have been a wonderful tonic. Later, in 1910, Sidney commented on her condition: 'Her illness progressed favourably, and though she has never been able to walk from that day, she still, in a recumbent posture, enjoys her existence.'

Ada was not the only sibling about whom Clarence was worried. Percy's finances had always been dubious, even if Clarence was his constant enabler, but this time he was facing ruin. Sidney wrote 'My nephew Herman had spread a report that his uncle Percy, my brother, was nearly bankrupt. I had always believed Percy to be a rich man, for he had always lived luxuriously like one, and I knew that he inherited about £120,000 from his father as well as an old established lucrative business. So I took this to be merely a specimen of that unfounded malicious gossip some members of the family often relieve their *malaise* by indulging in.' It was not unfounded gossip. When Sidney confronted him, Percy admitted to 'having spent too freely, having helped his sons too liberally, and kept two houses.' That was the least of it. He owed money everywhere, especially to Clarence, although Clarence's loans were more in the nature of gifts, and was guilty of gross mismanagement of his father's business.

Sidney continues: 'This was so incredible, so astounding, that it left me only lamenting that a son of my most honourable father, his partner, executor and trustee, a residuary legatee, would fall so low in immorality and crime . . . Several of us contributed, as gifts, large sums to keep my brother from becoming a bankrupt. I acted at once with energy – a quality no other member of my family possesses . . .' and here Sidney enumerates the family's losses, and launches into a description of his efforts to staunch the flow of funds. 'If I had not insisted on more punctual payment . . . I think in all probability our losses might have grown to vastly greater dimensions and perhaps we might all finally have been involved in one common ruin. The family owe me a deep debt of gratitude, but they have never acknowledged it, or thanked me by a single word.'

In 1907, Percy finally liquidated his father's business and retired. Naturally, Sidney commented 'So came to an end a business carried on for more than a century, raised to great prosperity by my father solely, and which brought him the noble fortune of about half a million . . . I am sure Percy's dishonesty and folly would have broken his heart.'

Angry, acidulous, not a pleasant man, Sidney had another, surprisingly admirable side – that of the explorer. He had Clarence's curiosity and determination, and he went even further in his world exploration. In 1904, and after a long and detailed report of an operation to remove five inches of his intestine, he listed other occasions when he was in danger of his life. These were: storm on Lake Neuchatel; storm on Lake Killarney; collision in steamer outside New York; suffocation by gas in a Brandfold well; showers of stones; bridges over crevasses in the Alps; change of weather on Monte Rosa; bridges and precipices in the Andes; steam engine in Cornish mine, accident; carried out to sea at Brighton; falling into the River Ouse.

He then enumerates the mountains he ascended: Mont Blanc; Monte Rosa; Matterhorn; Breithorn; Strahlhorn; Oberrothorn; Adler pass; Grand Combier; Triftjoch; Valpellini Pass and Tête Blanche; Col du Géant, several times; direct descent from Dent du Géant to Courmayeur; direct descent from summit of Cima di Jazzi to Macugnaga; Col d'Hérens; Jungfrau; Etna, at Xmas; Vesuvius, 10 times during eruptions; Lesser Atlas Mountains; Mount Lebanon; Mount Washington, U.S.; Mount Pedro (Pidurutalagala), Ceylon; and Sendakphu, Darjeeling, India.

Many a modern mountaineer would be hard pressed to top Sidney's total. And surely none has achieved his ten times of summiting Mount Vesuvius – while it was erupting! This display of courage makes one almost admire him.

~

'Hoping that the New Year will bring you more happiness, and your path blossom like the daisy in meadows. C. Bicknell.' These were Clarence's good wishes to the Baroness von Taube for 1911; unfortunately, they were not fulfilled. Her husband's health declined dramatically and her daughter Helene's condition continued to be a source of great anxiety.

Clarence was called to England at the beginning of April because of Ada's perilous health. It was a doomed trip. The day after his arrival at Fairseat, Ada's new home in Kent, he was stricken with sciatica so painful that he was condemned to bed for the next ten days, and unable to spend time with Ada. Not only was he in pain, he suffered feelings of guilt about being a nuisance in a crowded house where his sister's condition was so serious that she was being tended by her daughter Maud, a friend, and a trained nurse. In desperation, he telegraphed Luigi to come for him, and Luigi duly showed up. Once Clarence's condition had improved enough for him to travel, they made the journey back to Bordighera.

'I have just received the latest issue of the *Revue préhistorique*, sent to me by my bête noire, M. Stiegelman, and I note that he is at Tussat-les-Bains, a place that is in dangerous proximity to all your beautiful caves', wrote Clarence in a letter of warning to Cartailhac on 7 June. 'I hope he is not there to vandalise nor to "discover" anything that you discovered long ago!' This bête noire was Adolphe Stiegelman; the reason Clarence loathed him was because he had defaced rock engravings in the Val Fontanalba and the Merveilles by scratching a gigantic 'S' on them, thus claiming possession to them. Cartailhac, too, had fallen afoul of him; after Stiegelman's death, he wrote to Clarence: 'I agree that we have lost a dangerous being. He had become unpleasant to me personally, very much so . . . I am going to see if I can retrieve the objects he took from our caves at Ariège, and I will also help his wife whom I believe to be more worthy of esteem. She was perhaps his victim.'[288] On 13 August 1908, Stiegelman had visited Clarence, who graciously and innocently took him on a tour of the rock engravings.[289] Nevertheless, the opportunist struck at both Clarence and Cartailhac.

Baron Otto von Taube died on 1 August 1911, and Helene wrote immediately to inform Clarence. He responded on the 7th in the manner familiar to many widows – by resorting to platitudes: 'It was a great shock to me yesterday to receive your sad news – if it is sad– sad for you and yours, of course, but I think your dear husband's life had for some time been only wretched for him and that he must have [been] glad to give it up . . . I know your life will be very different now after so many years of married happiness, but your children will be a consolation to you.'

Then it was Clarence's turn to inform Helene about his losses. His brother Percy, Nora's father, the man whom he had bailed out financially on so many occasions, died on 10 August. This death was followed by the death of his beloved Ada on 13 September. His pride in his sister and her accomplishments beams forth in his letter to Helene on the 21st: 'I shall miss her greatly, but I cannot mourn much. She had, to my mind, lived a very full, useful, brave life, and her work was done. Her children are good & mostly doing well, and she had lived to see the triumph of many things for which she had fought and suffered – more religious toleration, improvement in education & condition of the working classes. The spread of scientific ideas, &c.'

Clarence then described Ada's final days. 'Her last adventure in life which no doubt caused her death, was strange. A great friend, a lady doctor, who manages a sanatorium for consumptive patients in the country [the Sanatorium Nayland in Colchester], told my sister she thought it would do her no harm to come on a visit to her on a motor omnibus. My sister, always fond of travelling, an excellent horsewoman, walker &c.

*Pimpinella bicknellii* 'collected by Clarence Bicknell and Luigi Pollini in May 1899 on Majorca at a height of 4–500 metres on rocky slopes on the northern side of the hills between the two farms of Ariant (near Pollenza) and the sea, the locus classicus where Bicknell first discovered it in 1897', according to Ignaz Dörfler who provided the sample to Oxford University. This plant, endemic to Majorca, was named after Bicknell in 1898 by John Briquet, Director of the Botanical Garden of Geneva.

and fond of adventure and risk, was delighted with the idea, after 5 years of only being wheeled round her garden. She said she would go. A son & daughter thought it a great risk, *but if she wished it, what did it matter*? So, she who had never been in a motor and hated the idea of the rush and noise and shaking went on a 4 hour journey!' Ada thoroughly enjoyed the experience and the change of scene, 'But the day after she had a fresh paralytic stroke. She recovered from that, but then relapsed and in 2 or 3 days died quietly and painlessly, glad to end her life and hoping to find her husband & others gone before in another world so-called.'

'So-called' gives a glimpse into Clarence's opinion of the afterlife.

He continued: 'I am sad nevertheless at losing my best-loved sister, whose home was a centre for me to meet her children. We are now 4, a brother in England [Sidney] aged 79 in October who will probably not survive the winter, another 77 [Edgar], and a sister 71 [Lucinda] in Paris whom I never see. And so before long we shall all have gone away.'

Clarence also informed Burnat of Ada's death, but on 26 October returned to the topic of *Pimpinella bicknellii,* informing Burnat that an American botanist had hunted the plant down in Majorca and had written, insisting that the plant was not a true *Pimpinella,* but rather a plant of a new genus. 'Donc, c'est la chance!' [That's the way it goes!], shrugged Clarence. But despite the American's claim, the name that John Briquet gave to the species remains in standard use.

Clarence was correct in foreseeing Sidney's death. On 29 October, he wrote to Helene: 'On Thursday I received a letter urging me to go at once to England, as a brother wanted to see me. I was not very well, in the doctor's hands to cure a cough, and replied I would start as soon as possible. Happily I was unable for this reason to start at once for in the afternoon came a telegram: "Do not come – he is dead." So I have lost 2 brothers and my loved sister since the middle of July – too many all at once – and I feel left very much alone.'

Needing distraction and a change of scene, Clarence took Luigi to Rome for a week to see the art and ethnological exhibitions, and to visit a botanist friend at Tivoli. In the same postcard of 28 November to Helene telling her about this, he expressed hope that she and her ailing daughter were well settled in Hyères, where they planned to spend the winter. Writing to her again on 18 December, Clarence was pleased to note, 'In Italy they are trying now to preserve the rare plants, which the florists destroy, digging them up by thousands.' He then launched into a description of what it was like to be in Italy as a result of the Italo-Turkish war. This war had broken out in September, and was Italy's attempt to wrest colonies in North Africa from Ottoman rule. Although this war was not a large-scale, long-term engagement, it was one of the factors leading to the First World War because it became a destabilising factor in the Balkan states.

Clarence's brother Sidney Bicknell (1832–1911) in about 1910.

It is not very pleasant in Italy now. Every English person seems to be looked upon as an enemy because some of the English papers did not approve of the war, and some believed in lying reports of the atrocities. Of course the Italians are now very sensitive & have a little lost their heads. I love and trust them & think they conduct the war very well & that the soldiers are excellent young fellows, but now we are expected to believe that everybody is a hero or a genius, and everything in politics government, art &c &c very well done – and the papers, I think, greatly exaggerate what we have said – I am sure Italian rule in Tripoli will be better than Turkish – but I am not in favour of wars of aggression, and I think it is anyhow very wrong to talk about *Christian* influence, for Christ certainly never approved of killing one's enemies &c.

The last, long, run-on sentence sounds spewed out, as Clarence, the pacifist, poured out his disgust for wars of aggression. He was frightened, and he turned for comfort from families, not just the lost humans of his blood family, but his Italian family, the botanical and archaeological families he knew so well, as well as lists of things, the rigour of a regular work schedule, his home in Bordighera, the idea of peace.

He continued in the same vein on 17 February 1912: 'This long Italian war, that is no nearer an end than it was months ago, and the everlasting jealousies & fears & suspicions between *our nations* are terrible. I love every country and people and cannot understand these antipathies. It seems to me incredible that *we* could ever think of hitting one another . . . and we go on spending millions, while our people are starving, in order to have more ships.' He then turned to the situation in Ireland: 'We might heal the troubles of Ireland, and be at peace at home in our own houses if only people would have a little more love and trust, instead of fancying that all sorts of awful things will happen if there is a parliament in Ireland for Irish affairs.'

In the short space of six months, death continually stalked Clarence and Helene's families, striking again in January 1912, when the baroness's daughter died in Hyères of the tuberculosis against which she had struggled so valiantly for so long. Clarence immediately wrote to Helene: 'Resquiescat in pace *and* pax vobiscum, deeply grieved at your sorrow and loss', and sent poems of sympathy, one of which had botanical resonance for them both: 'Yet, if you grieve for me with flowers,/Remembering all the happy hours/They gave me living; pray you, bring/Your garlands to my burying.'

In a subsequent letter on 17 February, Clarence was less platitudinous than about the loss of her husband, more 'Buck yourself up, dear', saying 'Well, my good friend, your life must be very sad, I know, but many people still want you, so you must be brave and live as you did before, helping them all. We have all to live for those who come after us, and leave the world a little better.'

CHAPTER SEVENTEEN

# GOOD DEEDS
# AND THE WAR YEARS

LEAVING THE WORLD A BETTER place had been Father Giacomo Viale's goal, and one he accomplished in full measure. All his life he worked tirelessly for the poor, while also maintaining the fabric of the churches in Bordighera – restoring the parish church and the chapel of St Ampelio, enlisting Charles Garnier to design the church of the Terrasanta, and building a little sanctuary to the Virgin Mary, 'La Castellana di Montenero', in the hills above Bordighera, to which Clarence donated a bell.[290]

The elderly poor were his main concern in later years because the Casa di Provvidenza, a place of refuge for the elderly poor of Bordighera, was gobbled up by the hospital in 1905, leaving them without resource. Working hand in hand, Father Giacomo and Clarence were determined to remedy the situation. It took a long time, but when an old house became available, in deplorable condition but conveniently located next to the hospital, they made their move. On 26 March 1911 they purchased the house with funds provided in large part by Clarence, along with contributions from other members of the foreign community. (The locals were not responsive to fund-raising, much to Clarence's disgust.) Later that year, Padre Giacomo formed a committee to seek further funds to restore the house, and the first meeting was held in the Museo Bicknell on 7 December. Committee members included the mayor of Bordighera, the artist Baron Friederich von Kleudgen, the hotelier Adolph Angst, Captain Alberto Pelloux, and other luminaries. And Clarence, of course.

On 18 February 1912, St Joseph's Home for the Aged Poor was officially inaugurated by the Bishop of Ventimiglia.[291] Clarence attended the ceremony, but unfortunately Padre Giacomo was ill in bed. On the 24th, in great pain, he was rushed by automobile to hospital in San Remo, protesting mightily about being removed from Bordighera. He was operated on immediately, and spent the next six uncomfortable weeks convalescing in the hospital. On 31 March Clarence was able to write to Helene: 'Padre Giacomo was brought back in an automobile a week ago and I have been to see him. *He is better* but I do not know if he will recover. We are in a great fix *as he will not make his will* and the houses which were bought for the Asilo are in his name . . . If he leaves them to me or any other individual, succession death duties must be paid, and the difficulty will be as great as before.'

Clarence then left on a long-anticipated trip to France and Spain with Luigi, stopping at Lourdes. Being both a man of God and open-minded, not averse to discussions of mysticism, he would be expected to stop there. He went on to Bayonne, Burgos, Toledo, and stayed nearly a week in Madrid. He suffered throughout the trip from a hacking cough, but nonetheless managed to find several plants he had never seen before, and spent enough time looking at paintings in the Prado to become disillusioned by the paintings of Velázquez. On 29 April, he wrote to Helene: 'I was v. disappointed . . . they do not to my mind touch Van Dyck or Rembrandt & many others. I think [his] 'Forge of Vulcan' a wretched picture . . . and 'The Surrender of Breda' (or *Las Lancas*) certainly not one of the finest historical pictures ever painted . . . the botanical gardens are nice.'

He inveighed against what he saw at Lourdes and the trends in modern church teaching. 'These multiplied devotional pilgrimages, excitement of miracles . . . What have they to do with the religion of the heart & the welfare of the people and the increase of interest in the poor & suffering? I think that *miracle* superstition is very unhealthy, and all the advertising of Lourdes very bad.'

While Clarence was away, the Baroness wrote him a long letter from the Convento delle Suore di Santa Croce in Rome, where she had gone to seek comfort from her bereavements. It appears from her draft that she had spent time with him on her way south. She wrote:

> You have been good to me, you have not opened and trampled on my wounds, you let me sit before your fire and gave me the beautiful flower-book to read. I thank you for all your delicate kindness and for your goodness to one who has much suffered and shall suffer much. God bless your kind heart . . . I greeted Rome, the Campagna so beautiful beneath the flaming sky at sun-set with tears and the remembrance of happy days . . . yet Rome is beautiful seen also with sad eyes and the calm and silence among the good sisters in this house of peace is so appeasing.

However, Helene did not spend all her time grieving. 'I see much my nieces and go much into the villa Borghese . . . I like to sit near the solitary fontana del bosco where the cows come sometimes to drink water and where I write and read . . . I have not been in galleries but very much in churches . . . In the churches and villas one finds quiet hours, but [not] in the streets [of] modern Rome with the disgusting smell and noise of rushing automobiles and clouds of dust. There was beauty before in elegant Roman ladies driving in open carriages conducted by stately horses, but now the ugliness of these monsters makes beauty and grace a legend . . .

'As you don't mention Padre Giacomo's health, I hope, he is not worse.' He was, of course, and on returning from Spain, Clarence had to write to Helene: '

> Dear Padre Giacomo died about a week ago [16 April]. Pulmonite set in. I believe there was a grand funeral. Everyone professes to love him very much, but no one seems disposed to do what he wished, and all the people in Bordighera have only given 200 lire towards the Asilo. I shall much miss Padre Giacomo. It has been a sad time . . . And now comes the awful disaster to the *Titanic*. I know one man who perished in it. He is mentioned in the papers as having been one of the most devoted in helping others and who met his death with courage. But Why should we fear to die? *Living is the most difficult.*

'I am always sorry to leave home, and my books and begin the life of a savage in the wilds, but the wild life is very pleasant, and one quickly reverts to an ancestral simian type (at least I do)', wrote Clarence to Helene on 4 June 1912. He was heading up to the gentians and anemones of Val Casterino with niece Nora; Capi, the dog; Luigi and Mercede. He planned to find and preserve more flowers and to finish typing his article about his latest finds among the rocks. Clarence had invested in a typewriter! He also had good news: all the debts on St Joseph's home had been paid off – apart from the succession duties – and it would be furnished in the autumn; and the famous Belgian sculptor and artist Jules Pierre van Biesbroeck had fashioned a magnificent, life-like bust of Padre Giacomo as a present to the Commune.

The bust of Padre Giacomo Viale in the heart of Bordighera old town.

In 1914, Biesbroeck would make his home in Bordighera, after fleeing from the German invasion of his home town of Ghent. In his villa, 'Our Nest', he continued to sculpt and paint. Clarence, always wanting to improve his artistic skills, began taking lessons from him and learned how to employ a new technique in red chalk called *sanguine* for his views of Casterino. Biesbroeck made his mark on Bordighera by painting the *Deposition* in the new Terrasanta Church in Bordighera, designed by Charles Garnier. Clarence devoted a page to him in his *Book of Guests in Esperanto*.

'My sight is failing', he wrote in a letter to the Berrys.[292] 'I can see the sheep well on the Sabbione hills or men on the sky line, but I've taken to rapid flower drawing with a brush & seem able to make a [connection?] but then I can't see, so they may not be good.' He was clearly concerned about his sight because on 6 October, he asked Helene if she would tell him if she could read his writing. 'It seems to me it is getting very illegible, and that I must be more careful and not write so rapidly for I think it is as rude to write as to speak badly.'

C.B., Sketch of the Val Casterino in 'sanguine', a red chalk containing iron oxide. September 1917.

Clarence's admission comes as no surprise to those of us who have had to transcribe so much of his handwriting. He never refers to failing eyesight again, and it certainly did not impede his accomplishments during that summer.

On 8 September 1912 Clarence wrote to Helene:

I have read many interesting books, collected many plants, & done much house painting. I am now finishing some walls covered with a rough design of *Cirsium eriophorum*

C.B., watercolour of *Psalliota xanthoderma*, 'The Yellow-Stainer' which is described as poisonous to most people. Worryingly, Clarence writes 'edible' alongside the mushroom. UniGen.

& orange butterflies . . . I have not found very much to draw, but have lately been doing some funghi. I have no microscope to see the spores, but . . . it is a joy to use such bright colours . . . Next month, October I shall be 70. Shall I ever come up here again, I ask every year?

Clarence began communicating with his sister Lucinda ('Linda') again after the death of her husband, and when he heard she would spend part of the winter in Rome, he put her in touch with Helene who was already there, telling Helene: 'I like English & German to meet & promote *l'entente cordiale*.' But getting a response from Lucinda was challenging. 'She is the worst of correspondents & hardly ever writes to me . . . but Ethel, her daughter [who was both deaf and dumb], is very good & has written twice from Rome. They seem to be sightseeing all day & as Linda has a wonderful constitution & is never ill, she never seems to be tired – *She has no nerves*.'

After the eventual meeting between Helene and Linda in Rome, the city began to attract Clarence, so when Nora expressed interest in travelling there, they set off in March. His letter to the Berrys describing their trip is perhaps the most droll he ever wrote.

We had a heavy fall of snow on Tuesday & there has been rain at intervals since, but I think Nora has enjoyed herself. We lunched with Aunt Linda & Ethel & have been to see the Baroness Taube . . . 2 days more will quite finish me up. We've been 4 times to the Cinema & seen many *emozianti* dramas & we've seen the zoo, where the lions and tigers walk about on rocks & you would think every minute they could jump on to you, but there are cleverly concealed chasms between.

Then we have walked along the new walls to keep in the Tiber, and seen all the modern houses & streets where the ghetto & other picturesque things used to be – and I've shown Nora the gasworks and a splendid large new manufactory of pasta – and we've done a little shopping & I bought a new hat & sponge – and we have been up the 265 steps of the Capitol tower to get a view . . .

Nora likes our quiet inn & restaurant & she eats huge pieces of cheese. All the chickweed here seems to be the [*var.*] *grandiflora* with very large flowers. It is one of the best things in Rome but Baedeker does not mention it.

So much for the Forum and St Peter's!

Clarence made a trip to England in April, and described its challenges to Helene: 'I have been away more than 3 weeks & paid 66 visits to relations & seen very many others & friends, and I am so tired of trains, & automobiles & rushing about with no rest, and besides I have a troublesome cough & cold ... It was very difficult, and just like putting together a "jig-saw puzzle".' On the way home, he stopped at Stresa to meet up with Luigi and Mercede, planning to travel back to Bordighera together, but he found that Mercede had undergone two operations and was still recuperating in Milan. He left Luigi with her until she was fit to travel. Clarence was doubtful about the result of the operations, telling Helene: 'I only *hope* she will really be quite cured now, but every doctor she has seen in these last years has done something that was to be *the last* ... My nephew James Berry, one of the 6 best surgeons in London, is so against all these operations.' He also wrote to Burnat, 'I do not have much faith in these female operations, they never end.'

Against Clarence's expectations, by June Mercede had recovered and accompanied Luigi and Clarence to Casterino. 'It is a delightful life up here', Clarence declared to Helene, '& I already feel much better than at Bordighera & the gout in my foot seems to be giving up ... the 3 hours climb up here did not tire me.' Clarence was 73 at this point, an age at which many another 73-year-old would have found a three-hour climb quite a challenge. But he came to grips with his limitations in a letter to Helene: 'Luigi and I have been camping out for 2 nights, 4 hours away, and again exploring the rock figures, and we had 3 interesting days, but I came home very tired. The fact is I cannot do quite so much as ten years ago, and I shall before long begin to confess that I am getting old, but I intend to fight on as long as possible.'

He and Rosa Junck attended the Esperanto congress in Bern that summer, although he was silent about it in his correspondence. He began writing to Hungarian and Finnish Esperantists, but, as he complained to Burnat, it was annoying that German botanists were unwilling to communicate in any language but German, which he did not speak. His commitment to the international language remained firmer than ever. In October, he wrote to Helene, 'Tonight we begin our Esperanto meetings. These tire me very much and are not very satisfactory ... some who can best help me cannot come regularly. Eileen Daly is not well enough, and Sra Junck always is tired after her lessons so that the thing chiefly devolves on me, and I am too old and not sufficiently energetic, although my interest in Esperanto and *desire* to help in spreading it never flags, and every year I am more and more delighted with the language and more sure of its ultimate triumph.'

On his birthday, three days later, he launched himself on a new project: collecting poetry about mountains, and asking Burnat if mountains had inspired Swiss poets. 'I think that before the last century, people regarded mountains with fear. They were terrible, menacing, barriers, enemies ... It seems that no English poet was in love with mountains before Shelley in 1816 ... [Perhaps] there is no beautiful poetry about mountains because one cannot write about them. The soul feels much, but cannot express itself.'

He celebrated his birthday by hosting a dinner at the Villa Rosa for his faithful Giacomo, Luigi's father, aged 74; Maddalena's father, aged 79; Maddalena, Luigi, and Mercede. He called them 'the family', and referred to himself as Luigi's second father. The family soon suffered the loss of Giacomo when he died the following February. 'I shall miss my dear old Giacomo very

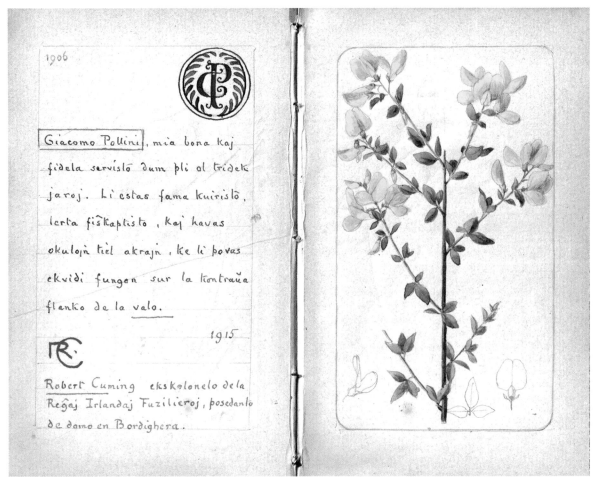

Clarence's floral watercolour and words in Esperanto for Giacomo Pollini, Luigi's father, who 'has eyes so sharp that he can see fungi on the far side of the valley'. *Book of Guests in Esperanto*,

much', Clarence told Helene. '34 years is a long time and he was always faithful and true – I think of the English words of the gospel *'Well done good and faithful servant'*. I am truly grateful to anyone who understands, but there are many, even those that knew him well and always saw him here, who think it is not worth while troubling about *only a servant*.'

About Giacomo, Clarence had written the following in the *Book of Guests in Esperanto*: 'Giacomo Pollini, a good and faithful servant for more than thirty years. He is a famous cook, a skilled fisherman, and has eyes so sharp that he can see fungi on the far side of the valley.'

Clarence spent Christmas in Florence, visiting his old friend, Dr Agnetti. He also took in some interesting sights such as watching dancers perform the tango at the Grand Hotel. As he wrote to Stefano Sommier on 1 January 1914, 'Even the bishops with their *vietato* [prohibition] have done much to advertise the dance. The figures I saw were all beautiful, much better than the stupid waltz and polka, and I wish everybody would learn the Tango. If some figures are *indecente*, it is not necessary to learn them.'[293]

He was also intrigued by a ceremony at Santa Maria Novella on Christmas day, describing it to Sommier in the same letter and asking about its significance.

> Before the reading of the gospel the two acolytes with their great candles went out and solemnly reconducted [*sic*] a banner or gonfalone ricamato [embroidered banner] which stood behind the gospel book and afterwards for a long time in front of the altar, hiding the priests . . . So solemnly was it brought in, that more could hardly have been done to conduct a living bishop or the Pope himself. Qua doctrines I am quite an agnostic but am always very much interested in all rites and liturgies and traditional beliefs and ceremonies.

Clarence, who in the past had been a participant in ritual in the Anglican church, had become instead a witness to ritual in a wide religious context.

Clarence returned from Florence with a nasty cough. Dr Odelli, his physician since the departure of Dr Agnetti, prescribed medicines that Clarence shunned. 'I do not much believe in medicines which pass into the stomach to help affections of the air passages', he told Helene. 'However I inhale at night, keep warm, and *take care of myself*. At least Luigi takes care of me. He is an excellent nurse.'

While he was ill, he started planning a trip to Japan by the Trans-Siberian railway, a country he wanted to visit more than any other. He later scuttled his plans because he felt Luigi should not leave his dying father. 'After all what does it matter if I ever see Japan or not?' he asked Helene. 'I am more and more convinced that one spends too much money on one's own pleasures – not that I think "charity" so-called, the giving of money, is much of a gift. I only really admire the people who give themselves to try and ameliorate the condition of the world.' Examples of those people were his new friends, the Russian activists, Peter and Sophia Kropotkin, the 'angel anarchists', who were staying next door.

> What a life he has had of study, work, imprisonment & exile, for his beloved 'scientific anarchism'. I think he is quite right in his theories, but not in his proposed methods of improving matters. That a great change, a great revolution will come & that the order of things will be very different some day I do not doubt, but not yet . . . after all must not even this planet come to an end & be remade into nebula &c. in the eternal system of life & death?

Conversations with the Kropotkins must have been quite a change from those with the tea-party gossips. His friendship with them

Peter A. Kropotkin (1842–1921) and his wife Sophia Grigorievna in their house at Dmitrov, north of Moscow, c. 1919.

Clarence's symmetrical composition of the dandelion, a watercolour in one
of the Fitzwilliam albums.

led the police of Imperia to classify him as 'friendly to subversives.' Imperia is the province in
which Bordighera is situated.

Clarence did not sympathise with violent anarchism because he loathed violence of any sort.
And, although much in favour of votes for women, he abhorred militant suffragettes and must
have been particularly disturbed by their attack on the tea house at Kew Gardens in 1913; their
unproven but probable attack on three orchid houses at Kew the same year; and their bombings
at the Glasgow Botanic Gardens in January 1914. 'More women ought to revolt', he told Helene
on 10 July 1914, 'and they will, against the tyranny of men & their slavery. I can approve of all
methods except what seem to me the senseless ones of destroying the world's treasures & ruining
innocent people.'

Clarence's final letter to Helene, at least among the collection at the Natural History Museum,
was also written in Italian, and sent on 20 April 1915, one month before Italy declared war on
Austria/Hungary. He told her there were few foreign visitors in Bordighera and the town had the
feel of the aftermath of an earthquake. 'Oh God, it is so difficult . . . but let us not talk of the dark
night, always hoping for the brighter morning.' In true form, he followed up with a discourse on
the sheer brilliance of the dandelion and his work on an album about it, as always finding comfort for her and himself in wildflowers. Clarence may well have written more letters to Helene,
and she to him; if that is the case they never made it past the censors.

Letters to and from his other correspondents became sadder and sadder as the Great War
deepened. No one was left untouched by loss, and Clarence reminded Burnat how lucky he was
to live in Switzerland.

'I try everything in my power to be friendly to my German acquaintances, but naturally one cannot discuss the war with them, nor with anyone who believes in propagating culture and civilization by force. And it is even more useless to discuss what caused the war.'[294] Clarence had read with distaste General Friedrich von Bernhardi's book, *Germany and the Next War,* with its claim that war was a biological necessity that fulfilled the laws of the struggle for existence. '[Bernhardi] says clearly "We Germans are the first people of the world, we must advance, and it is only by force that this can be done".'

Brute force was anathema to Clarence, and German brute force in particular. In a letter to Alberto Pelloux written in 1915, he lashed out, 'We shall conquer that arch-liar the Kaiser some day . . . If he is not a scoundrel he must be mad.' And he told Burnat, 'I cannot have relations with these Germans, Baron von Kleudgen excepted . . . my friend for more than 30 years; he does not speak about the war, his son is Italian, pro-Italy, doing his military service, but Madame and their daughter are *very* German . . . It is impossible to be friendly with people who approve of all the horrors of these savages.'

Italy finally declared war on the German Empire on 28 August 1916. In the build-up, the atmosphere was tense and apprehensive, with Italy prevaricating over which side to take, that of Germany or that of the Allied Powers. The eventual decision to join the Allied Powers cost the Italians, already weakened by the Italo-Turkish war, hundreds of thousands of lives and led them into socio-economic collapse and the rise of Fascism. For Clarence, living in Italy, the war years were a sort of limbo: his letters were censored; he could not return to England; even a quick trip across the border into France became a nightmare of bureaucracy. But nothing stopped him from going up to Casterino.

'Here we are, well established with everything in order', he wrote to Caterina Pelloux in 1915, 'even the little plants brought from Bordighera, beets, lettuce, onions, leeks, etc. and the potatoes are out in the open under the earth. Blessed are they . . . I'm not accustomed to hard work, and I'm a bit tired, but perhaps the reason is that I'm well old at 72 1/2 . . . On Saturday we went up the Val Casterino and collected plums, and came home with about 3800!! Yesterday, Sunday, I rested!' Up there, the war receded and Nature was king.

The eminent botanist and gentian specialist, Lino Vaccari, paid a visit to Casa Fontanalba that summer, gathered seeds, and disabused Clarence of the idea that Saint Bernards were actually rescue dogs. 'How many times, showing pictures of them with my magic lantern have I insisted that it was "an article of faith" that they looked for and saved travellers lost in the snow . . . Apparently these dogs are lazy, greedy and beautiful. That's all!' Clarence told Burnat on 21 September. He was very proud of his lantern slides, and longed to show Burnat his rich collection. 'If we don't have anyone to show them to, Luigi and I have a session just for ourselves . . . It's strange, but very often the prehistoric engravings are much more clear in the photographs than they are to the naked eye.'

Clarence's magic lanterns, his slide projectors, were handed down through Luigi Pollini to the Gozzini family in Bordighera.

Clarence's 1915 Christmas card to Alberto Pelloux, with this stencil of a bird, was not sent until 30 December. IISL.

Although he insisted that he had finished his explorations of the engravings, he could not leave them alone; that summer he discovered around 200 new ones in Val Fontanalba, making a total of over 7,300 there. 'And in the Meraviglie we know 5,140, so in all more than 12,600! all copied! it is a great number!' he exulted to Burnat. But even as he delighted in new discoveries in his remote valley, Clarence was ground down by dismal news. 'Oh, the war! I have a nephew who directs a hospital in Serbia – one in the Dardanelles – one killed in the trenches – two in France.'

The nephew in Serbia was Sir James Berry, at the time head of the British-Serbian hospital and supervisor of six other hospitals. In October, he and his doctor wife May, along with other doctors and nurses, were imprisoned by the authorities. After five months in captivity, the Berrys were released and made their way back to London via Switzerland. As soon as they could leave again, they joined the British Red Cross Unit in Romania and Russia.[295]

Clarence also received disquieting news about Fritz Mader, the young friend who had alerted him to the rock engravings in the Val Fontanalba in the first place. The Italian police had visited his parents in Tende and had found correspondence that compromised Fritz. They did not arrest him, but he decided it was in his own interest to leave Tende and return to Germany. 'I cannot believe that Fritz Mader was a spy', wrote Clarence to Burnat on 25 October 1915. 'He was well thought of by the Italian officers, he had permission to photograph everywhere, he knew the Maritime Alps very well, he worked hard for Baedeker and he often wrote for the Alpine Club. All this naturally meant that he wrote about passages, roads, summits, etc. But I am convinced that he did everything for the sake of geography. But who knows? The espionage system has been so well organised.'

Without the steady supply of British goods to Bordighera, Christmas 1915 was a sparse affair. Clarence's Christmas postcard, naturally promoting Esperanto, bore the words 'In wartime, there's no turkey or plum pudding.'

Clarence made it to Casterino again in 1916 but, as he told Sommier, his peace was shattered by labourers 'damming the lakes for electric works and alas! spoiling our quiet valleys, and there are workmen everywhere . . . It has been very cold here, and it will not rain, there are hardly any flowers and the grass is short, and our vegetables will not grow. It seems as if everything is at war. And so many of my malgari [cow-herd] young friends are away, and 2 are dispersi [missing] killed or prisoners – who knows?'[296]

Once back in Bordighera, Clarence busied himself with philanthropy and volunteer aid. He worked for the Red Cross; he rolled bandages and made slippers – and presumably caught up with his knitting; he collected medicinal and aromatic plants to sell in benefit of the Red Cross;

he made little bags that he filled with sphagnum, a moss, to apply to wounds – apparently one of the best cures – but complained that no one wanted to collect the moss without payment; and he visited the sick and comforted the weary. He described to Edward, not without a certain macabre humour, one of his visits to the sick: 'Mrs Bonsignore had [her] finger poisoned by a white-thorn spine (probably other poison getting into wound) till at last the finger was cut off & we talked nearly all the time of this cheerful subject, but washed it down with some good wine, while we gazed at the relic of her finger & bone carefully preserved in her purse.'

He turned his museum over to convalescing soldiers, and noted to Alberto Pelloux that there were army horses in the public garden, and that the Victoria Hall and the Casino were full of the wounded. 'What a good thing it is to see useless or mischievous places being turned to good account', he said censoriously. Ever since his first visit to the casino in Monte Carlo, he had loathed gambling and the harm it did.

'We have over 500 refugees! What are we to do to help them to live and be clothed and *work*, which is the most important, if they are not to follow the example of the Bordighotti and become thieves? I really do not know if our unpatriotic town will do its duty or *is worthy* to have these people . . . We shall all be glad when this night is over and the day breaks, *as it must some day*.' Clarence had no patience with the *dolce far niente* attitude of the locals. In his opinion, everyone, man, woman, and child should pitch in.

He was constantly aware of the sad condition of the refugees. 'They seem to have nothing, most of them', he told Edward Berry, 'but a few had a sack & I saw one man with 2 fowls, poor things. What would Albrecht [Adolph Angst] think of his hotel becoming a fowl-house? How they can all be fed, clothed etc. I know not . . .' Then he changed his tune: 'I am coining money!! Sold my olives, picked up by ourselves for 67.20 and I suppose they have not half fallen yet.'

By March 1917, Clarence was worrying about whether he would be able go to Casa Fontanalba that summer, whether he could hire a mule to carry provisions, whether there would be any provisions to carry. He did find the mule and provisions, he did go to Casa Fontanalba, and so did many others. Thirty people – botanists, soldiers and Pollini relations – signed the visitors' book that year.

At the end of 1917, Clarence described the scene in Bordighera to Alberto Pelloux, 'On Monday we had a distribution of Xmas presents to the Italian hospital patients, and on Xmas day I went to see our Tommies eating at the H. Angst. They had not eaten such a good meal for 3 years. The wounded from the front are coming here and Bordighera is quite full of men and movement. What a change.' This feeling of movement was a tonic for Clarence, and energised him. He was 75 years old, and in his correspondence during the war years, he never mentions sickness or aches and pains.

The enormous Hotel Angst was already in a dilapidated state when Ezio Benigni took this photo in about 1910. BibCiv.

CYTISUS SESSILIFOLIUS L.

*Papilionacea.*
*Cytisus sessifolius*
(L)
*coast form*

Clarence made this watercolour on 12 July 1918, just five days before he died. His note on the back reads 'This plant in the mountains has a very different aspect to the same by the coast. It is a low compact bush very much branched with great quantity of flowers, and is a very striking feature of the hillsides.' UniGen.

# CHAPTER EIGHTEEN

# THE BALCONY

ENOUGH MULES AND PROVISIONS WERE ON HAND to allow Clarence, Luigi, Mercede and Maddalena to return to Casa Fontanalba in the summer of 1918. Life in Casterino resumed its customary rhythm: gardening, painting, botanising, a little fossicking around for engravings. People came to visit: a clutch of four Englishwomen in mid-June, an Italian family at the end of the month.

Doctor Boris Emanuele signed the *Casa Fontanalba Visitors' Book* on 17 July. Alas, this was not a social call; he was there to sign Clarence's death certificate.

The following day, neighbours from the valley streamed into the house to pay their respects, and Luigi wrote a heart-breaking memorial in the visitors' book.

> Your own Luigi, who for almost 24 years lived happy and proud in being your companion, hopes that he has been of service to you. He always tried to follow all your desires and begs pardon if he sometimes failed.
>
> Good soul, rest in peace. Rare among the rare, soul of virtue and honesty, I lose you in the flesh but never in the spirit. I shall always remember our journeys, the pleasant and unpleasant things shared in various circumstances. I shall remember your holy and kindly thoughts, the way you showed me to follow, the good you always did me. And if one day we meet afresh, I shall be most happy to start again and to go through another life with you.
>
> Farewell, or better, till we meet again, Luigi.

Luigi could not leave it at that and made three additions:

> ii. I add your dear 'Casa Fontanalba' where you lived more happily and contented than an emperor, among your mountains, your prehistoric rock engravings and especially your much-beloved flowers which long occupied your thoughts to the profit of mankind, throwing light on them in scientific works and in poetry too. Till we meet again, your Gigi.

I:  Il tuo Luigi, che da quasi 24 anni visse felice ed orgoglioso d'essere tuo compagno, spera d'esserti stato utile, ha sempre provato di assecondare tutti i tuoi desideri, e se qualche volta ha mancato, ti chiede perdono.

Riposa in pace, anima buona, rara fra le rari, di virtù, d'onestà, ti perdo materialmente ma mai moralmente, ricorderò sempre i nostri viaggi, i piaceri e dispiaceri diviso nelle varie circostanze, ricorderò le tue idee sante e benevoli, ricorderò il cammino che m'indicasti da seguire, il bene che m'hai sempre fatto e se un giorno c'incontreremo nuovamente, sarò felicissimo di ricominciare e continuare una nuova vita con te.

Addio, o meglio, arrivederci,  L.

II:  Aggiungo la tua cara "Casa Fontanalba," ove vivevi felice e contento più d'un Imperatore, fra i tuoi monti e le rocce colle incisioni preistoriche ed in special modo i tuoi tanto amati fiori, che lungamente occuparono i tuoi pensieri a profitto dell'umanità, illuminandoli scientificamente e anche poeticamente. Tis la rendo, via Gigi

III:  "Capi" memoras nian honecon

Luigi Pollini's tribute to Clarence in the *Casa Fontanalba Visitors' Book*.

iii. 'Capi' says 'I remember your kindness'. (This was written in Esperanto.)
iv. I include dedications, photographs (one of my father), and a postcard of Casa
Fontanalba as company for you in your coffin, the last time I could see you, 20 July 1918.

Clarence had wanted to be buried in Casterino, but it appears that the authorities insisted he
be buried at the cemetery in Tende. A rumour circulated around the village that Clarence's coffin was filled with stones for the burial in Tende, but that he was, indeed, buried in Casterino.
This rumour is discredited by Luigi's note about seeing him in his coffin. Another of Clarence's
wishes, reported forty years later by Enzo Bernardini, was that he should 'lie forever at Casterino
to be near to the mountains where he had so often walked, and beside his faithful companion,
Miss Alice Campbell.'[297]

Clarence's sudden death immediately plunged the village into more speculation, with mushroom poisoning being the favoured culprit. Fortunately, Edward Berry wrote to Émile Burnat a
week later, detailing the actual circumstances:

24 July, 1918  Villa Monte Verde, Bordighera

My dear Monsieur Burnat,

I very much regret to inform you that my dear uncle Clarence Bicknell died at Casa
Fontanalba, Tenda the 17th of this month. I was in Rome at the time and on the 18th I
received a telegram that he was dead.

I went immediately to Val Casterino and we buried him in the cemetery of Tenda on
Monday.

On the 14th of this month, he took a six hour walk and tired himself a little too much
perhaps. On Monday he stayed at home; on Tuesday he did not feel well, and Luigi called
for the doctor from Tenda on Wednesday morning, who examined him minutely and
pronounced that there was nothing to fear.

The same afternoon he went to rest on a chaise longue on the balcony in plain view of the
mountains and a quarter of an hour later he ceased to live without suffering.

One cannot imagine a better death for him – he had been able to continue his ordinary
occupations up until three days before his death and was full of the joy of living until the
last moment.

His three faithful and affectionate domestics were with him at Casa Fontanalba (Luigi,
Maddalena and Mercede) and you can imagine their grief.

For me he was like a dear father since 1890 and my wife also loved him like a daughter.
Many warm greetings to you and Jean. Your affectionate friend, Edward E. Berry

Clarence on the balcony of the Casa Fontanalba with a rubbing of a rock engraving in his hand, wildflowers at his elbow and Capi at his feet.

# AFTER CLARENCE

Marcus Bicknell

'THE BALCONY' WAS THE END OF CLARENCE'S LIFE, but not the end of his story.

Margaret and Edward Berry were permitted to continue using the Casa Fontanalba, despite the house passing back to the Count Guido d'Alberti della Briga upon Clarence's death, and the Visitors' Book is signed by the Berry family and friends in most years up to 1931. Clarence's will had been established in Britain and was executed there but the Berrys wound up Clarence's estate in Italy. For many years they made sure that the Museo Bicknell, and other Bordighera institutions in which Clarence had played a role, were looked after. They were active in further fundraising for the museum.

Edward Berry died in Rome in 1931. Margaret Berry returned to Taplow in Britain and died there in 1957, not before she gave to Peter Bicknell, the grandson of Clarence's brother Percy, her entire collection of Clarence's diaries, notebooks, sketchbooks, watercolours, personal items, three of Clarence's albums and two similar Berry albums. At Peter's death in 1995 this Bicknell Collection passed to his nephew Marcus who had been organising family trips to the Merveilles and Bordighera in the footsteps of Clarence.

The family collection is not the half of it. It was known and respected that Clarence, with Luigi's help, had found, copied and catalogued 12,000 of the rock engravings in the high mountains of the Mont Bégo area. But in 2013 Marcus started logging Clarence's bequests elsewhere, and the total of his output turns out to be of an unimaginable quantity. Thirty-six museums and universities in a dozen countries and nine private owners have more than 38,000 of Clarence's rubbings of rock engravings, watercolours of flowers or landscapes, albums, letters, diaries, notebooks, sketchbooks, photos and personal items. The complete list is published online. Genoa University alone has 3,165 sheets of copies of rock engravings, over 10,000 plant samples and 3,428 botanical watercolours. Clarence was keen that his findings, material or recorded on paper, be available to other students; the quantity and quality of his legacy continues to be appreciated and looked after.

Clarence Bicknell has been known from Genoa to Bordighera primarily as an archaeologist; he remains the researcher/cataloguer of reference for the rock engravings of the Mont Bégo area. The research into his life leading up to his 2018 centenary and this biography has reminded people of his achievements as a botanist and has revealed what a good artist he was. In 2017 the Fitzwilliam Museum, Cambridge University, rediscovered the seven vellum-bound albums (which Peter Bicknell had given them in 1980) and the extraordinary watercolours of flowers, stories and Victorian whimsy they contain. Our commissioning of photographs of some of them enabled Fitzwilliam experts to see them for the first time and fall in love with them. The images will be featured in the Fitzwilliam's 2018 botanical art exhibition. Greetings cards and a Clarence Bicknell 2019 calendar will contribute to the celebration of the centenary of his death.

The efforts since 2013 to bring Clarence's work to a wider public are based on the conviction that Clarence's intangible cultural heritage is worth preserving and spreading, while his tangible cultural heritage (like the Museo Bicknell for which fund-raising appeals are on-going, and the Casa Fontanalba, which is not open to the public) is worthy of support and recognition. As a result, Clarence is better known in 2018 than he was in 1918.

# ACKNOWLEDGEMENTS

IN 2012, MARCUS BICKNELL, Clarence's great-great nephew and guardian since 1995 of the family's collection of Clarence's art and books, retired from full-time work and found himself in need of a captivating project. He decided to bring Clarence Bicknell to a wider public – and to celebrate the centenary of his death – with the publication of this biography; a film *The Marvels of Clarence Bicknell*; exhibitions; and a reproduction of Clarence's *Casa Fontanalba Visitors' Book*. Having set up an excellent research-pooling website and an association, he then put together a team.

It is to this team that I owe my deepest debt. We are six: Marcus, the driving force; Susie Bicknell, researcher, specialising in Clarence's art; Graham Avery, mountain walker, botanist, writer and researcher; Helen Blanc-Francard, landscape designer, writer, picture researcher; Christopher Chippindale, archaeologist, author and Clarence specialist; and myself, the principal writer. Biography is usually a lonely profession, but being a part of this team took care of that. Its members offered me encouragement when my spirits flagged and new material when I got stuck. I cannot imagine working with a kinder, more competent, more supportive group of people.

Marcus is my fourth cousin once-removed, and I found him in August 2000 when researching my book on Phiz, Clarence's uncle. Already by April 2001 we were corresponding about the Vallée des Merveilles and Bordighera, but it was not until I finished my book on Bodoni in early 2014 that I got cracking on Clarence. I spent many weeks, on many different trips, from my home in the U.S. working with Marcus and Susie near London, poring over the material in the Bicknell collection. We talked about Clarence all day, every day, arguing about the details and mysteries in Clarence's life. Marcus was unflagging in his research; he left no stone unturned. Susie took on many special projects that I have incorporated into the manuscript. By the way, their hospitality is world class.

Graham Avery is a wise and scrupulous researcher and writer, and has held me to a high standard. His essays on many aspects of Clarence's life can be found on the Clarence Bicknell website,[298] essays to which I have turned time and again. His discovery of Clarence's letters to Burnat, has led to much of the narrative of the second half of Clarence's life. Without them, I would have been fumbling in the dark, a prey to speculation. He has contributed notably to recent work on Clarence.

It was through walking in the Alps in 2008 that Graham encountered Clarence's name in the Vallée des Merveilles. His interest in alpine flora led him to investigate Reginald Farrer's publications on botanical excursions in Europe in the period 1899 to 1913, including the book *Among The Hills: A Book of Joy in High Places* (1911) in which Farrer recounted a tour of the Alps in 1910, including a visit to Val Casterino to meet an enigmatic un-named person. Wishing to elucidate this, Graham googled the search-terms 'Reginald Farrer' and 'Clarence Bicknell' and found that the Casa Fontanalba visitors' book – of which a transcript had been posted online by Marcus– does indeed have Farrer's signature for 19 July 1910. Graham contacted Marcus, and began his research into Clarence's botanical activities. Realising that dried specimens of flowers collected by Clarence are to be found in herbaria in many countries, he wrote to Geneva's Botanical Garden which conserves the herbarium of the Swiss botanist Émile Burnat, including specimens contributed by Clarence. Geneva informed Graham that they had in their archives nearly seven hundred letters and postcards from Clarence to Burnat!

After discovering this bounty, Graham transcribed and published a selection of about three hundred, which are quoted frequently in this biography. He also found 31 letters from Clarence to the Italian botanist Stefano Sommier in the library of the University of Florence and, following up the fact that the visitors' book displays the names of three botanists from Bristol who visited Casa Fontanalba, he discovered five letters from Clarence in the archives of Bristol University and the Bristol Naturalists' Society. To have had access, thanks to Graham, to so much primary material has been a singular blessing.

Helen Blanc-Francard is a brilliant photo researcher, whose discoveries have lent a visual, and even aural, dimension to the book. She is uncannily able to feel her way into a scene, and her illustrated messages have always enlivened my job and my day. Some of the brighter passages in the biography have been snatched wholesale (with her permission) from her correspondence.

Christopher Chippindale, a devoted student of and writer about Bicknell since the 1980s at Cambridge University, provided archaeological expertise to the effort, and his work on Clarence and the rock engravings in the Alpes Maritimes has been invaluable.

In Britain I trod Clarence's path from Herne Hill to Cambridge to his first church postings in the UK before he left for Bordighera. I was greatly helped by the staff of Trinity College Cambridge; the Rev. Katy Hacker Hughes at St Paul's Walworth, London; the Rev. Andy Ackroyd, warden Jan Wattleworth and Janice Bradley at St Peters Stoke-upon-Tern, Shropshire; Liz Young and Karen Young, Shropshire Archives in Shrewsbury; John Rooney, Archivist at the University of Southampton for information on Broadlands; Philip Bye of the East Sussex Record Office at The Keep; and Martyn Webster, who alerted us to the diaries of Clarence's brother Sidney there; and Mark Bicknell (Marcus's first cousin) who provided information on Elhanan, the *Whalers*, and the photo of the bust of Clarence's mother Lucinda.

In early 2014, I settled into research at the Museo Bicknell. It was the coldest winter in 55 years and I needed and enjoyed support (including a heavy down jacket and a hot water bottle) from the friends I made there. I am indebted to the Museum's director Dr Daniela Gandolfi and to her colleagues at the Istituto Internazionale di Studi Liguri, Dr Elena Riscosso, Dr Giovanni Russo, Franca Porrà, Dr Marta Garulli and Dr Bruna di Paoli. Special thanks go to Bruna for prying me away from book research and leading me into the hills to follow in Clarence's footsteps in the beautiful countryside surrounding Bordighera.

Giuseppe Bessone, architect, art collector, Bicknell specialist and for me the spirit of Bordighera, has been an immense source of facts, encouragement and hospitality. Many others in Bordighera also deserve my thanks, including Pier Rossi; Gisella Merello; Luca Moreno; Maria Pia Luly Jones; Marco Re; Simona Beghelli of the Biblioteca Civica Internazionale; and Elisabetta Gozzini. A few kilometers along the coast towards France are two of the world's most famous gardens where I found friendship and botanical intelligence from Carolyn Hanbury (Hanbury Gardens) and Ursula Salghetti Drioli Piacenza (Boccanegra Gardens). Carolyn's deliciously warm kitchen and good humour brightened my way as I trudged along. At the Università degli Studi di Genova, where Clarence's archaeological field notebooks and huge collections of pressed flowers and botanical watercolours are held, Professor Mauro Mariotti, Director of Genoa University's Department for the Earth, Environment and Life Sciences, and a prolific writer on botanical issues, has been a vital source of images and information.

Others who helped the project are Pierre Machu of the Institut National du Patrimoine in Paris; the staff at the Musée des Merveilles in Tende, especially the director Charles Turcat and Silvia Sandrone; the staff of Parc National du Mercantour; Conseil Départemental des Alpes-Maritime in Nice; Mairie de Tende; researchers in Tende like Françoise Villain Rinieri and Nadine Valentini; Dominique Aviotti of the Auberge Val Casterino; and André and Natalie Boulanger (and his parents Michel and Elise) in the Hotel des Mélèzes. Dr Robert Hearn and Dr Raffaella Bruzzone, teaching and researching at the University of Nottingham and the Università degli Studi di Genova, buoyed us up with their enthusiasm for Clarence's botanical art and his place in the geo-history of the Alpine region between Italy and France.

Special thanks go to the rock engraving guide Franck Panza who escorted me and my cousin Petra Molloy to the Casa Fontanalba, unfortunately closed, but at least we saw the house in its lovely setting, and then up into the Val Fontanalba for what was one of the most memorable days of our lives. It was 1 June and the park had just opened for the season. We hiked up through fields of gentians, up and up, until the engravings began appearing. Franck pointed them out, and still we climbed higher until he had to cut steps in the snow so that we could see even more. Everywhere was the sound of melting water rushing beneath the snow as the thaw took hold. The sky was bright blue, the air was crystal clear, and we understood the magic of the place.

I thank the Hingham, MA, Public Library; the British Museum (Natural History) for Baroness von Taube's letters; Christopher Mills at the Royal Botanic Gardens, Kew; the Fitzwilliam Museum and the enthusiasm there of Hettie Ward, Emma Darbyshire and Camay Chapman-Cameron; authors Michael Nelson (the Riviera); Brian Green (Herne Hill); Mark Howard (whales); Selby Whittingham (Turner's art); and Maddalena Cataldi (archaeology).

Special thanks to the collections where Graham Avery found so much new material: Oxford University Herbaria; the Conservatory and Botanical Garden of Geneva; the Botanical Library of the University of Florence; the Botanic Garden of Meise, Belgium; London Metropolitan Archives; Bristol Naturalists' Society.

The active team of Esperanto experts has been headed by Olga Kerzjuk at the British Library; Professor Humphrey Tonkin of the University of Hartford, CT; Leland Bryant Ross; Nicola Minnaja; Bill Chapman; Angela Tellier; Wera Blanke; and the late Paul Gubbins.

Nick Humez, my indexer, and Sally Salvesen, the book's editor and production director, have added their invaluable expertise and polish. I am so grateful to have had such professional support in completing the book. I alone am responsible for errors in translation from French and Italian of the many letters, articles and books I read in those languages.

Deep gratitude goes to my readers: the researchers in the team of six, of course; my children, the writers Toby Lester and Alison Jean Lester; Bruce Kennett for his eagle eye, design sense, and shoulder-to-shoulder encouragement; Diana Phillips, whose knowledge, sense of style, and ability to nose out clichés and anachronisms is paramount; Marcia and Geoff Thompson, who provided laughter, great meals and a perfect writer's refuge, complete with swimmable pond at the end of their lane on Cape Cod. My friends Sarah deLima, Mary Ann Frye and Michael MacPherson have kept me sane by prying me away from my desk and taking me for bracing walks.

It is to Marcus and Susie Bicknell that I owe my deepest gratitude for their inspiration, drive and support. We have had so much fun.

V.L.

*April 2018*

# NOTES

1. Valerie Lester, the author of this biography, also wrote *Phiz: The Man Who Drew Dickens* (2004), in which she proved that Phiz was Clarence's cousin and not his uncle. His natural mother, Kate, permitted her mother to adopt him to avoid a scandal.

2. Algernon Sidney Bicknell, *Autobiography*. This handwritten volume can be found at The Keep, the East Sussex County Archives. All quotations from Sidney Bicknell come from the autobiography.

3. Margaret Berry, Biographical sketch. Bicknell collection.

4. Patricia M. Jenkyns, 'The Bicknells of Herne Hill', May 1986. Bicknell collection.

5. Edgar Browne, *Phiz and Dickens*. London: Nisbet, 1913, p. 58.

6. C.G. Browne and A.S. Bicknell, *Notes to Assist the Future Authors of the Huguenot Family of Browne*. Handwritten manuscript, 1903, p. 93.

7. E. Browne, p. 56.

8. E. Browne, p. 57.

9. E. Browne, p. 59.

10. G.B. Briano, *Vita esperantista di Genova e Liguria dal 1900 al 1975*. Liguria: Sabatelli, 1976, p. 52.

11. The National Archives. These two letters are in the William Etty letter collection, held at the York City Art Gallery. C1810-46 (150). Ref. EC.

12 A.S. Bicknell, letter to *The Athenaeum,* 9 January 1909.

13. In Katherine Baetger, *British Paintings in the Metropolitan Museum of Art, 1577–1875*. New York: Metropolitan Museum, 2009, p. 233.

14. The bust is in the collection of Mark Bicknell.

15. Robert S. Levine, ed., *The New Cambridge Companion to Herman Melville*. New York: Cambridge University Press, 2014, p. 181.

16. Michael Shelden, *Melville in Love*. New York: Harper Collins, 2016, p. 116.

17. Hull University Whale Fishery History Project database.

18. Katharine Sim, *David Roberts R.A. 1796–1864*. London: Quartet, 1984, p. 291.

19. *The Gentleman's Magazine*. Vol. 211. July–December 1861, p, 318.

20. *The Christian Reformer,* New Series, Vol. XVII. London: James Whitfield, 1861, p. 378.

21. Sim, p. 311.

22. *The Christian Reformer*, Vol. XVIII. 1862, p. 56.

23. *The Art-Journal:* New Series, Vol. I. London: James S. Virtue, p. 46.

24. Entry for Clarence Bicknell in *Alumni Cantabrigienses,* Part 2, vol. i. Cambridge Univ. Press, 1922.

25. Sim, p. 312.

26. *The Fine Arts Quarterly Review*. London: Chapman and Hall, 1863, p, 420.

27. *Art Journal of London*. London: Virtue, 1863, p. 121.

28. *Art Journal,* p. 121.

29. *Fine Arts,* p. 122.

30. Christie's sale 7235. British Art on Paper Including *The Blue Rigi* by J.M.W. Turner, R.A. 5 June 2006. London, King Street.

31. *Fine Arts,* p. 420.

32. John Pemble, *The Mediterranean Passions; Victorians and Edwardians in the South*. London: Faber, 1987, p. 55.

33. Obituary in *The Times*. See trinitycollegechapel.com/about/memorials/brasses/lightfoot/

34. Entry by Fenton John Anthony Hort on Joseph Barber Lightfoot in *Dictionary of National Biography*, 1885–1900, Vol. 33.

35. Email from Jonathan Smith, archivist, Trinity College, 28 Feb. 2017.

36. Geoffrey R. Treloar. *Lightfoot the Historian: The Nature and Role of History in the Life and Thought of J.B. Lightfoot*. Tübingen: Mohr Siebeck, 1998, p. 39.

37. Treloar, p. 41.

38. Susan Maitland, 'Clarence Bicknell e la sua attività pastorale in Inghilterra (1866–1876)'. In *Clarence*

*Bicknell: La Vita e le Opere.* Eds. Daniela Gandolfi and Mario Marcenaro. Bordighera: Istituto Internazionale di Studi Liguri [IISL], 2003, p. 29.

39. *Church of the People and The People's Magazine,* May, 1857, to December 1858. London: Kent, 1859, p. 491.

40. Marcus Donovan, *A History of S. Paul's, Lorrimore Square and S. Agnes', Kennington Park.* London: 1930, p. 16.

41. Donovan, p. 26.

42. Maitland, p. 30.

43. Donovan, p. 15.

44. Maitland, p. 28.

45. *The Church Association Monthly Intelligencer,* July 1868.

46. Margaret Hardy in the *Shropshire Magazine,* undated article, c. 1950.

47. C. Milner, 'Some nineteenth-century post-Tractarian clergy in the Archdeaconry of Salop, Diocese of Lichfield with particular reference to the *Societas Sancti Spiritus* 1869–79, its members and its founder, the Rev. Rowland William Corbet M.A. Rector of Stoke upon Tern, Salop, 1869–1901', 1972, p. 70. Thesis for M.Phil degree, Leeds University, 1972.

48. Hardy, *Shropshire Magazine.*

49. Maitland, p. 32.

50. Milner, pp. 118–120.

51. Minute Book of the Guild of the Holy Redeemer (being the Stoke-upon-Tern branch of the Church of England Temperance Society.) The minute book is held in Shrewsbury at the Shropshire archives.

52. Herman Bicknell, *Háfiz of Shiraz.* London: Trübner, 1875, p. xii.

53. Rolland Hein, *George MacDonald: Victorian Mythmaker.* Eugene: Wipf and Stock, 2014, p. 35.

54. Carolyn W. de la L. Oulton, *Let the Flowers Go: A Life of Mary Cholmondeley.* London: Chatto & Pickering, 2009.

55. This information comes from the Broadlands Archives at the University of Southampton.

56. Emilia Russell Gurney. *Letters of Emilia Russell Gurney.* London: Nisbet, 1902, p. 144.

57. *Proceedings of the Society for Psychical Research.* Vol. XIII. 1897–1898. London: Kegan Paul, 1898, p. 39.

58. *Psychical Research,* Vol. 4, 1886–1887. London: Trübner, 1887.

59. University of Southampton, Hartley Library. Broadlands Archives. [16/122 JMR] MS62 BR49/4/7

60. Giovanni Battista Semeria, *Storia Ecclesiastica Di Genova E Della Liguria Dai Tempi Apostolici Sino All'anno 1838.* Genoa: Canfari, 1838, pp. 236–240.

61. This reference and most of the others that follow in this chapter come from Clarence Bicknell's diary of his first season in Bordighera during 1878/9. The diary itself is missing, but the transcript by Libby Peachey is in the Bicknell collection. Unfortunately,

this is the only diary to detail his daily existence, although he did write an account of his trip to Egypt in 1889/90.

62. sotonopedia.wikidot.com/page-browse:fanshawe-reverend-charles

63. Giuseppe E. Bessone. 'Tra Neogotico e Cottages. L'architettura "inglese" della Riviera'. In: *La Vita ...,* p. 217.

64. Bessone, p. 219.

65. Mario Marcenaro, 'Bordighera e il Museo-Biblioteca dell'Istituto Internazionale di Studi Liguri da Clarence Bicknell al rinnovamento attuale.' Bordighera: IISL, 1990, p. 11.

66. Umberto Folena, 'Giacomo Viale, "U fratin" servo di Dio.' *Avenire.it,* 8 July 2016.

67. Andrea Folli and Gisella Merello, *Charles Garnier et la Riviera.* Genoa: Erga, 2000, p. 47.

68. For details of Clarence's period of service at All Saints Church, including his entries in the Chaplain's Book, and for the history of the church from 1868 to 1911, see G. Avery, 'Clarence Bicknell in the Archives of All Saints' Church, Bordighera'.

69. Louise Jopling, *Twenty Years of my Life. 1867–1887.* London: Bodley Head, 1925.

70. Margaret Berry. Article in Bicknell collection.

71. *Journal de Bordighera,* 26 February 1914.

72. C.B., *Book of Guests in Esperanto.* Bicknell collection.

73. C.B. sketchbook. Bicknell collection.

74. Università degli Studi di Genova, DISTAV.

75. Edward Berry's biographical sketch. Bicknell collection.

76. Jopling.

77. Frederick Fitzroy Hamilton, *Bordighera and the Western Riviera.* London: Stanford, 1883, p. 270.

78. C.B. to Arturo Issel, 1897-12-27. In *La Vita ...,* p. 77.

79. C.B. to Arturo Issel, 27.12.1897. In *La Vita ...,* p. 75.

80. C.B. to Arturo Issel, 20.11.1898. In *La Vita ...,* p. 75.

81. Claude Monet to Alice Hoschedé in *Monet by himself.* Ed. Richard Kendall. Trans. Bridget Strevens Romer. London: Little, Brown, 1995, p. 108.

82. *Monet by Himself,* p. 108.

83. Paul Hayes Tucker, *Claude Monet, Life and Art.* New Haven and London: Yale, 1995, p. 119.

84. *Monet by Himself,* p. 109.

85. Ed. Mrs Harry Coghill. *The Autobiography and Letters of Mrs M.O.W. Oliphant.* Edinburgh & London: Blackwood, 1899, p. 315.

86. Richard H. Reis, *George MacDonald.* Woodbridge, CT: Twayne, 1972, p.23.

87. Hein, p. 327.

88. Hein, p. 328.

89. Angela R. Barone, 'The Oak Tree and the Olive Tree: The True Dream of Eva Gore-Booth'. Dublin City University, PhD thesis, 1990.

90. Ronald MacDonald, *From a Northern Window.* Escondido, CA: Sunrise, 1989.

# NOTES

91. *The Spectator,* Vol. 95, Oct. 7, 1905, p. 526.

92. Greville MacDonald, *George MacDonald and His Wife.* London: Allen & Unwin, 1924, p. 509.

93. 'George MacDonald at Bordighera.' *The Critic and Good Literature,* V, 2 Feb. 1884, pp. 54–55.

94. Hein, p. 338.

95. Linda Villari. *Soggiorno a Bordighera.* London: Allen, 1893, p. 28.

96. Greville MacDonald, p. 508.

97. Hein, p. 327.

98. Hein, p. 339.

99. Hein, p. 338.

100. Greville MacDonald, p. 558.

101. C.B. to Baroness von Taube, 1912-6-10. This item comes from a collection of autograph letters written by Bicknell to the baroness during the period 1909–1914. They are held at the Natural History Museum in London, call number: NHM, 92 BIC.

102. See G. Avery, 'Clarence Bicknell and Botany: an appreciation' for an account of Clarence's work in this field, his botanical publications and friends, and how his experience as a botanist contributed to his work as an archaeologist.

103. Susan Orlean, *The Orchid Thief.* New York: Ballantine, 2009, p. 68.

104. John Traherne Moggridge, *Contributions to the flora of Mentone, and to a winter flora of the Riviera, including the coast from Marseilles to Genoa.* London: Reeve, 1871.

105. *Journal of Botany, British and Foreign,* Vol XXII, 1885, p. 382.

106. *The Gardeners' Chronicle,* Vol. XXIV, 12 December 1885, p. 754.

107. C.B., *Flowering Plants and Ferns of the Riviera and Neighbouring Mountains.* London: Trübner, 1885, p. viii.

108. Villari, p. 33.

109. Honoré Arduino, *Flore Analytique du Département des Alpes-Maritimes.* Menton: Bertrand & Queyrot, 1879. Clarence's personal copy of this book is in the Bicknell collection.

110. C. Bicknell, botanical watercolours at University of Genoa, DISTAV.

111. C.B. to Burnat. 1896-06-22.

112. See G. Avery, '"Cher Monsieur": Clarence Bicknell's correspondence with Emile Burnat 1886–1917,' for transcripts of about 300 of the 690 letters and postcards held in the archives of Geneva's Botanical Garden (*Conservatoire et Jardin Botaniques de la Ville de Genève*).

113. C.B. to Burnat, 1885-04-28.

114. John Briquet and François Cavillier, *Émile Burnat: autobiographie publiée avec un étude sur le botaniste et son oeuvre, des souvenirs e documents divers Émile Burnat.* Geneva: Conservatoire Botanique, 1922, p. 99.

115. C.B. to Burnat, 1885-04-28.

116. G. Avery, '"Cher Monsieur"...,' p. 5.

117. C.B. to Burnat, 1886-09-03.

118 Quentin Groom in G. Avery, '"Cher Monsieur"...,' p. 7.

119. C.B. to Burnat, 1886-12-28.

120. M. Berry, 1918 biographical sketch.

121. For fuller information, see G. Avery, 'Bristol Botanists at Casa Fontanalba.'

122. See G. Avery, 'Clarence Bicknell and *Pimpinella bicknellii.*'

123. Fielding-Druce Herbarium in the Oxford University Herbaria.

124. Alessandro Bartoli, *The British Colonies in the Italian Riviera in '800 and '900.* Savona: Ferraris, 2008, p. 131.

125. Marcenaro, 'Bordighera e il Museo-Biblioteca', p. 28.

126. Email from Gozzini family, Bordighera, 2016.

127. Humphrey Tonkin, 'Clarence Bicknell, Philanthropist and Person of Ideas.' A talk given to the Twilight Club, Hartford, Connecticut, 2014, p. 2.

128. *Alberi di Liguria, monumenti viventi della natura.* Genoa: Erga, 2003, p. 92.

129. Pierre Damon, *Pasteur.* Paris: Fayard, 1995.

130. Patrice Lebré, *Louis Pasteur.* Baltimore: John Hopkins, 1994.

131. Daniela Gandolfi, 'La Raccolta Archeologica di Clarence Bicknell'. *La Vita . . . ,* p. 95.

132. Bernardini, p. 12.

133. Founded by Louisa Boyce (1822–1891), a visitor to Bordighera. See http://www.studivaldesi.org/dizio-nario/evan_det.php?evan_id=33

134. Marcenaro, p. 26.

135. Arturo Issel in Enzo Bernardini, *Clarence Bicknell; Edward e Margaret Berry.* Bordighera: IISL, 1972, p. 12.

136. Gisella Merello, *L'immagine turistica di Bordighera attraverso le cartoline illustrate e la letteratura.* Bordighera: IISL, Lions Club, 1995, p. 25.

137. Arturo Issel, *Il Terremoto del 1887 in Liguria.* Rome: Tipografia Nazionale di Reggiani & soci, 1888, p. 106.

138. Domenico Capponi, *Ricordo del terremoto in Liguria del 23 febbraio 1887.* Genoa: Tipografia della Gioventù, 1887.

139. Kathy Triggs, *The Stars and the Stillness: A Portrait of George MacDonald.* Cambridge: Lutterworth, 1986, p. 25.

140. Issel, p. 128.

141. C.B. to Burnat, 1887-03-08.

142. C.B. to Burnat, 1888-01-20.

143. C.B. to Burnat, 1888-04-25.

144. C.B., *Journal of Botany,* 1891.

145. C.B. to Burnat, 1889-04-18.

146. 'The Egypt Diary leans heavily on quotations from Clarence's handwritten and illustrated Egypt diary in the Bicknell collection.

147. C.B. to Burnat, 1890-01-12.

148. C.B. to Burnat, 1889-04-03.

149. Notice in *Journal de Bordighera*, 11 November 1909, p. 4.

150. M. Berry, 1918 biographical sketch.

151. C.B. to Burnat, 1896-03-01.

152. Pierre de Montfort of Tours (fourteenth century) in a letter to his wife. In Gabriella Parodi, 'Il laboratorio paleontologico di Arturo Issel e le lettere di Clarence Bicknell.' *Ligures: rivista di archeologia, storia, arte e cultura ligure*. Bordighera: IISL, 2003, p. 273.

153. Clarence Bicknell, *A Guide to the Prehistoric Rock Engravings of the Italian Maritime Alps*. Bordighera: Bessone, 1913, p. 25.

154. Parodi, p. 273.

155. Edmond Blanc. 'Études sur les sculptures préhistoriques du Val d'Enfer'. In Enzo Bernardini, *Monte Bego: storia di una montana*. Club Alpino Italiano. Bordighera: 1971.

156. Christopher Chippindale, *A High Way to Heaven: Clarence Bicknell and the 'Vallée de Merveilles.'* Tende: Musée Départmental des Merveilles, 1998, p.32.

157. C.B., *A Guide ...*, p. 14.

158. C.B., *A Guide ...*, p. 14.

159. Giovanni Russo, 'La Biblioteca personale di Clarence Bicknell. Indagini bibliografiche nelle biblioteche di Bordighera.' *Ligures*. Bordighera: IISL, 2014/2017, pp. 13–14.

160. C.B. to Burnat, 1897-06-01.

161. C.B., *A Guide ...*, p. 22.

162. C.B. to Issel, 1897-09-16. In *La Vita ...*, p. 71.

163. C.B. to Burnat, 1897-08-04.

164. Reginald Farrer, *Among the Hills: A Book of Joy in High Places*. London: Headley Brothers, 1911, p. xx.

165. Christopher Chippindale, 'Clarence Bicknell: archaeology and science in the 19th century.' *Antiquity*. LVIII, 1984, p. 185.

166. Chippindale, 'Clarence Bicknell: archaeology ...', p. 186.

167. C.B., *A Guide ...*, p. 37.

168. C.B., *A Guide ...*, p. 96.

169. M. Berry, biographical sketch.

170. C.B., *A Guide ...*, p. 25.

171. C.B. to Burnat, 1897-08-04.

172. *Les Inscriptions Préhistoriques des Environs de Tende par M. Fritz Mader*. Annales de la Société des lettres, sciences et arts des Alpes-Maritimes, Nice, 1903, pp. 15–18.

173. C.B. to Burnat, 1900-04-27.

174. Emanuele Celesia, 'Escursioni alpine.' In *Bulletin of the Ministry of Public Education*, May 1886.

175. C.B., *A Guide ...*, p. 22.

176. C.B., *A Guide ...*, p. 22.

177. C.B., *A Guide ...*, p. 26.

178. Chippindale, *A High Way ....*

179. C.B., *The Prehistoric Rock Engravings in the Italian Maritime Alps*. Bordighera: Gibelli, 1902.

180. C.B. to Arturo Issel, 1897-11-18. In *La Vita ...*, p. 72.

181. C.B., *A Guide ...*, p. 26.

182. British Museum. G51/dc10, museum number 1897,1229.1.

183. C.B., *A Guide ...*, p. 24.

184. 'Clarence Bicknell on some rock drawings at Val Fontanalba (Italy).' Proceedings of the Society of Antiquaries of London. Volume 17, June 1899, pp. 43–50.

185. Christopher Chippindale, *A High Way ...*, p. 44.

186. C.B. to Burnat, 1899-01-26.

187. C.B., *A Guide ...*, p. 27.

188. Bicknell family collection.

189. M. Berry to Rosa Fanshawe Walker, 1901-08-15. Bicknell collection.

190. C.B. to Pelloux, 1902. C.B.'s letters to Alberto Pelloux are housed in the archives of the International Institute of Ligurian Studies in Bordighera.

191. C.B. to Pelloux, 1903-02-05.

192. Arturo Issel, 'Le rupi scolpite nelle alte valli delle Alpi Marittime.' *Bullettino di Paletnologia Italiana*, Anno XXVII. Oct.–Dec. 1901. N.i., pp. 10–12.

193. C.B., *A Guide ...*, p. 39.

194. *A Guide ...*, p. 30.

195. *A Guide ...*, p. 70.

196. *A Guide ...*, p. 73.

197. In Pierre Machu, 'Clarence Bicknell, Émile Cartailhac et les autres ... au pays des Merveilles.' *Antiquités Nationales*. 2006–7, vol. 38, p. 210.

198. C.B. to Burnat, 1898-04-17.

199. C.B. to Burnat, 1898-12-18.

200. See G. Avery, 'The Burnat/Bicknell Nature Reserve in the Marguareis Natural Park'.

201. *Journal de Bordighera*, 8 Feb. 1900.

202. *Journal de Bordighera*, 1 March 1900.

203. C.B. to Sommier, 1904-04-10.

204. C.B., 'Una gita primaverile in Sardegna.' *Bulletino della Società botanica italiana*. Florence: 1904, pp. 193–202.

205. C.B. to Burnat, 1904-07-24.

206. C.B. to Pelloux, 1903? IISL, Doc. 10.

207. C.B. to Pelloux 1905-10?-24. Doc. 3.

208. Sir Arthur Evans to C.B., Archivio IISL, Bordighera. Fondo Bicknell-Berry, 2.

209. C.B., *A Guide ...*, p. xi.

210. C.B.'s letters to Cartailhac are in the Archives de l'Association Louis BEGOUËN, Laboratoire de Préhistoire de Pujol (Montesquieu-Avantès - France), Lettres: Clarence BICKNELL à Emile CARTAILHAC. Transcribed by Pierre Machu. Also

on the Clarence Bicknell website, under the heading 'Documents.'

211. Émile Cartailhac, 'La grotte d'Altamira, Espagne. Mea culpa d'un sceptique.' *L'Anthropologie*. 1902. 13, pp. 348–354.

212. Photo: Breuil, Cartailhac (1907).

213. C.B. to Cartailhac, 1907-01-31.

214. C.B. to Cartailhac, 1907-03-09.

215. This and much other useful information about Niaux, Combarelles and Font-de-Gaume, on which I have relied, has been collected by Don Hitchcock, and can be seen on his generous website: donsmaps.com

216. C.B. to Cartailhac, 1907-03-09.

217. Machu, *Antiquités Nationales*, p. 221.

218. C.B. to Cartailhac, 1907-03-13.

219. C.B. to Burnat, 1907-04-03.

220. C.B. to Burnat, 1907-04-26.

221. Merello, *L'immagine...*, p. 25.

222. C.B.'s letters to Ellen Willmott are held at the archives in Berkeley Castle near Stroud, Gloucestershire (www.berkeley-castle.com).

223. Audrey Le Lièvre, *Miss Willmott of Warley Place*. London: Faber & Faber, 2008, p. 122.

224. Le Lièvre, p. 93.

225. *La floro de l'pasinto*. Basel: Geering, 1906.

226. C.B. to Pelloux, 1906-05-08.

227. Livio Mano, ed. *Nel Paese delle Meraviglie. Novel Temp. Quaderno di cultura e studi occitani alpini*. Sampeyre: Soulestrelh, 1990.

228. Incident recounted by Enzo Bernardini in an email to Giuseppe Bessone on 9 June 2016.

229. A summary of research on the identity of Alice Campbell is kept updated at http://www.clarence-bicknell.com/images/downloads_news/alice_campbell.pdf

230. C.B. to Sommier, 1910-02-05.

231. C.B. to Pelloux, 1903-03-01.

232. C.B. to Burnat, 1903-06-10.

233. See G. Avery, '"Caro Dottore": Clarence Bicknell's correspondence with Stefano Sommier 1903–1918', for transcripts and translations of 31 letters and postcards held in the archives of the Botanical Library of the University of Florence (Biblioteca di scienze, sede Botanica, Università degli Studi di Firenze).

234. C.B. to Burnat, 1903-07-14.

235. C.B. to Abbott Antonio Carestia, 1903-09-14. C.B.'s letters to Carestia are found in the State Archives Section at the Calderini Museum of Varallo, deck 11. Thanks to Giuseppe Sitzia for finding, transcribing, and informing us about this collection.

236. C.B. to Carestia, 1903-11-30.

237. C.B. to Carestia, 1903-12-17.

238. See G. Avery, 'Clarence Bicknell's Botanical Exchanges' for the location of botanical specimens collected by Clarence, and a description of the botanical exchange networks with which he was involved.

239. C.B. to Burnat, 1898-09-17.

240. See G. Avery, 'Clarence Bicknell and Reginald Farrer, 19 July 1910', for a full account of this episode.

241. Farrer, *Among The Hills ...*

242. Reginald Farrer, *The English Rock Garden*. Vol. 2. London & Edinburgh: T.C. & E.C. Jack, London & Edinburgh, 1919, pp. 153–154.

243. William Morris, *The Lesser Arts of Life*, 1882.

244. C.B. to Baroness von Taübe, 1912-09-08.

245. See G. Avery, 'Clarence Bicknell and *Iridomyrmex bicknelli*' for a description of this species and its naming by Carlo Emery in 1898.

245. C.B., 'Notes on Casa Fontanalba.' Undated handwritten notes describing the building of the house, the planting, and the decoration of the shutters and the interior walls with images of horns, wildflowers, and sayings in Esperanto. Bicknell collection.

246. C.B. to Pelloux, 1906-06-15.

247. C.B. to Burnat, 1906-08-12.

249. Helen Patricia MacDonald, *Possessing the Dead: The Artful Science of Anatomy*. Melbourne Univ. Publishing, 2010, p. 133.

250. *Launceston Examiner*, Wed. 9 March, 1892, p. 3.

251. 'Return of Dr. Bingham Crowther.' *The Mercury*, Hobart, 28 March 1902, p. 5.

252. C.B. to Burnat, 1907-01-01.

253. Clarence Bicknell, 'Notes on Casa Fontanalba.' Handwritten catalogue, 1916.

254. G. Avery, 'Clarence Bicknell and Reginald Farrer.'

255. Graham Avery's translation of page 18 of Bernardini (1972), apparently derived from a book by Minozzi dedicated to his father.

256. A.F. Mummery, *My Climbs in the Alps and Caucasus*. London: Nelson, 1908, ch. 14.

257. C.B. to Burnat, 1907-09-10.

258. *Esperanto*, 1918, 9/10, p.111. Trans. Paul Gubbins.

259. *The Casa Fontanalba Visitors' Book* is in the Bicknell collection, as is *The Book of Guests in Esperanto*. A facsimile of the first is available for purchase at clarencebicknell.com

260. C.B. to Pelloux, 1906-07-19.

261. C.B. to Burnat, 1907-07-07.

262. In Marjorie Boulton, *Zamenhof: Creator of Esperanto*. Trans. Boulton. London: Routledge and Kegan Paul, 1960, p. 6.

263. Aleksander Korzenkov, *The Life, Works and Ideas of the Author of Esperanto*. New York: Mondial, 2010.

264. Giuseppe Bessone, 'Passione per l'esperanto a Bordighera', *Ligures*, 2010, pp.193–194.

265. See G. Avery, 'Bristol Botanists at Casa Fontanalba' for more on them and their visits to Casa Fontanalba in 1907 (Thompson) and 1911 (White and the Bucknalls).

266. C.B. to Cedric Bucknall, 1903-12-19.

267. C.B. to Sommier, 1903-12-06.

268. This, and much of the information that follows, comes from the 'Compte-rendu extrait de la Presse', from the 1st Esperanto World Congress, Boulogne-sur-Mer, 1905. The material is held in the Department of Planned Languages at the Österreichische Nationalbibliotek in Vienna. https://www.onb.ac.at/en/library/ collections/planned-languages/digital-media/ esperanto-world-congresses/

269. Bessone, 'Passione . . . ', p.193.

270. Tonkin, p. 7.

271. *Cambridge Daily News,* 15 August 1907, p.23.

272. Corrispondenza tra Clarence Bicknell e Edward E. Berry. IISL, Bordighera.

272. Listo de la kongresanoj. Online reading of the Esperanto World Congresses. Österreichische Nationalbibliothek, Department of Planned Languages. onb.ac.at

273. See G. Avery, 'Kew & Clarence Bicknell' for an account of the botanical specimens, publications and correspondence of Clarence held by the Royal Botanic Gardens at Kew, which includes a letter from him to Prain.

274. Basil Morgan, 'Farrer, Reginald John (1880–1920)', *Oxford Dictionary of National Biography.* Oxford University Press, 2004 (online edition, 2012).

275. Reginald Farrer, *In Old Ceylon.* London, E. Arnold, 1908, p. 1.

276. C.B. to Burnat, 1908-01-11.

277. J.C. Willis, *Ceylon: A Handbook for the Resident and the Traveller.* Colombo: Colombo Apothecaries Company, 1907, p. 48.

278. C.B. to Burnat, 1908-01-11.

279. Professor Francis Ramaley, University of Colorado. 'The Botanical Gardens of Ceylon.' *Popular Science Monthly,* September 1908, p. 203.

280. C.B. to the Baroness von Taübe. ND. Probably 1909, the year in which they began corresponding.

281. C.B. to John Ferguson, 1911-08-23. ICS 86, Ferguson Papers. Institute of Commonwealth Studies, University of London.

282. See https://archiveshub.jisc.ac.uk/data/gb101-ics86.

283. C.B. to Burnat, 1908-02-20.

284. Cartailhac to C.B., early 1908.

285. Daniela Gandolfi, 'La Raccolta Archeologica' di Clarence Bicknell. *La Vita . . . ,* p. 107.

286. C.B. to Cartailhac, 1908-17-05.

287. C.B. to Burnat, 1908-01-16.

288. Cartailhac to C.B., 1913-06-03.

289. Adolphe Stiegelman to C.B., 1908–1909.

290. Umberto Folena, *Padre Giacomo Viale. L'Avventura di un parroco francescano.* Genoa: Grafica Fassicomo, 1997, p. 57.

291. The information about St Joseph's home comes from 'L'Ospizio per i poveri.' www.fondazionesangiuseppebordighera.it/ospizio

292. Corrispondenza tra Clarence Bicknell e Edward E. Berry. IISL, Bordighera.

293. C.B. to Sommier, 1914-01-01.

294. C.B. to Burnat, 1914-10-17.

295 Anatoly Romanchishen et al., 'Sir James Berry (1840–1946)'. Jaypeejournals.com 10.5005/ jp-journals-10001-1005

296. C.B. to Sommier, 1916-06-28.

297. Bernardini, p. 20.

298. www.clarencebicknell.com >documents

# BIBLIOGRAPHY

This bibliography has three sections: primary sources; the original research conducted during the preparation of the biography; the works cited. A further bibliography of Clarence-related books and journals that Marcus Bicknell and Dr Giovanni Russo have been assembling since 2013, can be found at www.clarencebicknell.com/en/the-man/bibliography.

## PRIMARY MATERIAL

BERRY, E., Biographical sketch of C.B.. Bicknell collection.

BERRY, E., Corrispondenza tra Clarence Bicknell e Edward E. Berry. IISL, Bordighera.

BERRY, E., Letter to Émile Burnat on C. Bicknell's death, 1918. Held with C.B.'s letters to Burnat in the archives of the *Conservatoire et Jardin Botaniques de la Ville de Genève*, www.clarencebicknell.com/images/downloads_news/berry_burnat_1918_juillet-24.pdf

BERRY, M., *Fontanalba Diary 1906*. Transcribed by M. Bicknell 2014. Bicknell collection. www.clarencebicknell.com/images/downloads_news/margaret_berry_diary_july_1906.pdf

BERRY, M., Biographical sketch of C.B.,1918. Bicknell collection.

BERRY, M., Letters to Rosa Fanshawe Walker. Bicknell collection.

BICKNELL, A.S., *Autobiography*. The Keep, East Sussex County Archives, ACC 8490.

BICKNELL, C., diary. *Stoke-upon-Tern/Bordighera (1878–1879)*. Transcribed Libby Peachey 1998. Bicknell collection. www.clarencebicknell.com/images/downloads_news/clarence_bicknell_diary_1878-9_vols_1-4_lp_compiled_mb.pdf

BICKNELL, C., diary. *Notes of a Tour in Italy, Egypt &c. 1889–1890*. Transcribed M. Bicknell & V. Lester 2017. Bicknell collection. www.clarencebicknell.com/images/downloads_news/clarence_bicknell_nile_cruise_diary_1890.pdf

BICKNELL, C., Letters to Abbot Carestia – 1903. Transcribed M. Bicknell, 2014. www.clarencebicknell.com/images/downloads_news/letters_1903_carestia_english_rough.pdf

BICKNELL, C., Letters to Émile Burnat 1886–1917. www.clarencebicknell.com/images/downloads_news/burnat_letters_from_bicknell.pdf

BICKNELL, C., Letters to Émile Cartailhac. Transcribed by P. Machu 2014. www.clarencebicknell.com/images/downloads_news/clarence_letters_cartailhac_pierre_machu_mb_nov2014.pdf

BICKNELL, C., Letter to John Ferguson, 1911. Transcribed by M. Bicknell, 2014. www.clarencebicknell.com/images/downloads_news/john_ferguson_from_clarence_bicknell_23_aug_1911.pdf

BICKNELL, C., Letters to Louisa MacDonald. George MacDonald Collection. General Collection, Beinecke Rare Book and Manuscript Library, Yale University.

BICKNELL, C., Letters to Alberto Pelloux. Archivio IISL,Bordighera. www.clarencebicknell.com/images/downloads_news/pelloux_bicknell_letters.pdf

BICKNELL, C., Letters to Baroness Helene von Taube. London, Natural History Museum. Call number: NHM, 92 BIC.

BICKNELL, C., *Casa Fontanalba Visitors' Book 1906–1918*, and C. Bicknell, *Book of Guests in Esperanto*. Bicknell collection. www.clarencebicknell.com/images/downloads_news/casa_fontanalba_visitors_books.xls

BICKNELL, C., 'Notes on Casa Fontanalba.' Bicknell collection.

BICKNELL, C., seven albums of watercolours made for Margaret Berry. Cambridge, Fitzwilliam Museum.

BICKNELL, C., Sketchbooks. Bicknell collection.

BICKNELL, C., botanical watercolours, 3,428 of them in albums and loose-leaf, many of them marked with the date and location, at the Università degli Studi di Genova, DISTAV.

BICKNELL, C., 9 archaeological field diaries, Mont Bego area, at the Università degli Studi di Genova, Legate Bicknell.

BROWNE, C.G. and A.S. BICKNELL, *Notes to Assist the Future Authors of the Huguenot Family of Browne.* Handwritten manuscript, 1903.

ETTY, W., Letters to Elhanan Bicknell. National Archives. York City Art Gallery. C1810–46 (150). Ref. EC.

EVANS, Sir Arthur, to C.B., Archivio IISL, Bordighera. Fondo Bicknell-Berry, 2.

JENKYNS, Patricia M., 'The Bicknells of Herne Hill', May 1986. Bicknell collection.

Minute Book of the Guild of the Holy Redeemer (being the Stoke-upon-Tern branch of the Church of England Temperance Society.) Shrewsbury, Shropshire archives.

ORIGINAL RESEARCH

AVERY, G., 'Augusto Béguinot on Clarence Bicknell.' www.clarencebicknell.com/images/downloads_news/beguinot_article_on_clarence_bicknell_note_avery_jan2015.pdf

AVERY, G., 'Clarence Bicknell in the Archives of All Saints' Church, Bordighera.' www.clarencebicknell.com/images/downloads_news/all_saints_archives_april2017.pdf

AVERY, G., 'Clarence Bicknell and Botany: an appreciation.' www.clarencebicknell.com/en/botanist

AVERY, G., 'Botanical. Exchanges.' www.clarencebicknell.com/images/downloads_news/clarence_bicknell_botanical_exchanges_avery.pdf

AVERY, G., 'Bristol Botanists at Casa Fontanalba.' www.clarencebicknell.com/images/downloads_news/bristol_botanists_at_casa_fontanalba.pdf

AVERY, G., '"Caro Dottore": Clarence Bicknell's correspondence with Stefano Sommier 1903–1918.' www.clarencebicknell.com/images/downloads_news/bicknell_sommier_avery_april2017.pdf

AVERY, G., '"Cher Monsieur": Clarence Bicknell's correspondence with Emile Burnat 1886–1917.' www.clarencebicknell.com/images/downloads_news/burnat_letters_from_bicknell.pdf

AVERY, G., 'Clarence Bicknell and *Iridomyrmex bicknelli.'*

www.clarencebicknell.com/images/downloads_news/iridomyrmex_bicknelli_avery.pdf

AVERY, G., 'Clarence Bicknell & Kew.' www.clarencebicknell.com/images/downloads_news/kew_clarence_bicknell_avery.pdf

AVERY, G., 'Clarence Bicknell and *Pimpinella bicknellii.'* www.clarencebicknell.com/images/downloads_news/clarence_bicknell_pimpinella_bicknellii_avery_2017.pdf

AVERY, G., 'Clarence Bicknell and Reginald Farrer.' www.clarencebicknell.com/images/downloads_news/obh12_avery___bicknell_and_farrer_v4.pdf

AVERY, G., "The Burnat/Bicknell Nature Reserve in the Marguareis Natural Park" www.clarencebicknell.com/images/downloads_news/botanical_reserve_burnat_bicknell_avery.pdf

AVERY, G., and V. LESTER, 'Clarence Bicknell to Louisa MacDonald from the Yale collection.' www.clarencebicknell.com/images/downloads_news/clarence_letters_to_louise_macdonald_yale_april2017.pdf

BICKNELL, S., 'Clarence Bicknell – His Art', 2016. www.clarencebicknell.com/images/downloads_news/clarence_bicknell_his_art_Susie_Bicknell.pdf

BICKNELL, S., 'Letters from Clarence Bicknell to Ellen Willmott', 2016. www.clarencebicknell.com/images/downloads_news/clarence_bicknell_letters_to_ellen_willmott.pdf

CHIPPINDALE, C., 'Clarence Bicknell – Una Vita Sacra: Discovery of Rock Art', 1985. www.clarencebicknell.com/images/downloads_news/chippindale_una-vita-sacra_1985.pdf

MACHU, P. 'Clarence Bicknell, Émile Cartailhac et les autres . . . au pays des Merveilles.' *Antiquités Nationales,* 38, 2006-2007. www.clarencebicknell.com/images/downloads_news/antiquits_nationales_38_pierre_machu_2007_compressed.pdf

WORKS CITED

*Alberi di Liguria, monumenti viventi della natura.* Genoa: Erga, 2003.

*Alumni Cantabrigienses,* Part 2, Vol. iI. Cambridge Univ. Press, 1922.

ARDUINO, Honoré. *Flore Analytique du Departement des Alpes-Maritimes.* Menton: Bertrand & Queyrot, 1879.

*The Art-Journal:* New Series, Vol. I. London: James S. Virtue.

BAETGER, Katherine. *British Paintings in the Metropolitan Museum of Art, 1577–1875.* New York: Metropolitan Museum, 2009.

BARONE, Angela R. *The Oak Tree and the Olive Tree: The True Dream of Eva Gore-Booth.* Dublin City University, PhD thesis, 1990.

BARTOLI, Alessandro. *The British colonies in the Italian Riviera in '800 and '900*. Savona: Ferraris, 2008.

BERNARDINI, Enzo and Giuseppe E. Bessone, eds. *Bordighera Ieri*. Genoa: Stabilmento Tipigrafico, 1971.

BERNARDINI, Enzo. *Clarence Bicknell, Edward e Margaret Berry*. Bordighera, IISL, 1972.

BERNARDINI, Enzo. *Monte Bego, storia di una montagna*. Sezione di Bordighera: Club Alpino Italiano, 1971.

BESSONE, Giuseppe E. 'Passione per l'esperanto a Bordighera', *Ligures*, 2010, pp. 193–194.

BESSONE, Giuseppe E. 'Tra Neogotico e Cottages. L'architettura "inglese" dell Riviera.' In *La Vita*.

BICKNELL, A.S. *Five Pedigrees*. London: Sherwood, 1912

BICKNELL, A.S. Letter to *The Athenaeum,* 9 January 1909.

BICKNELL, C. 'Una gita primaverile in Sardegna.' *Bulletino della Società botanica italiana*. Florence: 1904.

BICKNELL, C. *The Common Fig Tree*. Bordighera: Bessone, 1912.

BICKNELL, C. *The Prehistoric Rock Engravings in the Italian Maritime Alps*. Bordighera: Gibelli, 1902.

BICKNELL, C. *A Guide to the Prehistoric Rock Engravings in the Italian Maritime Alps*. Bordighera: Bessone, 1913.

BICKNELL, C. *Flowing Plants and Ferns of the Riviera*. London: Trübner, 1885.

BICKNELL, C. *Flora of Bordighera and San Remo*. Bordighera: Gibelli, 1896.

BICKNELL, Herman. *Hafiz of Shiraz*. London: Trübner, 1875.

BLANC, Edmond. 'Études sur les sculptures préistoriques du Val d'Enfer.' In Enzo Bernardini, *Monte Bego: storia di una montana*. Club Alpino Italiano. Bordighera: 1971

BLESSINGTON, Marguerite, Countess of. *The Idler in Italy*, Vol. I. London: Coburn, 1839

BOULTON, Marjorie. *Zamenhof: Creator of Esperanto*. Trans. Boulton. London: Routledge and Kegan Paul, 1960.

BOYER, Marie-France. 'Vallée de Merveilles', *The World of Interiors,* June 1990.

BRADLEY, John Lewis, ed. *The Letters of John Ruskin to Lord and Lady Mount-Temple*. Ohio State University, 1964.

BRANDOLINI, Maurizia et al. *Le incisioni rupestri a Monte Bego nei diari di campagna di Clarence Bicknel* (sic). Genoa: Dipteris, 2002.

BRIANO, G.B. *Vita esperantista di Genova e Liguria dal 1900 al 1975*. Liguria: Sabatelli, 1976.

BRIQUET, John and François Cavillier, *Émile Burnat: autobiographie publiée avec un étude sur le botaniste et son oeuvre, des souvenirs et documents divers Émile Burnat*. Geneva: Conservatoire Botanique, 1922.

BROWNE, Edgar. *Phiz and Dickens*. London: Nisbet, 1913.

*Cambridge Daily News,* 15 August 1907.

CAPPONI, Domenico. *Ricordo del terremoto in Liguria del 23 febbraio 1887*. Genoa: Tipografia della Gioventù. 1887.

CARTAILHAC, Émile. 'La grotte d'Altamira, Espagne. Mea culpa d'unsceptique.' *L'Anthropologie*. 1902, 13.

CELESIA, Emanuele. 'Escursioni alpine . . . Fontanalba.' In *Bulletin of the Ministry of Public Education,* May 1886.

CHIPPINDALE, Christopher. *A High Way to Heaven: Clarence Bicknell and the 'Vallée de Merveilles.'* Tende: 1998.

CHIPPINDALE, Christopher. 'Clarence Bicknell: archae-ology and science in the 19th century.' *Antiquity*. LVIII, 1984,

*The Christian Reformer,* New Series, Vol. XVII. London: James Whitfield.

*The Christian Reformer*, Vol. XVIII. London: James Whitfield.

*The Church Association Monthly Intelligencer*. July 1868.

*Church of the People and The People's Magazine,* May 1857, to December 1858. London: Kent, 1859.

*Corriere di Porto Maurizio,* II, 1890, number 47.

COGHILL, Mrs Harry, ed. *The Autobiography and Letters of Mrs M.O.W. Oliphant*. Edinburgh & London: Blackwood, 1899.

DAMON, Pierre. *Pasteur*. Paris: Fayard, 1995.

*Dictionary of National Biography*, 1885–1900, Vol. 33. Entry on Joseph Barber Lightfoot.

DONOVAN, Marcus. *A History of S. Paul's, Lorrimore Square and S. Agnes', Kennington Park*. London: 1930.

*Esperanto*, 1918, 9/10.

FARRER, Reginald. *In Old Ceylon*. London: E. Arnold, 1908.

FARRER, Reginald. *Among the Hills: A Book of Joy in High Places*. London: Headley Brothers, 1911.

FARRER, Reginald. *The English Rock Garden*. London: Nelson, 1919.

*The Fine Arts Quarterly Review*. London: Chapman and Hall, 1863.

FOLENA, Umberto. 'Giacomo Viale, "U fratin" servo di Dio.' *Avenire.it*, 8 luglio 2016.

FOLENA, Umberto. *Padre Giacomo Viale. L'Avventura di un parroco francescano*. Genoa: Grafica Fassicomo, 1997.

FOLLI, Andrea and Gisella Merello, *Charles Garnier et la Riviera*. Genoa: Erga Edizioni, 2000.

GANDOLFI, Daniela and Mario Marcenaro, eds. *Clarence Bicknell: La Vita e le Opere. Atti del Convegno di Studi 1998.* Bordighera, 2003.

*The Gardeners' Chronicle,* Volume XXIV, 12 December 1885

*The Gentleman's Magazine.* Vol. 211. July–December, 1861.

'George MacDonald at Bordighera.' *The Critic and Good Literature,* v, 2 Feb. 1884.

GREGORY, James. *Reformers, Patrons and Philanthropists: The Cowper-Temples and High Politics in Victorian England.* London: Tauris, 2009

GURNEY, Emilia Russell. *Letters of Emilia Russell Gurney.* London: Nisbet, 1902,

HARDY, Margaret. *The Shropshire Magazine,* undated article, c. 1950.

HAMILTON, Frederick Fitzroy. *Bordighera and the Western Riviera.* London: Stanford, 1883.

HEIN, Rolland. *George MacDonald, Victorian Mythmaker.* Eugene: Wipf and Stock, 1993.

HEWITSON, Robert. *John Ruskin, the Argument of the Eye.* London: Thames and Hudson, 1976.

HOARE, Philip. *England's Lost Eden: Adventures in a Victoian Utopia.* London: Harper, 2005.

ISSEL, Arturo. *Il Terremoto del 1887 in Liguria.* Rome: Tipograpfia Nazionale di Reggiani & soci, 1888.

ISSEL, Arturo. 'Le rupi scolpite nelle alte valli delle Alpi Marittime.' *Bullettino di Paletnologia Italiana,* Anno XXVII. Oct.–Dec. 1901. N. 1.

JOPLING, Louise. *Twenty Years of my Life. 1867–1887.* London: Bodley Head, 1925.

*Journal de Bordighera,* 8 February 1900; 1 March 1900; 11 November 1909; 26 February 1914.

*Journal of Botany, British and Foreign,* Vol. XXII, 1885.

KENDALL, Richard, ed. *Monet by himself.* London: Little, Brown, 1995.

KORZENKOV, Aleksander. *The Life, Works and Ideas of the Author of Esperanto.* New York: Mondial, 2010.

LARROQUE, C., O. Scotti, and M. Ioualalen, 'Reappraisal of the 1887 Ligurian earthquake (western Mediterranean) from macroseismicity, active tectonics and tsunami modelling.' *Geophysical Journal International.* Vol. 190, Issue 1.

*Launceston Examiner,* Wed. 9 March 1892.

LEVINE, Robert S., ed. *The New Cambridge Companion to Herman Melville.* New York: Cambridge University Press, 2014.

LEBRÉ, Patrice. *Louis Pasteur.* Baltimore: John Hopkins, 1994

LE LIÈVRE, Audrey. *Miss Willmott of Warley Place.* London: Faber, 2008.

MACDONALD, Greville. *George MacDonald and his Wife.* London: Allen & Unwin, 1924.

MACDONALD, Helen Patricia. *Possessing the Dead: The Artful Science of Anatomy.* Melbourne Univ. Publishing, 2010.

MACDONALD, Ronald. *From a Northern Window.* Escondido, CA.: Sunrise, 1989.

MADER, Fritz. 'Les Inscriptions Préhistoriques des Environs de Tende par M. Fritz Mader.' *Annales de la Société des lettres, sciences et arts des Alpes-Maritimes,* Nice, 1903.

MAITLAND, Susan 'Clarence Bicknell e la sua attività pastorale in Inghilterra (1866–1876).' In *La Vita.*

MANO, Livio, ed. *Nel Paese delle Meraviglie. Novel Temp. Quaderno di cultura e studi occitani alpini.* Sampeyre: Soulestrelh, 1990.

MARCENARO, Mario. *Bordighera e Il Museo-Biblioteca dell'Istituteo Internazionale di Studi Liguri da Clarence Bicknell al rinnovamento attuale.* Bordighera: IISL, 1998.

MASSIE, James and Shirley Maxwell. *Arts and Crafts.* London: Abbeville, undated.

MERELLO, Gisella. *L'immagine turistica di Bordighera attraverso le cartoline illustrate e la letteratura.* Bordighera. IISL, Lions Club, 1995.

MILNER, C. 'Some nineteenth century post-Tractarian clergy in the Archdeaconry of Salop, Diocese of Lichfield with particular reference to the *Societas Sancti Spiritus* 1869–79, its members and its founder, the Rev. Rowland William Corbet M.A. Rector of Stoke-upon-Tern, Salop, 1869–1901,' 1972. Thesis for M.Phil degree, Leeds University, 1972.

MOGGRIDGE, John Traherne. *Contributions to the flora of Mentone, and to a winter flora of the Riviera, including the coast from Marseilles to Genoa.* London: Reeve, 1871.

MONTGOMERY, John. *Abodes of Love.* London: Putnam, 1962.

MUMMERY, A. F. *My Climbs in the Alps and Caucasus,* 1908.

NELSON, Michael. *The French Riviera: A History.* Kibworth Beauchamp: Matador, 2017.

ORLEAN, Susan. *The Orchid Thief.* New York: Ballantine, 1998.

OULTON, Carolyn W. de la L. *Let the Flowers Go: A Life of Mary Cholmondeley.* London: Chatto & Pickering, 2009.

PARODI, Gabriella. "Il laboratorio paleontologico di Arturo Issel e le lettere di Clarence Bicknell." *Ligures: rivista di archeologia, storia, arte e cultura ligure.* Bordighera: IISL, 2003.

PEMBLE, John. *The Mediterranean Passion: Victorians and Edwardians in the South.* London: Faber, 1987.

*Proceedings of the Society for Psychical Research.* Vol. XIII.

1897–1898. London: Kegan Paul, 1898.

*Psychical Research,* Vol. 4, 1886–1887. London: Trübner, 1887.

RAMALEY, Francis. 'The Botanical Gardens of Ceylon.' *Popular Science Monthly,* September 1908.

REIS, Richard H. *George MacDonald.* New York: Twayne, 1972.

'Return of Dr. Bingham Crowther.' *The Mercury,* Hobart, 28 March 1902.

RINIERI, Françoise. *C'est un Grand Mystère.* Turin: Hapax, 2013.

RIX, Martyn. *The Golden Age of Botanical Art.* London: Deutch, 2012.

RUSSO, Giovanni. "La Biblioteca personale di Clarence Bicknell. Indagini bibliografiche nelle biblioteche di Bordighera." *Ligures.* 2014/2017.

SCHOR, Esther. *Bridge of Words: Esperanto and the Dream of a Universal Language.* New York: Holt, 2016.

SEMERIA, Giovanni Battista. *Storia Ecclesiastica Di Genova e Della Liguria Dai Tempi Apostolici Sino All'anno 1838.* Genoa: Canfari, 1838

SHELDEN, Michael. *Melville in Love.* New York: Harper Collins, 2016

SHULMAN, Nicola. *A Rage for Gardening. The Story of Reginald Farrer.* Boston: Godine, 2004.

SIM, Katharine. *David Roberts R.A. 1796–1864.* London: Quartet, 1984.

*The Spectator, Vol. 95,* 7 Oct. 1905.

THOMPSON, H. Stuart. *Flowering Plants of the Riviera.* London: Longmans, 1914.

TONKIN, Humphrey. 'Clarence Bicknell, Philanthropist and Person of Ideas.' Talk given to the Twilight Club, Hartford, CT, 2014.

TRELOAR, Geoffrey R. *Lightfoot the Historian: The Nature and Role of History in the Life and Thought of J.B. Lightfoot.* Tübingen: Mohr Siebeck, 1998

TRIGGS, Kathy. *The Stars and the Stillness. A Portrait of George MacDonald.* Cambridge: Lutterworth, 1986.

TUCKER, Paul Hayes. *Claude Monet, Life and Art.* New Haven: Yale University Press, 1995.

VILLARI, Linda. *Soggiorno a Bordighera.* London: Allen, 1893

WHITEHOUSE, Rosie. *Liguria.* London: Bradt, undated.

WILLIS, J.C. *Ceylon: A Handbook for the Resident and the Traveller.* Colombo: Colombo Apothecaries Company, 1907.

# INDEX

C.B. = Clarence Bicknell.
Page numbers in italics refer to illustrations; those followed by M indicate maps.
C.B.'s lengthy correspondence with Émile Burnat has been one of our major resources, and some of the many references
to it are noted below. For further information about the letters, go to Documents in the Clarence Bicknell website and see
G. Avery, 'Clarence Bicknell – Correspondence with Emile Burnat (1886–1917) 2016'.

# ABBREVIATIONS AND
# IMAGE CREDITS

Every effort has been made to trace or contact all copyright holders.
We shall be pleased to rectify at the earliest opportunity any omissions or errors brought to our notice

**Abbreviations in the captions and end credits**

| | |
|---|---|
| **BibCiv** | courtesy of the Biblioteca Civica Internazionale, Bordighera |
| **Bicknell Collection** | property of the estate of Clarence Bicknell, a collection passed down through Margaret Berry to Peter Bicknell and now enlarged and looked after by Marcus Bicknell, copyright © 2018, all rights reserved |
| **C.B.** | Clarence Bicknell |
| **IISL** | courtesy of the Istituto Internazionale di Studi Liguri, Museo Bicknell, Bordighera |
| *La Vita* | *Clarence Bicknell: La Vita e le Opere*. Eds. Daniela Gandolfi and Mario Marcenaro. Bordighera: Istituto Internazionale di Studi Liguri [IISL], 2003 |
| **Met** | courtesy of the Metropolitan Museum of Art, New York |
| **OxHerb** | University of Oxford Herbaria |
| **ShropArch** | Shropshire Archive, Shrewsbury |
| **Tate** | courtesy of the Tate Gallery, London |
| **UniGen** | courtesy of the Università degli Studi di Genova, DI.S.T.A.V. |
| **V&A** | Victoria and Albert Museum, London |
| **Vintners** | Vintners' Company, London |

ii   Outside Casa Fontanalba, left to right: Marco Novello, Clarence Bicknell, Capitano Alberto Pelloux, Signora Bianca Pelloux, Luigi Pelloux. Bicknell Collection.

ix   J.M.W. Turner, *The Blue Rigi, Sunrise*. Public Domain. This copy via Creative Commons CC-BY-NC-ND (3.0 Unported). Tate.

x   The family tree 'Clarence Bicknell and his Close Family' was drawn for this book by Gwyneth Hibbert. Bicknell Collection.

2   Denning, *The six children of Elhanan Bicknell Esquire, an art patron*. Courtesy of the V&A, number P.18-1934.

2   Thomas Philips R.A., oils, *Elhanan Bicknell*. Photo by Darren Woolway, courtesy of the Vintners' Company, London.

3   Photo by A.S. Bicknell, *The Garden at Herne Hill*, print in the Bicknell Collection.

3   Photo by A.S. Bicknell, *Herne Hill*, print in the Bicknell Collection.

5   J.M.W. Turner, *Giudecca*. Public domain. Private collection (sold by Christies in 2006 to an anonymous buyer). Photo courtesy of The Bridgeman Art Library via www.wikiart.org.

5   This mezzotint of William Bicknell by W. Ward, from the painting by Samuel Drummond, is the property of Marcus Bicknell and reproduced with his permission.

6   Samuel Drummond, *Elhanan Bicknell*. Photo in the Bicknell Collection. The location of the original painting is unknown.

6   William John Huggins, *Whalers*, 1845. Oil painting, the property of Mark Bicknell and reproduced with his permission.

7   Phiz. Public domain, photo courtesy of Valerie Lester.

8   Clarence with his donkey in 1850. Unknown photographer. Bicknell Collection.

10   D'Orsay, *Turner in Mr E. Bicknell's drawing room*. An original print, by J. Hogarth, of d'Orsay's drawing from Sir Edwin Landseer's sketch, in the Bicknell Collection.

10   J.M.W. Turner, *Whalers*. Public domain. Creative

Commons CC-BY-NC-ND. Courtesy of the Metropolitan Museum of Art, New York, 96.29, Catharine Lorillard Wolfe Collection, Wolfe Fund, 1896. Turner's painting was probably inspired by William John Huggins, *Whalers*, 1845 (on page 6 of this book) made available to Turner by Elhanan Bicknell.

13  Bust of Lucinda, with Huggins's *Whalers* behind it. Courtesy of Mark Bicknell. Photo by Marcus Bicknell.

18  Christie and Mansons sale from *The Illustrated Times*, 1863. Public domain. Bicknell Collection.

18  The Prospectus for the Christie's sale. Public domain. Bicknell Collection.

19  Trinity College. Photo by Valerie Lester, 2016.

20  Rev. Joseph Barber Lightfoot. Public domain. This stained glass window by Burlison & Grylls showing Lightfoot is in the chapel of Auckland Castle, the Bishop of Durham's palace. Courtesy of Auckland Castle and the office of Bishop of Durham. Photo by Dave Webster on www.flickr.com/photos/davewebster14 used with his permission.

21  St Paul's, Lorrimore Square. Courtesy of British History Online, in *Survey of London: Volume 25, St George's Fields* ed. Ida Darlington (London, 1955). www.british-history.ac.uk/survey-london/vol25/plate-84.

22  Rev. John Going. Public domain. Wikimedia.

23  Mary Ann Girling. Public domain. This copy courtesy of the St Barbe Museum & Art Gallery, Lymington, Hampshire (https://www.stbarbe-museum.org.uk) published in *Emotions, Ghosts, Guest Posts, Modern, Religion, Witchcraft* by Kristof Smeyers, 2017, at https://innerlives.org/2017/06/21

24  Rev. Rowland Corbet. Public domain via the Corbet family photo collection of 'Cistercian' at https://www.flickr.com/photos/67209854@N03/7354239136.

24  C.B., *St Peter's Church*. Watercolour from a pocket sketchbook in the Bicknell Collection.

25  The Shropshire Giant. Photographer unknown, public domain, via www.whitchurch-heritage.co.uk and www.shropshirehistory.com.

25  Photo by Marcus Bicknell, *St Peters Church, Stoke-upon-Tern, Sunset and Storm*, 2016.

26  Photo by Marcus Bicknell of Henry Slocombe's *Thursday (Monks Fishing)* etched from a painting by Walter Dendy Sadler, courtesy of St Peter's Church, Stoke-upon-Tern where it hangs.

27  Photo by Dr Giovanni Russo of Clarence's copy of Thomas Moore, *The Handbook of British Ferns*, courtesy of the Biblioteca Civica Internazionale, Bordighera.

29  William and Georgina Cowper-Temple. Public domain. This copy courtesy of the University of Southampton https://specialcollectionsuniversityofsouthampton.wordpress.com/tag/georgina-cowper-temple/.

30  *Broadlands* from Morris's *Country Seats* (1880). Public domain. This copy by Merchbow~commonswiki via Wikimedia.

32  Map, From England to Bordighera, drawn by Martin Brown, © 2018 The Estate of Clarence Bicknell, Bicknell Collection.

34  Unknown artist, *Saint Ampelio Church on Cape Bordighera*, c. 1870. Courtesy of Ing. Giuseppe E. Bessone of Bordighera, from his collection.

35  Henri Giffard's *Captive Balloon at the Tuileries, Paris*, 1878. Public domain. This copy courtesy of La Boite Verte www.laboiteverte.fr/le-ballon-captif-dhenri-giffard-au-dessus-de-paris-en-1878/.

37  The Villa Rosa in Bordighera. Photo by Valerie Lester 2016.

37  The Chapel of St Ampelio. Public domain, unknown photographer, courtesy of Bordighera.net, Pier Rossi.

38  C.B., *Rocks near St Ampelio's Church*. Watercolour, 1900. Bicknell Collection.

40  *The English Church in Bordighera in about 1900* is one of a collection of photographs by Bordighera photographer Ezio Benigni housed in the Biblioteca Civica Internazionale in Bordighera, reproduced with their permission.

40  Photo of Padre Giacomo Viale is in the public domain and available at several websites e.g. immacolata-concezione.it, bordighera.net and avvenire.it.

42  The watercolour *Tennis net under olive trees* of 1877 is attributed to Albert Trachsel (1863–1929) by its owner Ing. Giuseppe E. Bessone of Bordighera, reproduced with his permission.

42  *The English Church and the tennis club in about 1905*, is one of series of complex and exotic pen and ink drawings by Genovese artist Sandro Migliarini published in 2017 in his book *Genoa and the Italian Riviera – Tales of British Voyagers* featuring C.B. among many others. © 2016, reproduced with his permission. More at sandromigliarini.com

42  *The SIRT tennis racquet-makers at Bordighera*. Photograph by Ezio Benigni, Biblioteca Civica Internazionale in Bordighera, reproduced with their permission.

42  Metal pin badge of the Bordighera Tennis Club dated 1878. Bicknell collection.

45  Photo of Garnier by Gaspard-Félix Tournachon (1820–1910), known by the pseudonym Nadar. Public domain. This copy from Wikimedia, scan by Jean-Michel Leniaud in 2003, courtesy of the Bibliothèque Nationale de France.

45  Portrait by Millais of *Louise Jane Jopling* (1843–1933; née Goode, later Rowe), 1879. Public domain. Original in National Portrait Gallery: NPG 6612.

46  *Giovanni Ruffini*. Public domain, from Jessie W. Mario, *Della Vita di Giuseppe Mazzini*, 1891.

48  *Emelia Russell Gurney* by G. F. Watts and engraved by Hollyer. Public domain. This photo by Charles Matthews available on WikiMedia.

50  Photo by Degioannini Giovanni of C.B. Original in the Bicknell collection.

54  C.B., *Cliffs at Finalmarina*. Watercolour in the Bicknell collection

55  Claude Monet, *Villas at Bordighera*. Public domain. This copy © RMN-Grand Palais (Musée d'Orsay) / Hervé Lewandowski from WikiMedia.

56  Nestel, *The Sasso Valley*, hanging in the headquarters of the Istituto Internazionale di Studi Liguri (IISL) in Bordighera. Photo provided by the IISL.

57  William Jeffrey, *George MacDonald*, an albumen print of the 1860s. Public domain. Original in the National Portrait Gallery, London, NPG P36. This copy from WikiMedia uploaded by Materialscientist.

57  Louisa Powell MacDonald. Public domain. Photographer and location unknown. This copy courtesy of the George MacDonald Informational Web, georgemacdonald.info/wife.

59  Casa Coraggio. Public domain. Source and location of original photo unknown. This copy from the Clarence Bicknell Association www.clarencebicknell.com.

61  Map, Bordighera around 1900, drawn by Martin Brown, © 2018 The Estate of Clarence Bicknell, Bicknell Collection.

64  Vasculum in the Bicknell Collection. Photo by Marcus Bicknell.

65  Moggridge brothers photo. Public domain. Courtesy of Llyfrgell Genedlaethol Cymru / The National Library of Wales, via Wikipedia.

66  C.B. watercolour of *Aristolochia* is one of a dozen hand-coloured proofs for his book *Flowering Plants and Ferns of the Riviera and Neighbouring Mountains*, 1884, in the Bicknell Collection. Photo by Marcus Bicknell. © 2018.

68  Émile Burnat. Public domain. This copy of the photo courtesy of the Stadtarchiv Schaffhausen, D I 02.521.04/2418.

69  Map, Bordighera to the Mont Bégo, drawn by Martin Brown, © 2018 The Estate of Clarence Bicknell, Bicknell Collection.

71  This watercolour of *Pimpinella bicknellii* by C.B. is one of 3,428 botanical watercolours donated by him to the Università degli Studi di Genova, DI.S.T.A.V. (University of Genoa) and is reproduced with their permission.

74  Sir Thomas Hanbury. Public domain. Photographer probably Alwin Berger, author of the book in which it appeared, *Hortus Mortolensis: Alphabetical catalogue of plants growing in the garden of the late Sir T. Hanbury at La Mortola, Ventimiglia, Italy* (1912), via WikiMedia JLaN.

74  C.B. early 1880s. Photographer unknown. Photo in the Bicknell Collection.

75  *Ficus macrophylla* at the Museo Bicknell. Photo courtesy of René Stannarius, Schmitten, Germany. https://www.flickr.com/photos/stannarius/.

75  *The wisteria on the face of the Museo Bicknell* is one of a collection of photographs by Bordighera photographer Ezio Benigni housed in the Biblioteca Civica Internazionale in Bordighera, reproduced with their permission.

76  Fireplace in the Museo. Photo courtesy of writer/historian Gisella Merello Folli of Bordighera.

76  Benigni, *Bordighera under snow*. Courtesy of the Biblioteca Civica Internazionale in Bordighera.

77  Butterflies in the Museo Bicknell. Still from the film *The Marvels of Clarence Bicknell* by Rémy Masséglia, 2016. Bicknell Collection.

77  The interior of the Museo Bicknell in 1902. Photo thought to be by Ezio Benigni. Courtesy of the Istituto Internazionale di Studi Liguri, Museo Bicknell, Bordighera.

78  Pietro Zeni. Public domain. Copy courtesy of Bordighera net, Pier Rossi.

80  *The Earthquake in the Riviera*, 1887, photo from the *Illustrated London News*. Public domain.

83  C.B., *San Bartolomeo di Pesio*, 1888. From one of 17 of Clarence's pocket sketch-books in the Bicknell Collection.

84  The Gibelli family with C.B. and Margaret Berry. The photo is probably by Luigi Pollini who accompanied C.B. on most of his expeditions. Bicknell Collection.

86  Chapter 8 is drawn from C.B.'s *Diary of Tour in Italy and Egypt 1889–1890* written in his own hand day-by-day in a soft-cover notebook 180 × 230mm in size and with 150 pages. 26 sketches from this diary are reproduced in this chapter. All are courtesy of the Bicknell Collection and are copyright © 2018 The Estate of Clarence Bicknell, all rights reserved.

87  *Train arriving at Bordighera,* photo by Ezio Benigni. Courtesy of the Biblioteca Civica Internazionale, Bordighera.

88  C.B., *On board P&O's Hydaspes*. Diary sketch.

88  Cook's Nile Cruise logo, courtesy of Thomas Cook Archive at Thomas Cook UK Ltd.

88  C.B., *Nile Village*. Diary sketch.

89  Louis Haghe, (1806–1885), lithograph after David Roberts R.A. (1796–1864), *Mosque of Sultan Hassan, Cairo,* 1838. Each of the 247 lithographs was after a watercolour by Roberts that was worked up from sketches made during his tour of the Near East in 1838–39. Images are in the public domain. This copy courtesy of the U.S.A Library of Congress and the Wikimedia Foundation.

89  C.B., *A mosque outside Cairo*. In addition to the diary sketches, Clarence painted watercolours on loose-leaf cartridge paper, many of them c. 300 × 220mm. All these watercolours are courtesy of the Bicknell Collection and are copyright © 2018 The Estate of Clarence Bicknell, all rights reserved.

90  C.B. *Pyramids*. Diary sketch.

90  C.B., *Pyramids and palm trees*. Diary sketch.

90  C.B., *The Great Sphinx of Giza*, watercolour.

91  Abdullah Brothers, *Climbing a Pyramid*. Public Domain. This copy of their photo courtesy of Cornell University Library, Division of Rare and Manuscript Collections, Daniel Willard Fiske papers, #13-1-1165, Box 18 - Abdullah Frères, *Ascension de Pyramide* No8, ca. 1885.

91  C.B., *Boys and Girls*. Diary sketch.

92  Cook's Nile poster, courtesy of Thomas Cook Archive at Thomas Cook UK Ltd.

92  C.B., *Sailor*. Diary sketch.

92  Cook's Nile passenger list, recto and verso, letterpress printing on card, original in the Bicknell Collection.

93  C.B., *Nile Cargo Boats*. Diary sketch.

93  C.B., *Beni Hassan from the river*. Diary sketch.

94  C.B., *Feluccas and River*. Diary sketch.

94  Thomas Cook's Nile ship *Oonas*. Photo courtesy of Thomas Cook Archive at Thomas Cook UK Ltd.

94  C.B., *Quarries and Tombs of Silsileh 8/1/90*. Diary sketch.

95  C.B., *Hills Behind Denderah, New Year's Day 1890*. Diary sketch.

96  C.B., *Camels at Assouan 7/1/90*. Diary sketch.

96  C.B., *At Keneh, 10/1/90*. Diary sketch. 'Keneh' is probably how C.B. heard the town of Qena pronounced (also Kaine or Caene in antiquity), 40 kms north of Luxor on the east bank and adjoining Denderah.

97  David Roberts (1796–1864*)*, *Column, Hall of the Temple at Karnak/Egypt*, 1838. Public Domain. This copy from Manfred Heyde, via Wikimedia Foundation. Whereabouts of original unknown.

97  C.B., *Boat laden with sacks*. Diary sketch, January 1890.

98  C.B., *Edfou*. Diary sketch.

98  C.B., *Pylon of the Temple of Horus at Edfou*. Diary sketch.

98  C.B., *Esneh 8/1/90*; Mosque, Pigeon House, Rising Water, Sycamore Tree and Windmills. Diary sketch.

99  C.B., *Nile near Assouan*. Diary sketch.

99  C.B., *Doum Palms*. Diary sketch.

99  C.B., *Boats at Assouan 6/1/90*. Diary sketch.

100  C.B., *Luxor by moonlight from the boat, 8/1/90*. Diary sketch.

100  C.B., *Pigeon house* and *a boat on the Nile*. Diary sketch.

101  C.B., *View from where we stuck on a sandbank 2pm 13/1/90*. Diary sketch.

103  C.B., *Acropolis*. Diary sketch.

104  C.B., diary excerpt 'Reached Home'.

106  Margaret and Edward Berry. Their passport photos are in the Bicknell Collection.

108  Algernon Sidney Bicknell in 1850. Photograph in his diary, courtesy of the East Sussex Record Office at The Keep, near Brighton, U.K. (Acc 8490).

108  Clarence with his bicycle, Villa Rosa, probably 1892. Photographer unknown. Photo in the Bicknell collection.

109  C.B.'s photo by Ezio Benigni is mounted on stiff card inscribed Formato Gabinetto which refers to a standard size for printing photos, 100 × 150mm, 'cabinet format'. Original in the Bicknell Collection.

*London News*, 11 January 1958.

151 Farrer and Elliott signatures in the *Casa Fontanalba Visitors' Book*, in the Bicknell collection.

152 Casa Fontanalba postcard from C.B. to Émile Burnat in the archives of the Conservatoire et Jardin botaniques de la Ville de Genève. Photo by Graham Avery. Reproduced with their kind permission.

154 Bingham Crowther, public domain photo from Flickr.com, uncredited.

156 Casa Fontanalba garden map. Photo by Marcus Bicknell from the original of his list of plants in *Wild Flowers* in the Istituto Internazionale di Studi Liguri, Bordighera.

159 H. Stuart Thompson. Photo by E.B. Mowll, courtesy of the Bristol Naturalists' Society, from their Proceedings of 1940.

160 The *Casa Fontanalba Visitors' Book* is in the Bicknell Collection. Photo by Marcus Bicknell.

161 Logo on the first page of the *Casa Fontanalba Visitors' Book*, Bicknell Collection. Photo by Marcus Bicknell.

162 First page of signatures and corresponding botanical
163 watercolours in CB's *Casa Fontanalba Visitors' Book*. The hand-drawn original 265 × 340mm is in the Bicknell Collection and a limited edition art reproduction is available for purchase.

164 C.B., watercolour of *Caltha palustris*, in the *Casa Fontanalba Visitors' Book*. Bicknell Collection.

165 Émile Cartailhac's page in the *Book of Guests in Esperanto* by C.B., 130 × 205mm. The logotype at the top combines his initials with the various forms of the rock engravings of the Mont Bégo region, which he had come to visit. Bicknell Collection.

166, An opening from C.B.'s *Children's Picture Book of*
167 *Wild Plants,* 250 × 330mm. Bicknell Collection.

168 *The Triumph of the Dandelion* from one of 7 vellum-bound albums by C.B. in the Fitzwilliam Museum, University of Cambridge, PD5-11 (1980), reproduced with their permission.

169 Grosvenor Berry in the *Book of Guests in Esperanto* by C.B. Bicknell Collection.

169 George Macdonald, poem from one of 7 vellum-bound albums by C.B. in the Fitzwilliam Museum, University of Cambridge, PD5-11 (1980) reproduced with their permission.

171 Symmetrical floral patterns from one of 7 vellum-bound albums by C.B. in the Fitzwilliam Museum, University of Cambridge, PD5-11 (1980) reproduced with their permission.

172 *Aquilegia alpina* in C.B.'s *Casa Fontanalba Visitors' Book*. Bicknell Collection.

174 Metallic lapel pin badge of the Esperanto star in the Bicknell Collection.

175 C.B. wears his Esperanto star. Photographer unknown. Bicknell Collection.

176 Ezio Benigni (attributed), *The Bordighera Tea Rooms adjacent to the tennis club*, c. 1905. Courtesy of the Biblioteca Civica Internazionale in Bordighera.

176 Esperanto postcard. Courtesy of the Conservatoire et Jardin botaniques de la Ville de Genève.

177 International Esperanto Congress, Boulogne, 1905. Photo by Henri Caudevelle in the public domain available via WikiMedia Commons uploaded by Zico.

177 C.B., photo by Ezio Benigni in the collection of the Biblioteca Civica Internazionale in Bordighera, reproduced with their permission.

178 Zamenhof group photo at Boulogne. Public domain. Courtesy of the BildArchiv Austria via WikiMedia,

photographer unknown.

179 Poster of the Universal Esperanto Congress in Geneva in 1906. Public domain. This copy courtesy of Liverpool Hidden History, Steven Horton.

180 Esperanto group in Bordighera. Photo in the public domain, copies in the Bicknell Collection and the Istituto Internazionale di Studi Liguri, Museo Bicknell, Bordighera.

180 Esperanto Congress in Cambridge. Public domain. Courtesy of the BildArchiv Austria via WikiMedia, photographer unknown.

181 Pages from the album of the Esperanto World Congress in Cracow, 1912. Public domain. This copy courtesy of the Austrian National Library.

181 Poster of the International Esperanto Congress in Barcelona in 1909. Public domain. This copy courtesy of modernism-modernity.org, Nico Israel.

181 Poster of the International Esperanto Congress in Paris in 1914. Public domain. This copy courtesy of nod050.org, Xavier Alcalde.

184 Sri Pada. Wikipedia Creative Commons. Photo by Bourgeois 2005.

185 Peradeniya Garden. Public domain. This copy from *Popular Science Monthly* (Volume 73, September 1908, The Botanical Gardens of Ceylon), photograph by Macmillan, via WikiSource.

186 Jade pendants and silver medal of the Societas Sancti Spiritus, in the Bicknell Collection, photo by Marcus Bicknell.

186 Cima Bicknell postcard in the Bicknell Collection.

187 Émile Burnat. Photo courtesy of the Stadtarchiv Schaffhausen.

190 Sample of *Pimpinella bicknellii*. Photo courtesy of Oxford University Herbaria, Department of Plant Sciences.

191 Sidney Bicknell. Photo in the Bicknell Collection.

195 Statue of Giacomo Viale. Photo by Marcus Bicknell.

195 C.B. *Val Casterino* in 'sanguine'. Bicknell Collection.

196 C.B. *Psalliota xanthoderma*. Watercolour in the collection given by Clarence to the Università degli Studi di Genova, DI.S.T.A.V.

198 Giacomo Pollini in Clarence's *Book of Guests in Esperanto*, Bicknell Collection.

199 Peter A. Kropotkin and his wife Sophia Grigorievna. Public domain. Source Тема 'Простая', Технологии, via http://scorsoinfo.blogspot.co.uk/2014/09/dmitrov-kropotkin-returns.html.

200 C.B. dandelion watercolour in one of the vellum-bound albums (PD7) in the Fitzwilliam Museum, University of Cambridge, reproduced with their permission.

201 C.B.'s magic lanterns, photo by Marcus Bicknell, courtesy of the Gozzini family.

202 C.B. Christmas card to Pelloux. Courtesy of the Istituto Internazionale di Studi Liguri, Museo Bicknell, Bordighera.

203 *Hotel Angst*. Photo by Ezio Benigni, courtesy of the Biblioteca Civica Internazionale in Bordighera.

204 C.B. watercolour of *Cytisus sessilifolius* in the collection given by Clarence to the Università degli Studi di Genova, DI.S.T.A.V., reproduced with their permission.

206 Pollini's tribute to Clarence in the *Casa Fontanalba Visitors' Book*. Bicknell Collection.

208 Clarence on the balcony of the Casa Fontanalba. Photographer unknown. Bicknell Collection.

246 C.B., *Arno River in Florence, 1885,* watercolour. Bicknell Collection.

Praise for *Marvels: The Life of Clarence Bicknell*

Rich in information and unpublished sources that enhance our knowledge of the great Clarence Bicknell and the history of Bordighera.

Gisella Merello Folli

*Marvels – The Life of Clarence Bicknell* is a fantastic book. The abundance of wealth in the text, the beautiful layout, the multitude of images; life's very perfume rises from the pages.

Giuseppe Bessone

A hugely readable book and a wonderful vignette on Victorian life.

Carolyn Hanbury

FRONT COVER: Photograph of Clarence Bicknell on the rock-slopes of Val Fontanalba; *Aquilegia alpina* by C.B. from the *Casa Fontanalba Visitors' Book*.

BACK COVER: Symmetrical floral pattern of gentians by C.B. (Fitzwilliam Museum, University of Cambridge).

ENDPAPERS: Rock engravings of a plough drawn by two oxen and *Le Sorcier* (*the Sorcerer*) recorded by C.B.

Cover design by Sally Salvesen; display typography by Bruce Kennett